PENGUIN BOOKS

THE VALMIKI RAMAYANA VOLUME 2

Bibek Debroy is a renowned economist, scholar and translator. He has worked in universities, research institutes, industry and for the government. He has widely published books, papers and articles on economics. As a translator, he is best known for his magnificent rendition of the Mahabharata in ten volumes, and additionally the *Harivamsha*, published to wide acclaim by Penguin Classics. He is also the author of *Sarama and Her Children*, which splices his interest in Hinduism with his love for dogs.

PRAISE FOR *THE MAHABHARATA*

'The modernization of language is visible, it's easier on the mind, through expressions that are somewhat familiar. The detailing of the story is intact, the varying tempo maintained, with no deviations from the original. The short introduction reflects a brilliant mind. For those who passionately love the Mahabharata and want to explore it to its depths, Debroy's translation offers great promise . . .'—*Hindustan Times*

'[Debroy] has really carved out a niche for himself in crafting and presenting a translation of the Mahabharata . . . The book takes us on a great journey with admirable ease'—*Indian Express*

'The first thing that appeals to one is the simplicity with which Debroy has been able to express himself and infuse the right kind of meanings . . . Considering that Sanskrit is not the simplest of languages to translate a text from, Debroy exhibits his deep understanding and appreciation of the medium'—*The Hindu*

'Debroy's lucid and nuanced retelling of the original makes the masterpiece even more enjoyably accessible'—*Open*

'The quality of translation is excellent. The lucid language makes it a pleasure to read the various stories, digressions and parables'—*Tribune*

'Extremely well-organized, and has a substantial and helpful Introduction, plot summaries and notes. The volume is a beautiful example of a well thought-out layout which makes for much easier reading'—*Book Review*

'The dispassionate vision [Debroy] brings to this endeavour will surely earn him merit in the three worlds'—*Mail Today*

'Debroy's is not the only English translation available in the market, but where he scores and others fail is that his is the closest rendering of the original text in modern English without unduly complicating the readers' understanding of the epic'—*Business Standard*

'The brilliance of Ved Vyasa comes through, ably translated by Bibek Debroy'—*Hindustan Times*

THE VALMIKI RAMAYANA 2

Translated by Bibek Debroy

PENGUIN BOOKS

An imprint of Penguin Random House

PENGUIN BOOKS

USA | Canada | UK | Ireland | Australia
New Zealand | India | South Africa | China

Penguin Books is part of the Penguin Random House group of companies
whose addresses can be found at global.penguinrandomhouse.com

Published by Penguin Random House India Pvt. Ltd.
4th Floor, Capital Tower 1, MG Road,
Gurugram 122 002, Haryana, India

Penguin
Random House
India

First published in Penguin Books by Penguin Random House India 2017

Translation copyright © Bibek Debroy 2017

All rights reserved

15 14 13 12 11 10

ISBN 9780143428053

Typeset in Sabon by Manipal Digital Systems, Manipal
Printed at Replika Press Pvt. Ltd, India

www.penguin.co.in

For Professor Shailendra Raj Mehta

Contents

Acknowledgements

This journey, with Penguin, started more than a decade ago. It is a journey of translating Sanskrit texts into English, in unabridged form. It commenced with the Bhagavad Gita in 2006, followed by the Mahabharata (2010 to 2014) and the Harivamsha (2016). It continues with the Valmiki Ramayana and will be followed by the Puranas. To the best of my knowledge, the great translator, Manmatha Nath Dutt (1855–1912), is the only other person who has accomplished the 'double' of unabridged translations of both the Valmiki Ramayana and the Mahabharata in English. In this journey with Penguin, special thanks to Meru Gokhale, Ambar Sahil Chatterjee and Paloma Dutta. All three have made this journey easier to traverse.

My wife, Suparna Banerjee (Debroy), has not only been *patni*, she has been *grihini* and *sahadharmini* too. Had she not provided an enabling and conducive environment, juggling professional commitments and carving out the time required for translating would have been impossible. यः तया सह स स्वर्गो निरयो यस्त्वया विना (2.27.16).

This translation is based on the Critical Edition brought out (between 1951 and 1975) by the Oriental Institute, now part of Maharaja Sayajirao University, Baroda. When I started work on translating the Mahabharata in 2009, there was a thought, however hazy, of attempting the Valmiki Ramayana too. Therefore, one had to acquire the seven published volumes of the Critical Edition. Those who have tried this acquisition will testify this is no mean task. Multiple channels and multiple efforts failed. The Oriental Institute is not known for its marketing and distribution successes.

context changed in 2015, because I joined the government. By
I had still not been able to get copies of the Critical Edition.
with joining the government, which made finding time
lt, and an inability to get the text, I remarked to my wife
stiny willed otherwise. A few months later, on a flight, I
found myself seated next to Shailendra Mehta, economist, scholar,
friend, and currently president, director and distinguished professor
at MICA, Ahmedabad. 'What next, after the Mahabharata?' asked
Shailendra and I described my frustration. A few weeks down the
line, Shailendra Mehta walked into my office, lugging a trolley bag,
with all seven volumes in them. 'All yours,' he said. What destiny
willed was clear enough. The dedication of this three volume set to
Shailendra is a paltry attempt to say thank you.

'What next, after the Valmiki Ramayana?' Life moves on to the
Puranas, beginning with the Bhagavata Purana. At one point, the
Mahabharata translation seemed like a mammoth task, stretching
to infinity. With the major Puranas collectively amounting to four
times the size of the Mahabharata, they are more monumental than
the mammoth. But as always, if it so wills, destiny finds a way.

Introduction

The Ramayana and the Mahabharata are known as *itihasa*s. The word itihasa means 'it was indeed like that'. Therefore, the word is best rendered as legend or history, and not as myth. This does not mean everything occurred exactly as described. In a process of telling and retelling and oral transmission, embellishments are inevitable. However, the use of the word itihasa suggests a core element of truth. There were two great dynasties—*surya vamsha* and *chandra vamsha*.[1] The first proper king of the surya vamsha was Ikshvaku and the Ramayana is a chronicle of the solar dynasty, or at least a part of its history. Similarly, the first king of the chandra vamsha was Ila and the Mahabharata is a chronicle of the lunar dynasty. The Puranas also describe the histories of the solar and lunar dynasties. Though there are some inconsistencies across genealogies given in different Puranas, the surya vamsha timeline has three broad segments: (1) from Ikshvaku to Rama; (2) from Kusha to Brihadbala; and (3) from Brihadbala to Sumitra. In that stretch from Ikshvaku to Rama, there were famous kings like Bharata (not to be confused with Rama's brother), Kakutstha, Prithu, Yuvanashva, Mandhata, Trishanku, Harishchandra, Sagara, Dilipa, Bhagiratha, Ambarisha, Raghu, Aja and Dasharatha. These ancestors explain why Rama is referred to as Kakutstha, Raghava or Dasharathi.

Rama had two sons—Lava and Kusha. Ikshvaku and his descendants ruled over the kingdom of Kosala, part of today's Uttar Pradesh. The Kosala kingdom lasted for a long time, with

---

[1] The solar and the lunar dynasty, respectively.

the capital sometimes in Ayodhya and sometimes in Shravasti. When Rama ruled, the capital was in Ayodhya. After Rama, Lava ruled over south Kosala and Kusha ruled over north Kosala. Lava's capital was in Shravasti, while Kusha's capital was in Kushavati. We don't know what happened to Lava thereafter, though he is believed to have established Lavapuri, today's Lahore. The second segment of the surya vamsha timeline, from Kusha to Brihadbala, doesn't have any famous kings. Brihadbala was the last Kosala king. In the Kurukshetra War, he fought on the side of the Kouravas and was killed by Abhimanyu. The third segment of the surya vamsha timeline, from Brihadbala to Sumitra, seems contrived and concocted. Sumitra is described as the last king of the Ikshvaku lineage, defeated by Mahapadma Nanda in 362 BCE. Sumitra wasn't killed. He fled to Rohtas, in today's Bihar.

The Ramayana isn't about these subsequent segments of the timeline. Though there are references to other kings from that Ikshvaku to Rama stretch, it isn't about all of that segment either. Its focus is on Rama. It is difficult to date the poet Kalidasa. It could be anytime from the first century CE to the fifth century CE. Kalidasa wrote a *mahakavya*[2] known as *Raghuvamsha*. As the name of this mahakavya suggests, it is about Raghu's lineage, from Dilipa to Agnivarna, and includes Rama. But it isn't exclusively about Rama. Ramayana is almost exclusively about Rama. That's the reason it is known as रामायण = राम + अयण. अयण means travel or progress. Thus, Ramayana means Rama's progress. There is a minor catch though. अयन means travel or progress and अयण is a meaningless word. The word used in Ramayana is अयण, not अयन. This transformation occurs because of a rule of Sanskrit grammar known as internal *sandhi*. That is the reason रामायन becomes रामायण.

Who is Rama? The word राम means someone who is lovely, charming and delightful. There are Jain and Buddhist versions (*Dasharatha Jataka*) of the Rama account and they differ in significant details from the Ramayana story. For instance, in Jain accounts, Ravana is killed by Lakshmana. In *Dasharatha Jataka*,

---

[2] Epic.

Sita is Rama's sister. In Ramayana and Purana accounts, Rama is Vishnu's seventh *avatara*.[3] Usually, ten avataras are named for Vishnu, though sometimes, a larger number is also given. When the figure is ten, the avataras are *matsya*,[4] *kurma*,[5] *varaha*,[6] *narasimha*,[7] *vamana*,[8] Parashurama, Rama, Krishna, Buddha and Kalki (Kalki is yet to come). In the cycle of creation and destruction, *yugas*[9] follow each other and one progressively goes down *krita yuga* (alternatively *satya yuga*), *treta yuga*, *dvapara yuga* and *kali yuga*, before the cycle starts again. In the list of ten avataras, matysa, kurma, varaha and narasimha are from the present krita yuga; Vamana, Parashurama and Rama are from the present treta yuga; Krishna is from dvapara yuga; and Buddha and Kalki are from kali yuga. Rama was towards the end of treta yuga. (In the 'Uttara Kanda', dvapara yuga has started.) Just as Krishna's departure marked the transition from dvapara yuga to kali yuga, Rama's departure marked the transition from treta yuga to dvapara yuga.

When did these events occur? It is impossible to answer this question satisfactorily, despite continuous efforts being made to find an answer. At one level, it is an irrelevant question too. There is a difference between an incident happening and it being recorded. In that day and age, recording meant composition and oral transmission, with embellishments added. There was noise associated with transmission and distribution. It is impossible to unbundle the various layers in the text, composed at different points in time. Valmiki is described as Rama's contemporary, just as Vedavyasa was a contemporary of the Kouravas and the Pandavas. But that doesn't mean today's Valmiki Ramayana text is exactly what Valmiki composed, or that today's Mahabharata text

---

[3] Incarnation, or descent.
[4] Fish.
[5] Turtle.
[6] Boar.
[7] Half-man, half-lion.
[8] Dwarf.
[9] Eras.

is exactly what Krishna Dvaipayana Vedavyasa composed. Therein lies the problem with several approaches to dating.

The first and favoured method of dating is undoubtedly the astronomical one, based on positions of *nakshatra*s and *graha*s,[10] or using information about events like eclipses. However, because layers of the text were composed at different points in time, compounded by precession of the equinoxes, this leads to widely divergent dates for an event like Rama's birth, ranging from 7323 BCE to 1331 BCE. Second, one can work with genealogies, notwithstanding problems of inconsistencies across them. One will then obtain a range of something like 2350 BCE to 1500 BCE. Third, one can work with linguistics and the evolution of language, comparing that of the Ramayana to other texts. Fourth, one can work with the archaeological evidence, such as the pottery discovered in sites known to be associated with the Ramayana. Even then, there will be a wide range of dates, from something like 2600 BCE to 1100 BCE. Fifth, one can consider geography, geology, changes in the course of rivers. Finally, there are traditional views about the length of a *manvantara*[11] or yuga. Given the present state of knowledge, it is impossible to impart precision to any dating of the incidents in the Ramayana. Scholars have grappled with the problem in the past and will continue to do so in the future. This may be an important question. But from the point of view of the present translation, it is an irrelevant one.

The present translation is about the Ramayana text. But what is the Ramayana text? After a famous essay written by A.K. Ramanujan in 1987 (published in 1991), people often mention 300 Ramayanas. It is impossible to fix the number, 300 or otherwise, since it is not possible to count satisfactorily—or even define—what is a new rendering of the Ramayana story, as opposed to a simple retelling, with or without reinterpretation. Contemporary versions, not always in written form, are continuously being rendered. There are versions of the Ramayana story in East Asia (China, Japan),

[10] Constellations/stars and planets.
[11] Lifespan of a Manu.

South-East Asia (many countries like Thailand, Indonesia and
Malaysia), South Asia (Nepal, Sri Lanka) and West Asia (Iran).
As mentioned earlier, there are Buddhist and Jain versions. Every
state and every language in India seems to have some version of
the Rama story. Our impressions about the Rama story are often
based on such regional versions, such as, the sixteenth-century
Ramcharitmanas by Goswami Tulsidas. (Many of these were
written between the twelfth and seventeenth centuries CE.) Those
depictions can, and will, vary with what is in this translation. This
translation is about the Sanskrit Ramayana. But even there, more
than one text of the Sanskrit Ramayana exists—Valmiki Ramayana,
Yoga Vasishtha Ramayana, Ananda Ramayana and Adbhuta
Ramayana. In addition, there are versions of the Ramayana story
in the Mahabharata and in the Puranas. With the exception of the
Ramayana story in the Mahabharata, the Valmiki Ramayana is
clearly the oldest among these. This is a translation of the Valmiki
Ramayana and yes, there are differences between depictions in the
Valmiki Ramayana and other Sanskrit renderings of the Rama
story.

If one cannot date the incidents of the Ramayana, can one at
least conclusively date when the Valmiki Ramayana was written?
Because of the many layers and subsequent interpolations, there is no
satisfactory resolution to this problem either. The Valmiki Ramayana
has around 24,000 *shloka*s, a shloka being a verse. The Mahabharata
is believed to have 100,000 shlokas, so the Valmiki Ramayana is
about one-fourth the size of the Mahabharata. These 24,000 shlokas
are distributed across seven *kanda*s—'Bala Kanda' (Book about
Youth), 'Ayodhya Kanda' (Book about Ayodhya), 'Aranya Kanda'
(Book of the Forest), Kishkindha Kanda (Book about Kishkindha),
'Sundara Kanda' (Book of Beauty), 'Yuddha Kanda' (Book about the
War) and 'Uttara Kanda' (Book about the Sequel). Kanda refers to a
major section or segment and is sometimes translated into English as
Canto. 'Canto' sounds archaic, 'Book' is so much better. This does
not mean the kanda-wise classification always existed. For all one
knows, initially, there were simply chapters. In this text itself, there
is a reference to the Valmiki Ramayana possessing 500 *sarga*s. The

word sarga also means Book, but given the number 500, is more like a chapter. (For the record, the text has more than 600 chapters.) Most scholars agree 'Uttara Kanda' was written much later. If one reads the 'Uttara Kanda', that belief is instantly endorsed. The 'Uttara Kanda' doesn't belong. This isn't only because of the content, which is invariably mentioned. It is also because of the texture of the text, the quality of the poetry. It is vastly inferior. To a lesser extent, one can also advance similar arguments for the 'Bala Kanda'. Therefore, the earlier portions were probably composed around 500 BCE. The later sections, like the 'Uttara Kanda', and parts of the 'Bala Kanda', were probably composed around 500 CE. It isn't the case that all later sections are in 'Uttara Kanda'.

There is a mix of earlier and later sections across all kandas. The word kanda also means trunk or branch of a tree. The Mahabharata is also classified into such major sections or Books. However, in the Mahabharata, these major sections are known as *parva*s. The word parva also means branch. However, parva suggests a smaller branch, one that is more flexible. Kanda suggests one that is more solid, less flexible. There may have been slight variations in shlokas across different versions of the Sanskrit Mahabharata, but fundamentally the Sanskrit Mahabharata is a single text. The original text expanded, like a holdall, to include everything. Those different versions have been 'unified' in a Critical Edition published by the Bhandarkar Oriental Research Institute, Poona (Pune). In the case of the Valmiki Ramayana, with its kanda-kind of classification, the evolution seems to have been different. If someone was unhappy with what Valmiki had depicted, he simply composed another Ramayana. In Sanskrit, mention has already been made of the Yoga Vasishtha Ramayana, Ananda Ramayana and Adbhuta Ramayana. This continued to happen with vernacular versions.

This translation is of the Valmiki Ramayana. It is necessary to stress this point. Both the Ramayana and the Mahabharata are so popular that one is familiar with people, stories and incidents. That doesn't necessarily mean those people, stories and incidents occur in the Valmiki Ramayana in the way we are familiar with them. Just as the Bhandarkar Oriental Research Institute produced a Critical

Edition of the Mahabharata, between 1951 and 1975, the Oriental
Institute, Baroda, produced a Critical Edition of the Valmiki
Ramayana. This translation is based on that Critical Edition,
published sequentially between 1958 and 1975. Producing a Critical
Edition meant sifting through a large number of manuscripts of
the Valmiki Ramayana. The editors had around 2000 manuscripts
to work with. Not all of these were equally reliable. Therefore, in
practice, they worked with fifty to hundred manuscripts, the specific
number depending on the kanda in question. It is not that there were
significant differences across the manuscripts and broadly, there was
a Southern Recension (version) and a Northern one, the latter sub-
divided into a North-Western and a North-Eastern one. The earliest
of these written manuscripts dates to the eleventh century CE. In
passing, the language may have been Sanskrit, but the script wasn't
always Devanagari. There were scripts like Sharada, Mewari,
Maithili, Bengali, Telugu, Kannada, Nandinagari, Grantha and
Malayalam. Since this translation is based on the Baroda Critical
Edition, it is necessary to make another obvious point. Even within
the Sanskrit Valmiki Ramayana, not everything we are familiar with
is included in the Critical text. For instance, the configuration of
nakshatras and planets at the time of Rama's birth is not part of the
Critical text. Nor is the bulk of one of the most beautiful sections
of the Valmiki Ramayana, Mandodari's lamentation. Those are
shlokas that have been excised. That's also the case with a shloka
that's often quoted as an illustration of Lakshmana's conduct. नाहं
जानामि केयूरं नाहं जानामि कुण्डलं । नूपुरं तु अभिजानामि नित्यं पादाभिवन्दनात॥ This
is a statement by Lakshmana to the effect that he cannot recognize
the ornament on Sita's head or her earrings. Since he has always
served at her feet, he can only recognize her anklets. This too has
been excised. There are instances where such excision has led to a
break in continuity and inconsistency and we have pointed them
out in the footnotes.

There are two numbers associated with every chapter. The
first number refers to the kanda, while the second number, within
brackets, refers to the number of the chapter (sarga) within that
kanda. Thus, Chapter 1(33) will mean the thirty-third chapter in

'Bala Kanda'. The table below shows the number of chapters and shlokas we have in the Critical Edition. The Critical text has 606 chapters, 106 more than the 500 sargas mentioned in the text itself. And there are 18,670 shlokas. If one considers chapters and shlokas from non-Critical versions, irrespective of which version it is, there are almost 650 chapters and just over 24,000 shlokas. Compared to such non-Critical versions, very few chapters have been excised from 'Bala', 'Ayodhya', 'Aranya', 'Kishkindha' or 'Sundara' kandas. The excision is primarily from 'Yuddha' and 'Uttara' kandas. The excision of shlokas is uniformly spread throughout the kandas, though most excision, relatively speaking, is from the 'Ayodhya', 'Yuddha' and 'Uttara' kandas.

Name of kanda	Number of chapters	Number of shlokas
Bala Kanda	76	1941
Ayodhya Kanda	111	3160
Aranya Kanda	71	2060
Kishkindha Kanda	66	1898
Sundara Kanda	66	2487
Yuddha Kanda	116	4435
Uttara Kanda	100	2689
Total	606	18,670

Valmiki is the first poet, *adi kavi*. By the time of classical Sanskrit literature, some prerequisites were defined for a work to attain the status of mahakavya. Kalidasa, Bharavi, Magha, Shri Harsha and Bhatti composed such works. Though these notions and definitions came later, the Valmiki Ramayana displays every characteristic of a mahakavya and is longer than any of these subsequent works. The story of how it came about is known to most people who are familiar with the Ramayana. The sage Valmiki had gone, with his disciple Bharadvaja, to bathe in the waters of the River Tamasa. There was a couple of *krouncha*[12] birds there, in the act of making

---

[12] Curlew.

love. Along came a hunter[13] and killed the male bird. As the female bird grieved, Valmiki was driven by compassion and the first shloka emerged from his lips. Since it was composed in an act of sorrow—*shoka*—this kind of composition came to be known as shloka. So the Ramayana tells us. Incidentally, this first shloka doesn't occur in the first chapter. It isn't the first shloka of the Valmiki Ramayana. The incident and the shloka occur in the second chapter. More specifically, it is the fourteenth shloka in the second chapter and is as follows. मा निषाद प्रतिष्ठां त्वमगमः शाश्वतीः समाः। यत्क्रौंचमिथुनादेकमवधी काममोहितम् ॥ 'O nishada! This couple of curlews was in the throes of passion and you killed one of them. Therefore, you will possess ill repute for an eternal number of years.'

Till a certain period of history, all Sanskrit works were in poetry or verse, not in prose. The Vedangas are limbs or auxiliaries and the six Vedangas are *shiksha*,[14] *chhanda*,[15] *vyakarana*,[16] *nirukta*,[17] *jyotisha*[18] and *kalpa*.[19] These are needed to understand not just the Vedas, but also Sanskrit works. Chhanda is one of these. Chhanda can be translated as metre and means something that is pleasing and delightful. Chhanda *shastra* is the study of metres or prosody. Sanskrit poetry wasn't about what we tend to identify as poetry today, the act of rhyming. Chhanda begins with the concept of *akshara*, akin to, but not exactly identical with, the English concept of syllable, that is, part of a word with a single vowel sound. Other than possessing a single vowel sound, an akshara must not begin with a vowel. Aksharas can be *hrasva* or *laghu*—light or L—and *guru*—heavy or G. Simply stated, with a short vowel, the akshara is L and with a long vowel, the akshara is G. There are some additional conditions, but we needn't get into those. Every verse consists of four *pada*s, the word pada meaning one quarter. Depending on how

---

[13] *Nishada.*
[14] Articulation and pronunciation.
[15] Prosody.
[16] Grammar.
[17] Etymology.
[18] Astronomy.
[19] Rituals.

many aksharas there are in a pada and the distribution of those
aksharas into L and G, there were a variety of metres. Depending
on the subject and the mood, the poet consciously chose a metre.
Analysing in this way, there were more than 1300 different metres.
One of the most popular was *anushtubh*. This figures prominently
in the Valmiki Ramayana, the Mahabharata and the Puranas. The
anushtubh structure meant eight aksharas in each pada, with a total
of thirty-two aksharas. In addition, for anushtubh, in every pada,
the fifth akshara would have to be L and the sixth akshara would
have to be G. In classical Sanskrit literature, conditions were also
applied to the seventh akshara, but such refinements came later. For
that first verse, the decomposition runs as follows: (1) L L L G L G
L G; (2) L G L G L G L G; (3) L L G G L G G L; (4) G G L L L G
G L. (1) *ma ni sha da pra tish tham*; (2) *tva ma ga mah shash vati sa
mah*; (3) *yat kroun cha mi thu na de ka*; (4) *ma va dhi ka ma mo hi
tam*. It is not that Valmiki only used anushtubh. There are actually
sixteen different metres in the Valmiki Ramayana.

   It is impossible to capture the beauty of chhanda in an English
translation. One can attempt to do a translation in verse, but it will
fail to convey the beauty. If the original text is poetry, one starts with
an initial question. Should one attempt a translation in verse or in
prose? This translation is based on the premise that the translation
should be as close as possible to the original Sanskrit text. One
should not take liberties with the text. This translation is therefore
almost a word-to-word rendering. If one sits down with the original
Sanskrit, there will be almost a perfect match. In the process,
deliberately so, the English is not as smooth as it might have been,
had one taken more liberties, and this is a conscious decision. Had
one attempted a translation in verse, one would perforce have had
to take more liberties. Hence, the choice of prose is also a deliberate
decision. As composers, there is quite a contrast between Valmiki
and Vedavyasa. Vedavyasa focuses on people and incidents. Rarely
does the Mahabharata attempt to describe nature, even if those
sections are on geography. In contrast, Valmiki's descriptions of
nature are lyrical and superlative, similar to Kalidasa. A translation
can never hope to transmit that flavour. There is no substitute to

reading the original Sanskrit, more so for the Valmiki Ramayana than for the Mahabharata.

Which occurred earlier, the incidents of the Ramayana or the Mahabharata? Which was composed earlier, the Ramayana or the Mahabharata? The Ramayana incidents occurred in treta yuga, the Mahabharata incidents in dvapara yuga. Rama was an earlier avatara, Krishna a later one. Hence, the obvious deduction is that the Ramayana incidents predated those of the Mahabharata—an inference also bolstered by the genealogy and astrological arguments mentioned earlier. However, and not just for the sake of being perverse, consider the following. Geographically, the incidents of the Mahabharata mostly occur along an east–west axis, along either side of what used to be called Uttarapath, the northern road, more familiar as Grand Trunk Road or National Highway (NH) 1 and 2. The incidents of the Ramayana often occur along a north–south axis, along what used to be called Dakshinapath, the southern road. Sanjeev Sanyal[20] has made the point that while Uttarapath remained stable over time, the Dakshinapath during Rama's time was different from the subsequent Dakshinapath, with the latter more like today's NH 44. To return to the point, the geographical terrain of the Mahabharata was restricted to the northern parts of the country, with the south rarely mentioned. The Aryan invasion theory has been discredited because of a multitude of reasons, but myths and perceptions that have lasted for decades are difficult to dispel. However, regardless of the Aryan invasion theory, the Ramayana reveals a familiarity with the geography of the southern parts of the country that the Mahabharata does not. The fighting in the Mahabharata, in the Kurukshetra War, is cruder and less refined. In the Ramayana, bears and apes may have fought using trees and boulders, but humans did not. A human did not tear apart another human's chest and drink blood. The urbanization depicted in the Ramayana is rarely found in the Mahabharata. We have cited these counter-arguments to make a simple point. Which incident

[20] *Land of the Seven Rivers: A Brief History of India's Geography*, Sanjeev Sanyal, Penguin, 2012.

occurred earlier and which text was composed earlier are distinct questions. They should not be confused. Even if the Ramayana incidents occurred before the incidents of the Mahabharata, that doesn't automatically mean the Ramayana was composed before the Mahabharata. The Rama story occurs in the Mahabharata, known as the 'Ramopakhyana' section. There is no such reference to the Mahabharata incidents in the Ramayana. This is the main reason for arguing that the Ramayana was composed before the Mahabharata.

The relationship between the 'Ramopakhyana' and the Valmiki Ramayana is also of scholarly interest. Which was earlier? Did one borrow from the other, or did both have a common origin? That need not concern us. What should be stressed is the obvious—the Valmiki Ramayana wasn't composed at a single point in time and there is a difference between the original composition and the present text, as given to us say in the Critical Edition. If bears and apes fought with the help of trees and boulders, and Angada suddenly kills someone with a weapon, that part is probably a later composition, with the composer having deviated from the original template. If a verse is in anushtubh, but deviates from the L–G pattern, this may have been a conscious decision, but in all probability, reflects the inferior skills of a subsequent poet. If we take the Critical text as it stands, while there are no direct references to the incidents of the Mahabharata, there are plenty of indirect allusions. There are shlokas reminiscent of the Bhagavatgita. When Bharata comes to Rama to inform him about Dasharatha's death, Rama asks him about the welfare of the kingdom, reminiscent of similar questions asked by Narada to Yudhishthira. In the Valmiki Ramayana, there are references to kings of the lunar dynasty (Yayati) and incidents (Ilvala and Vatapi) that are only described in the Mahabharata. The evidence may be circumstantial and speculative, but it is the following. It is as if the later composers knew about the Mahabharata incidents and the text, but consciously avoided any direct references.

Why is another translation of the Valmiki Ramayana needed? Surely, there are plenty floating around. That's not quite true. Indeed, there are several translations of the Valmiki Ramayana, including some recent ones, but they are abridged. In any act of abridgement, some sections are omitted or summarized. Abridged translations, no matter how good they are, are not quite a substitute for unabridged translations, which bring in the nuances too. To the best of my knowledge, the list of unabridged translations of the Valmiki Ramayana is the following: (1) Ralph T.H. Griffith;[21] (2) Manmatha Nath Dutt;[22] (3) Hari Prasad Shastri;[23] (4) Desiraju Hanumanta Rao and K.M.K. Murthy;[24] and (5) Robert P. Goldman.[25] Given the timelines, the Goldman translation is the only one based on the Critical Edition. Having translated the Mahabharata,[26] it was natural to translate the Valmiki Ramayana. The intention was to do a translation that was popular in style. That meant a conscious decision to avoid the use of diacritical marks, as would have been the case had one used IAST (International Alphabet of Sanskrit Transliteration). If diacritical marks are not going to be used, there may be problems rendering names, proper and geographic. We have sought to make the English renderings as phonetic as is possible. Thus, we use 'Goutama' to refer to the sage of that name—although others have often referred to him elsewhere as 'Gautama'. We have chosen Goutama on the logic that if Gomati is not Gamati, why should Goutama be rendered as Gautama? There remains the question of what one does with vowel sounds. How does one differentiate the short sound from the long? Should Rama be written as Raama and Sita as Seeta? That seemed to be too artificial and contrary to popular usage. On rare occasions, this does

---

[21] *The Ramayana of Valmiki, translated into English verse*, Ralph T.H. Griffith, E.Z. Lazarus and Company, London, 1895.

[22] *Valmiki Ramayana*, Manmatha Nath Dutt, R.K. Bhatia, Calcutta, 1891–92. Manmatha Nath Dutt (Shastri) was one of India's greatest translators (in English). He also translated the Mahabharata and several Puranas.

[23] *The Ramayana of Valmiki*, Hari Prasad Shastri, Shanti Sadan, London, 1952.

[24] This is net based, on the site http://www.valmikiramayan.net/ and leaves out 'Uttara Kanda'.

[25] *The Ramayana of Valmiki: An Epic of Ancient India*, Robert P. Goldman, Princeton University Press, 1984 to 2016.

[26] *The Mahabharata*, Bibek Debroy, Penguin (India), 10 volumes, 2010–2014, boxed set 2015.

xxiv   INTRODUCTION

cause a problem, with a danger of confusion between the ape Taara and his daughter Taaraa, Vali's wife. Such occasions are however rare and we have explained them. However, there are also instances where we have deviated from popular usage. Hanumat is a case in point, where Hanuman seemed to be too contrary to grammatical principles. There are some words that defy translation, *dharma* is an example. Hence, we have not even tried to translate such words. The Goldman translation is academic in style. This translation's style is more popular. Therefore, there is no attempt to overburden the reader with extensive notes. However, a straight translation may not be self-explanatory. Hence, we have put in footnotes, just enough to explain, without stretching the translation.

As with the Mahabharata, the Valmiki Ramayana is a text about dharma. Dharma means several different things—the dharma of the four *varna*s and the four *ashrama*s, the classes and stages of life; the governance template of *raja dharma*, the duty of kings; principles of good conduct, *sadachara*; and the pursuit of objectives of human existence, *purushartha*—dharma, *artha* and *kama*. As with the Mahabharata, the Valmiki Ramayana is a *smriti* text. It has a human origin and composer, it is not a *shruti* text. Smriti texts are society and context specific. We should not try to judge and evaluate individuals and actions on the basis of today's value judgements. In addition, if the span of composition was one thousand years, from 500 BCE to 500 CE, those value judgements also change. The later composers and interpreters may have had problems with what the earlier composers authored. A case in point is when Sita is being abducted by Ravana. At a certain point in time, men and women universally wore an upper garment and a lower one. When she is being abducted through the sky, Sita casts aside and throws down not just her ornaments, but her upper garment too. As this translation will illustrate, this caused problems for subsequent composers and interpreters.

To return to the notion of dharma—transcending all those collective templates of dharma—there is one that is individual in nature. Regardless of those collective templates, an individual has to decide what the right course of action is and there is no universal answer as to what is right and what is wrong. There are always contrary pulls of dharma, with two notions of dharma pulling in different directions. It is not immediately obvious which is superior. Given the trade-offs, an individual makes a choice and suffers the consequences. Why is there an impression that these individual conflicts of dharma are more manifest in the Mahabharata than in the Ramayana?

The answer probably lies in the nature of these two texts. What is the difference between a novel and a long story, even when both have multiple protagonists? The difference between a novel and a long story is probably not one of length. A novel seeks to present the views of all protagonists. Thus, the Mahabharata is a bit like a novel, in so far as that trait is concerned. A long story does not seek to look at incidents and actions from the point of view of every protagonist. It is concerned with the perspective of one primary character, to the exclusion of others.

If this distinction is accepted, the Valmiki Ramayana has the characteristics of a long story. It is Ramayana. Therefore, it is primarily from Rama's point of view. We aren't told what Bharata or Lakshmana thought, or for that matter, Urmila, Mandavi or Shrutakirti. There is little that is from Sita's point of view too. That leads to the impression that the Mahabharata contains more about individual conflicts of dharma. For the Valmiki Ramayana, from Rama's point of view, the conflicts of dharma aren't innumerable. On that exile to the forest, why did he take Sita and Lakshmana along with him? Was Shurpanakha's disfigurement warranted? Why did he unfairly kill Vali? Why did he make Sita go through tests of purity, not once, but twice? Why did he unfairly kill Shambuka? Why did he banish Lakshmana? At one level, one can argue these are decisions by a personified divinity and therefore, mere humans cannot comprehend and judge the motives. At another level, the unhappiness with Rama's decisions led to the composition of alternative versions of the Ramayana. Note that Sita's questions about dharma remained unanswered. If you are going to the forest as an ascetic, why have you got weapons with you? If the *rakshasas*[27]

---

[27] Demons.

are causing injuries to hermits, punishing the rakshasas is Bharata's job, now that he is the king. Why are you dabbling in this? Note also Rama's justification at the time of Sita's first test. It wasn't about what others would think, that justification came later. The initial harsh words reflected his own questions about Sita's purity. Thus, Rama's conflicts over dharma also exist. It is just that in the Valmiki Ramayana, it is about one individual alone.

In conclusion, this translation is an attempt to get readers interested in reading the unabridged Valmiki Ramayana. Having read abridged versions, and there is no competition with those, to appreciate the nuances better, one should read the unabridged. And, to appreciate the beauty of the poetry, one should then be motivated to read the text in Sanskrit. A translation is only a bridge and an unsatisfactory one at that.

CHAPTER THREE

Aranya Kanda

Chapter 3(1)

Rama, in control of his *atman*, entered the impenetrable and great forest of Dandakaranya[1] and saw a circle of hermitages of the ascetics. *Kusha* grass and bark were strewn around and the place was pervaded by all the signs of the *brahman*. It blazed and was difficult to look at, like the solar disc in the sky. The region was always the refuge of all creatures. Large numbers of *apsaras* always worshipped it and danced around there. There were large altars for sacrificial fires and ladles, vessels, deer skin and kusha grass. There were large trees and auspicious trees in the forest, laden with succulent fruit.

[1] This is the right place to mention the story of Dandakaranya. Ikshvaku's youngest son was Danda. Since he was wicked, his father exiled him. Danda went to the region around the Vindhya mountains and built a kingdom there, with a capital in Madhumanta. Danda consorted with the demons there and became the disciple of Shukracharya, the preceptor of the demons. However, he molested Shukracharya's daughter and was cursed by him. Madhumanta was destroyed and the area came to be known as Dandaka, *danda* also being punishment. The southern part of Dandakaranya, to the south of Madhumanta, was known as Janasthana. While Madhumanta was cursed, the southern part was exempted from the curse. Therefore, people began to reside in Janasthana, though Madhumanta was deserted. Ravana made Khara the ruler of Janasthana. When Rama entered Dandakaranya, with a desire that Rama should destroy the demons, the sages continually urged him towards the south, towards Janasthana. In the process, an area that was once under the Ikshvaku empire would again be brought under it.

Homage was rendered through sacrificial offerings and oblations. The place echoed with sounds of the brahman. Wild flowers were everywhere. There were female elephants with male elephants. It was populated by aged sages who possessed the radiance of the sun and the fire. They were self-controlled and were attired in bark and antelope skin, surviving on fruits and roots. The region was adorned by these sacred and supreme *rishi*s, who were restrained in what they ate. Resounding with the sound of the brahman, it was as remarkable as Brahma's abode. It was ornamented by those immensely fortunate *brahmana*s who knew about the brahman. The handsome Raghava saw that circle of hermitages of the ascetics. The immensely energetic one advanced, taking off the string from his great bow.

The *maharshi*s possessed divine insight. They were delighted to see that Rama and the illustrious Sita were approaching. The followers of *dharma* saw him,[2] like a rising moon. Firm in their vows, they received them, with all the auspicious rites. The residents of the forest were astounded on seeing Rama's form. He was handsome, powerful, prosperous and graceful and attired well. All the residents of the forest did not blink and were surprised to see Vaidehi, Lakshmana and Rama. All those immensely fortunate ones were engaged in the welfare of all beings and received the guest, Raghava, in their huts made out of leaves. Those immensely fortunate ones were like the fire. Following the indicated rites, the followers of dharma honoured Rama and received him properly, offering him water. All those in the hermitages knew about dharma. They offered the great-souled one roots, flowers and fruits from the forest. Joining their hands in salutation, they said, 'The king ensures adherence to dharma among the people. He is the immensely illustrious refuge. He is revered and worshipped. He wields the staff of chastisement and is a senior. O Raghava! He is a fourth part of Indra and protects the subjects.[3] Therefore, the king is worshipped by the people and enjoys the best among objects of pleasure. We reside in your kingdom and you are the one who will protect us.

[2] Rama.

[3] The king was created with one fourth of the parts from each of the guardians of the world, Indra being one of these guardians.

Whether you are in the city or whether you are in the forest, you
are the king and the lord of the people. O king! We have cast aside
our own staffs of chastisement. We have conquered anger and we
have conquered our senses. We, stores of austerities, must always
be protected by you, like a foetus inside a womb.' Having said
this, they worshipped Raghava and Lakshmana with fruits, roots,
flowers and many other kinds of forest fare. There were other
successful ascetics, who were like the fire. Following the proper and
appropriate rites, they worshipped him, like the lord of the gods.

Chapter 3(2)

Rama was thus treated to hospitality. When the sun arose, he
took leave of all the sages and entered the forest. It was full
of a large number of animals and frequented by tigers and wolves.
There were devastated trees, creepers and bushes and waterbodies
that were terrible to behold. The birds did not chirp, but the sound
of crickets could be heard. Followed by Lakshmana, Rama saw that
the centre of the forest was like that. In the middle of the forest,
surrounded by many such terrible animals, Kakutstha saw one who
lived off human flesh. He was like the summit of a mountain and
uttered a loud noise. His eyes were deep and his mouth was huge
and horrible. His stomach was also horrible. He was gruesome,
malformed, tall, hideous and horrible to behold. He was attired
in a tiger skin that was wet with fat and smeared with blood.
All creatures found him to be dreadful, like the Destroyer with a
gaping mouth.[4] His iron spear had impaled on it three lions, four
tigers, two wolves, ten spotted deer and the fat-smeared, tusked
and gigantic head of an elephant. He roared in a loud voice. On
seeing Rama, Lakshmana and Maithilee Sita, he became enraged
and rushed towards them, like the Destroyer towards beings. As he
roared loudly, the earth seemed to quake. He grasped Vaidehi in

---

[4] Yama.

his lap, went some distance away, and told them, 'You wear matted hair and are attired in bark. With your wife, you will not live for a long time. You have entered Dandakaranya with arrows, bows and swords in your hands.[5] What kind of an ascetic are you, since you are residing here with a woman? You are wicked and following *adharma*. You have defiled the status of a sage? With my weapons, I roam around in this impenetrable forest and am a *rakshasa*[6] named Viradha. I always devour the flesh of rishis. This beautiful woman will be my wife. The two of you are wicked. I will drink your blood in an encounter.' The insolent and evil-souled Viradha said this.

On hearing these proud words, Janaka's daughter was terrified. In her anxiety, Sita trembled, like a plantain tree in a storm. On seeing that the auspicious Sita was in Viradha's lap, with a dry mouth, Raghava addressed Lakshmana in these words. 'O amiable one! Look at the one who created herself from King Janaka.[7] She is my wife, auspicious in conduct. But she is in Viradha's lap. This illustrious princess was reared in a great deal of happiness. O Lakshmana! Kaikeyee had a cherished boon. Exactly as she had intended, the objective has swiftly befallen us today. She is a far-sighted person and was not content with obtaining the kingdom for her son. Though I am engaged in the welfare of all creatures, I was dispatched to the forest. My mother, the one in the middle,[8] has achieved her desire today. O Soumitri! Vaidehi being touched by another is a greater misery for me than my father banishing me or the loss of my own kingdom.' In a grieving voice that choked with tears, Kakutstha said this. Enraged, like a sighing serpent, Lakshmana said, 'You should not be like one without a protector. You are the protector of all creatures and are Vasava's equal. O Kakutstha! When I am serving you, why are you tormented? In my rage, I will now slay the rakshasa with my arrow. Viradha's life is over and the earth will drink his blood. I was angry with Bharata when he desired the kingdom. I will release that rage

---

[5] Pointing out the anomaly of ascetics (dressed in bark) wielding weapons and apparently finding pleasure with a wife.

[6] Demon.

[7] Since she was born from the earth and was not a biological daughter.

[8] This is an inconsistency, since Sumitra is the one in the middle.

on Viradha now, like the wielder of the *vajra* releasing the vajra on a mountain. This speedy and long arrow will receive a greater force from the strength of my arms. It will descend on his large chest and take away life from his body, which will then whirl around and fall down on the ground.'

Chapter 3(3)

At this, Viradha spoke again, making the forest echo with his words. 'You should ask yourself. Who are you and where are you going? Tell me.' The rakshasa's face blazed like the fire and Rama told him about himself and the Ikshvaku lineage, since the extremely energetic one kept asking. 'Know that we follow the conduct of *kshatriya*s, though we are roaming around in the forest now. However, we wish to know about you too. You roam around in Dandaka. Who are you?' Viradha replied to Rama, for whom, truth was his valour. 'O king! O Raghava! I will tell you. Listen. I am the son of Java and my mother is Shatahrada. All the rakshasas on earth refer to me as Viradha. Having performed austerities, I received the favours of Brahma. In this world, I would not be slain by any weapon, nor would it be able to penetrate me or slice through me. Cast aside this woman. Forget about her and go wherever you came from. Unless you run away, you will swiftly be robbed of your lives.' The rakshasa's eyes were red with rage. Viradha was wicked in intelligence and his body was malformed. Rama answered him. 'O inferior one! Shame on you. In the pursuit of something that is inferior, it is certain that you are looking for your death. Remain steadfast in the encounter. You will not be able to escape with your life.'

Rama strung his bow and affixed extremely sharp arrows to it. To slay the rakshasa, he aimed swiftly. From the excellent bow that had been strung, he released seven gold-shafted arrows that were extremely swift, like Suparna[9] or the wind. Tufted with peacock

[9] Garuda.

feathers and like fire, they penetrated Viradha's body and smeared with blood, fell down on the ground. He roared extremely loudly and raised a spear that was like Shakra's standard. Having seized it, he dazzled, like the Destroyer with a gaping mouth. That spear was like the vajra and blazed in the sky, like a fire. Rama, supreme among those who wielded weapons, severed it with two of his arrows. Soumitri severed the left arm of that terrible one. Rama swiftly severed the rakshasa's right arm. With his arms severed, the rakshasa quickly fainted and fell down on the ground like a cloud, resembling a mountain shattered by the vajra. Viradha uttered these words to Kakutstha, bull among men. 'O son![10] I know you to be Kousalya's excellent son and I also know the immensely fortunate Vaidehi and the immensely illustrious Lakshmana. I assumed this rakshasa body because of an extremely terrible curse. I am a *gandharva*[11] named Tumburu and was cursed by Vaishravana.[12] When I sought his favours, the immensely illustrious one[13] said, "Dasharatha's son, Rama, will kill you in an encounter and you will then obtain your natural form and go to heaven." Because I was attracted to Rambha,[14] I was not present when I should have been and King Vaishravana had angrily addressed me in this way. Through your favours, I have now been freed from that terrible curse and will go to my own abode. O scorcher of enemies! May you fare well. O son! The powerful Sharabhanga, with dharma in his soul, resides one-and-a-half *yojana*s[15] from here and that maharshi is as resplendent as the sun. Quickly go to him and he will tell you what is best for you. O Rama! Fling me into a pit and go safely. This is the eternal dharma for rakshasas who have lost their lives.[16] Those who are flung into pits obtain the eternal worlds.' Viradha, afflicted by arrows, spoke to Kakutstha in this way. The mighty-armed one

---

[10] The word used is *tata*. Though it means son, it is affectionately used for anyone who is younger or junior.

[11] Semi-divine species, companions of Kubera, celestial musicians.

[12] Kubera.

[13] Kubera.

[14] An apsara.

[15] A yojana is a measure of distance, between 8 and 9 miles.

[16] That is, rakshasas were buried.

gave up his body and reached heaven. The one with ears like cones emitted a loud roar from his throat. As Viradha was flung into a pit, he roared in a terrible tone. Having slain the rakshasa, the ones with the colourful and golden bows rescued Maithilee. Delighted, like the moon and the sun stationed in the firmament, they continued to travel through the great forest.

Chapter 3(4)

Having slain that fiercely strong rakshasa, Viradha, in the forest, the valiant one embraced Sita and comforted her. Rama spoke to his brother, Lakshmana, who blazed in his energy. 'This forest is impenetrable and difficult and we are not used to roaming around in the forest. We should quickly go to Sharabhanga, the store of austerities.' Raghava went towards Sharabhanga's hermitage, who possessed divine powers through his austerities and was in control of his atman. Near Sharabhanga's hermitage, he saw a great and wonderful sight. He saw the lord of the gods astride a chariot that did not touch the ground. His form was resplendent, like the complexion of the sun and the fire. The god dazzled in blazing ornaments and garments. He was worshipped by many divinities and great-souled ones. The chariot was yoked to tawny steeds and travelled through the sky. He could be seen from a distance, like a young and rising sun, like excellent and white clouds, or like the lunar disc. There was a white umbrella, colourfully decorated with garlands. Two excellent women held two superb and extremely expensive whisks above his head and fanned him. The god was in the sky and gandharvas, immortals, siddhas[17] and many supreme rishis praised him with their eloquent hymns.

On seeing Shatakratu, Rama told Lakshmana, 'We have earlier heard about Shakra Puruhuta's horses. These divine and

[17] Successful sages.

tawny ones that are in the sky must certainly belong to him. O tiger among men! There are hundreds and hundreds of young ones stationed around the chariot, sporting earrings and with swords in their hands. All of them are wearing blazing necklaces around their chests. O Soumitri! Their forms are blazing and they seem to be twenty-five years old. For the gods, the age always remains constant and these tigers among men are seen to be handsome. O Lakshmana! For a while, remain here with Vaidehi. Let me clearly find out who is the dazzling one on the chariot.' He asked Soumitri to remain there. Kakutstha then advanced towards Sharabhanga's hermitage. Shachi's consort saw that Rama was approaching. Having taken Sharabhanga's permission, he told the gods, 'This Rama is coming here. You should nudge him towards his vow.[18] Until then, he should not speak to me, or see me.[19] When he is victorious and successful, I will soon show myself to him. He has to perform an extremely great task and it is a task that anyone else will find extremely difficult.' Therefore, the wielder of the vajra[20] worshipped the ascetic and took his leave. Using the chariot that was yoked to horses, the destroyer of enemies went to heaven. The one with the one thousand eyes left.

Sharabhanga was seated near the *agnihotra* fire and Raghava approached him, with his companions.[21] Rama, Sita and Lakshmana touched his feet. Having obtained his permission, they sat down. They were also invited to stay there. Raghava asked about Shakra's arrival and Sharabhanga told Raghava everything about this. 'O Rama! That granter of boons wishes to take me to Brahma's world. Through my fierce austerities I have obtained that which is extremely difficult for those with uncleansed souls to get. O tiger among men! I knew that you were not very far away now. I will

---

[18] Of killing the rakshasas.

[19] This requires explanation. When soliciting a boon about who could kill him, Ravana forgot to mention humans and therefore, Ravana could only be killed by a human. Until this happened, if Indra spoke to Rama, Rama's divine nature would have been revealed and he wouldn't have been able to kill Ravana. This was to be avoided.

[20] Indra.

[21] Lakshmana and Sita. Once Indra had departed, they joined him.

not go to Brahma's world without first seeing my beloved guest. Having met, I will go to heaven, frequented by the gods. O tiger among men! I have obtained the auspicious and eternal world of Brahma and others in the vault of heaven. Accept them from me.' Raghava, tiger among men and accomplished in all the sacred texts, addressed the rishi Sharabhanga in these words. 'O great sage! I will also obtain all the worlds. I only wish that you indicate a residence for me in this forest.' He was thus addressed by Raghava, who was like Shakra in his strength. The immensely wise Sharabhanga again spoke these words. 'In this auspicious region meant for ascetics, go to Suteekshna. In this beautiful forest, he will tell you where you should reside.[22] O tiger among men! O son![23] That is your path. However, remain for a moment and see me give up my body, just as a snake casts off old skin.' With clarified butter, the one who knew about mantras ignited a fire. The immensely energetic Sharabhanga entered the fire. The fire consumed the great-souled one's body hair, hair, old skin, bones, flesh and blood. From the fire, a young and radiant Sharabhanga emerged and he was like the fire himself. He passed over the worlds where great-souled rishis offered oblations into the fire, and the world of the gods and went to Brahma's world. Going to the world meant for the performers of auspicious deeds, the bull among brahmanas saw the grandfather[24] and his companions. The grandfather also saw the brahmana and, happy and delighted, welcomed him.

Chapter 3(5)

When Sharabhanga went to heaven, a group of sages assembled and approached Kakutstha Rama, blazing in his

[22] With Sharabhanga dead, Rama could have resided there. But Sharabhanga directs him to Suteekshna and Suteekshna directs him to Agastya. This is part of the plan to make Rama head southwards.

[23] The word used is tata.

[24] Brahma.

energy. There were *vaikhanasas*,[25] *valakhilyas*,[26] *samprakshalas*,[27] *marichipas*,[28] *ashmakuttas*,[29] many sages who subsisted on leaves, *dantaulukhalinas*,[30] others who were *unmajjakas*,[31] sages who subsisted on water, others who subsisted on air, those who made their abodes under the open sky, those who slept on the bare ground, self-controlled ones who lived on high ground, those who were attired in wet garments, those who always meditated and performed austerities and those who tormented themselves with the five fires.[32] All of them possessed the radiance of the brahman and were firm in their devotion to *yoga*. Those ascetics came to Rama in Sharabhanga's hermitage. Those who knew about dharma approached Rama, supreme among the upholders of dharma. The large number of self-controlled sages spoke to the one who was supremely knowledgeable about dharma. 'You are a *maharatha*[33] on earth and belong to the Ikshvaku lineage. You are the foremost of protectors, like Maghavan among the gods. Your fame and valour is known in the three worlds. You are also invested with the truthful vow given to your father and all types of dharma. O great-souled one! O one who knows about dharma! O one who is devoted to dharma! O protector! We have approached you for a purpose and you should pardon us for this. O son![34] Great adharma befalls a king who receives a sixth part[35] as taxes, but does not protect the subjects like his sons.

---

[25] Sages believed to have been born from Brahma's nails.

[26] Sages believed to have been born from Brahma's hair. There are 60,000 such sages and they are the sizes of thumbs. They precede the sun's chariot.

[27] Sages believed to have been born from the water used to wash Brahma's feet.

[28] Those who subsist on the rays of the sun and the moon. There may also be some connection with the sage Marichi, who was born through Brahma's mental powers.

[29] Those who eat raw grain after it has been ground on stone.

[30] Those who use their teeth as mortars, that is, they eat raw grain that has not been ground.

[31] Those who perform austerities by submerging themselves in water.

[32] Those who performed austerities with four fires around them and the sun overhead.

[33] Great warrior, more specifically, a maharatha is someone who can single-handedly fight ten thousand warriors.

[34] The word used is tata.

[35] Of production.

He must protect their lives like his own life, like his own desires and like his own son. He must always be engaged in protecting those who reside within his kingdom. O Rama! Such a person obtains everlasting fame for many years. He attains Brahma's abode and achieves greatness there. Sages survive on roots and fruits and follow supreme dharma. A king who follows dharma and protects his subjects obtains a one-fourth share in their merits.[36] There are many great brahmanas who have resorted to *vanaprastha*.[37] O Rama! You are the protector. However, despite that, they are being fiercely slain by the rakshasas. Come and behold the bodies of the sages with cleansed souls. In this forest, there are many of them, who have been killed in many ways by the fierce rakshasas. This great carnage is going on among the abodes along the river Pampa, along Mandakinee and in the residences in Chitrakuta. We cannot tolerate this injury caused to the ascetics. In this forest, these are the horrible deeds being perpetrated by the rakshasas, who are terrible in their acts. You are the one who offers refuge. Therefore, in search of protection, we have come to you. O Rama! Protect us and slay the ones who roam during the night.' Kakutstha heard this from the ascetics who were performing austerities. The one with dharma in his soul told all the ascetics, 'You should not speak to me in this way. O ascetics! Command me. Roaming around as I willed, I have come here to accomplish your objective. I will thereby obtain great fruits from residing in the forest. In a battle, I wish to slay the rakshasas, the enemies of the ascetics.' With Lakshmana, the one whose soul was firm in its devotion to dharma granted this assurance to the stores of austerities. With the stores of austerities and with the one who was noble in conduct,[38] the brave one advanced towards Suteekshna.

---

[36] Of the merits obtained by the sages, though this is true of all subjects in general.

[37] In the four stages (*ashramas*) of life, *brahmacharya* is the first, followed by *garhasthya*, vanaprastha and *sannyasa*, in that order. Vanaprastha is when one resorts to the forest.

[38] Obviously meaning Sita.

Chapter 3(6)

With his brother and with Sita, Rama, the scorcher of enemies, went to Suteekshna's hermitage on foot, accompanied by the brahmanas. He travelled a long distance and crossed rivers with a lot of water. He saw a mountain that was as large as a tall cloud. With Sita, the two Raghavas, supreme among the Ikshvaku lineage, entered a forest that was always full of many kinds of trees. They entered that terrible forest, with trees laden with many flowers and fruits. In a lonely spot, they saw the hermitage, decorated with garlands of rags.[39] The ascetic was seated there, sporting matted hair and dirty lotuses that grow in the mud. Following the prescribed rites, Rama spoke to Suteekshna, store of austerities. 'O illustrious one! I am Rama and I have come here to meet you. O one who knows about dharma! O maharshi! O one for whom truth is his valour! Therefore, speak to me.' He looked at the brave Rama, supreme among those who uphold dharma and embraced him in his arms. He said, 'O brave one! O Rama! O supreme among those who uphold dharma! You are indeed welcome. With you suddenly having come to this hermitage, it is as if I have obtained a protector. O immensely illustrious one! O brave one! I have been waiting for you. Until you arrived, I could not cast aside my body on this earth and ascend to the world of the gods. I had heard that you have been dislodged from the kingdom and have reached Chitrakuta. O Kakutstha! Shatakratu, the king of the gods, came here and told me that because of my auspicious deeds, I have won all the worlds, cherished by the gods and the rishis. I have conquered them through my austerities. Through my favours, with your wife and with Lakshmana, find pleasure there.' Because of his fierce austerities, the maharshi, truthful in speech, blazed. Rama, in control of his soul, replied, like Vasava to Brahma. 'O great sage! I will myself obtain those worlds. I wish that you indicate a place where I can live in this forest. You are accomplished in every way and are engaged in the welfare of all beings. The great-souled Sharabhanga, descended from Goutama, told me this.'

---

[39] The word used is *cheera*, meaning bark or rags worn by ascetics as garments.

The maharshi, famous in the worlds, was addressed by Rama in this way. Overcome by great happiness, he replied in these sweet words. 'O Rama! This hermitage possesses all the qualities and you will find pleasure here. Large numbers of rishis wander around here and there are always roots and fruits. However, large numbers of excellent deer come to this hermitage. They are without fear. Having tempted us and wandered around, they return.' Having heard the words of the maharshi, Lakshmana's patient elder brother stretched his bow, with an arrow affixed to it, and said, 'O extremely fortunate one! When those large numbers of deer arrive, I will slay them with extremely sharp arrows that are as radiant as the vajra. However, because of your compassion, there may be no greater misery for you than this. Therefore, it is not befitting that I should dwell in this hermitage for a long time.' Rama spoke to the granter of boons in this way and meanwhile, evening arrived. Having worshipped the western *sandhya*,[40] he[41] fashioned an abode there. When evening was over, the great-souled Suteekshna saw that night had arrived. He himself treated them hospitably and gave the two bulls among men auspicious food that ascetics could eat.

Chapter 3(7)

With Soumitri, Rama was honoured by Suteekshna and spent the night there. He awoke when it was morning. At the right time, Raghava awoke with Sita and performed his ablutions in cool water that was fragrant with the smell of lotuses. At the appropriate time, in the refuge of the ascetics in the forest, Rama, Lakshmana and Vaidehi followed the rites and rendered offerings to the fire and the gods. Cleansed of sin, they saw that the sun had arisen. They went to Suteekshna and gently spoke these words. 'O illustrious one! We have been honoured by a revered one like you and have slept happily.

---

[40] Sandhya is any conjunction of day and night. Hence, it is dawn, as well as dusk.
[41] Rama.

Since the sages are hurrying us, we seek your permission to leave. We wish to quickly see the entire circle of hermitages, where the rishis, auspicious in their conduct, reside in Dandakaranya. We desire your permission so that we can leave with these bulls among sages. They are self-controlled and always devoted to dharma and austerities, like fires with flames. When the sun becomes too hot, it will be impossible to tolerate the scorching, like an ignoble person obtaining prosperity through undesirable means. We desire to leave before that.' With Soumitri and Sita, Raghava worshipped at the sage's feet and said this. When they touched his feet, the bull among sages raised them. Embracing them tightly, he affectionately addressed them in these words. 'O Rama! May you proceed safely along your path, with Soumitri and with this Sita, who is with you and follows you like a shadow. O brave one! Behold the beautiful hermitages of those who dwell in Dandakaranya. These ascetics have cleansed their souls through austerities. There are forests where fruits, roots and flowers grow well. There are extensive herds of deer and calm flocks of birds. There are clumps of blooming lotuses in placid waters. *Karandavas*[42] are spread out in the lakes and ponds. You will see beautiful waterfalls in the mountains. There are pleasant groves filled with the calls of peacocks. O child! Go. O Soumitri! You also go. However, when you have seen all this, come back to my hermitage again.' Thus addressed, Kakutstha, with Lakshmana, agreed. They circumambulated the sage and got ready to leave. The large-eyed Sita gave the brothers auspicious quivers, bows and sparkling swords. They girded those auspicious quivers and the bows that made loud sounds. Rama and Lakshmana emerged from the hermitage and left.

Chapter 3(8)

Having obtained Suteekshna's permission, the descendant of the Raghu lineage departed. Vaidehi addressed her husband

---

[42] Type of duck.

in gentle words. 'This dharma is extremely subtle and great and has been brought about by destiny.[43] It is possible to withdraw from a hardship that can come about through desire. There are three kinds of hardships that can come about through desire. False utterances are the most severe of these. However, there are two others that are also serious—intercourse with someone else's wife and fierceness without enmity. O Raghava! You have never uttered false words in the past, nor will you in the future. The desire for someone else's wife is destructive of dharma. How can you ever have that?[44] O mighty-armed one! Since you have conquered your senses, I know that you are capable of countering all of these. O one who is handsome to behold! I know all the senses are under your control. The third is the one of fiercely causing injury to the lives of others. That enmity may be due to confusion and it has presented itself before us. O brave one! You have given a pledge to the residents of Dandakaranya, for the sake of protecting the rishis, that you will slay the rakshasas in an encounter. It has been heard that this is the reason you are leaving for the Dandaka forest[45] with your brother, wielding a bow and arrows. On seeing that you are leaving in this way, my mind is full of worries. Thinking about what you will do, I am convinced that nothing beneficial will come out of this. O brave one! This departure towards Dandaka does not appeal to me. I will tell you the reasons. Listen to what I have to say. You will go to the forest with your brother, holding a bow and arrows in your hand. On seeing all those who roam around in the forest, you will exhaust your arrows on them. For kshatriyas on earth, a bow is like kindling offered into a fire. If it is near at hand, their energy and strength are greatly ignited. O mighty-armed one! In earlier times, there was an ascetic. He was pure and truthful in speech. Birds and animals used to frequent that auspicious forest. Indra, Shachi's consort, wished to create

[43] The dharma of kshatriyas to kill rakshasas. However, the rakshasas are being killed without any valid reason. They have caused no injury to Rama, Lakshmana and Sita.

[44] The only possibility that remains is fierceness without enmity.

[45] The southern parts of Dandaka.

an impediment for the ascetic.[46] He adopted the form of a warrior and went to the hermitage, with a sword in his hand. He left that excellent sword in the hermitage. Following the prescribed rites,[47] he left it with the virtuous ascetic. Having obtained the weapon in trust, he[48] thereafter sought to protect himself. Wishing to protect himself, he would hold it while roaming around in the forest. Wherever he went, even if it was to collect roots and fruits, because he desired to protect himself, he would not go without the sword. Always carrying the weapon around, gradually, the store of austerities abandoned his own intelligence and determination about ascetic pursuits and assumed a fierce trait. Because of attachment to the weapon, the confused sage became addicted to fierce pursuits and was dragged into adharma. He went to hell. I am not trying to teach. Because of affection and the great respect I hold for you, I am reminding you. You should never permit the act of picking up the bow and turn your mind towards causing enmity and slaying the rakshasas who have found a refuge in Dandaka. O brave one! In this world, it is not desirable to kill someone who has committed no crime. For kshatriyas and brave ones who have turned their minds to dwelling in the forest, the bow must only be taken up to protect those who are afflicted. What is this weapon? What is this forest? Who is a kshatriya? What are austerities? For us, all these are contradictory. The dharma of the country is what must be respected. O noble one! Association with weapons taints the intelligence. Follow the dharma of kshatriyas when you return to Ayodhya again. Let my affection for my father-in-law and mothers-in-law be eternal. Since you have given up the kingdom, become like a sage. *Artha* flows from dharma. Happiness results from dharma. Everything is obtained through dharma. Dharma is the essence of this universe. Those who are accomplished in dharma make attempts to control themselves and restrain their souls. Happiness cannot be obtained through the pursuit of

[46] Austerities lead to powers and Indra was always worried that ascetics would acquire powers and dislodge him. Therefore, he created impediments.

[47] For leaving something in trust. He would pick up the sword later.

[48] The ascetic.

happiness. O amiable one! Always follow pure intelligence and
observe austerities in the forest. You know everything about
the truth of the three worlds. I have told you this because of the
fickleness of feminine nature. Who is capable of telling you about
dharma? Use your intelligence to discuss this with your younger
brother. Without any delay, do what pleases you.'

Chapter 3(9)

Full of devotion, Vaidehi addressed these words to her husband.
Established in dharma, Rama heard this and then replied to
Maithilee. 'O queen! As is appropriate for you, you have spoken
gentle and beneficial words. O one who knows about dharma! O
Janaka's daughter! This befits your lineage. O queen! In response
to your words, I can say no more than the following. "As long as a
kshatriya wields a bow, the word affliction should not be heard."
The sages who reside in Dandakaranya are firm in their vows and
are afflicted. O Sita! Taking me to be a refuge, they have themselves
sought refuge with me. They are devoted to dharma. They reside
in the forest and survive on roots and fruits. They are terrified of
the rakshasas, the perpetrators of cruel deeds, and cannot find any
happiness. The terrible rakshasas subsist on human flesh and are
devouring them. The sages who live in Dandakaranya are being
eaten. The excellent brahmanas came to me and told me this. I heard
the words that descended from their mouths. Having worshipped at
their feet, I spoke those words to them. Show me your favours.
This is a source of great shame to me, that the brahmanas should
present themselves before me in that way. I asked that assembly
of brahmanas, "What should I do?" All of them, eloquent in
speech, addressed me in these words. "There are many rakshasas
in Dandakaranya and they can assume any form at will. O Rama!
They are oppressing us. Therefore, you should protect us. O
unblemished one! At the time of offering oblations and on other
auspicious occasions, those invincible rakshasas, who survive on

human flesh, oppress us. The sages and ascetics are thus oppressed
by the rakshasas. In searching for a solution, we found you to be
our supreme refuge. Through the strength of our austerities, we
are capable of slaying those who roam around in the night. But
we do not wish to diminish the store of austerities, earned over a
long period of time. O Raghava! Austerities are always extremely
difficult to perform and there are many impediments. Therefore,
even when we are eaten by the rakshasas, we do not pronounce
curses. The residents of Dandakaranya are thus oppressed by the
rakshasas. With your brother, protect us. You are our protector in
this forest." O Janaka's daughter! Hearing the words of the rishis
of Dandakaranya, I gave them my word that I would protect them
in every way. Having pledged to protect them, as long as I am alive,
I am incapable of not following the pledge that I have given to the
sages. I have always sought benefit in adherence to the truth. O
Sita! I am capable of giving up my life, you, or Lakshmana, but
not abandoning a pledge that I have given, especially one given to
brahmanas. It is certainly my task to protect the rishis. O Vaidehi!
I have given a pledge. What more remains to be said? Out of
affection and love, you have spoken those words to me. O Sita! I am
satisfied with you. Those who desire harm do not seek to instruct.
O beautiful one! You have been true to yourself and your lineage.'
The great-souled one spoke these words to the beloved Sita, the
princess of Mithila. With Lakshmana and with the bow, Rama left
for the beautiful hermitages in the forest.

Chapter 3(10)

Rama walked in front. The extremely beautiful Sita was in the
middle. With a bow in his hand, Lakshmana followed at the
rear. As they advanced with Sita, they saw many kinds of forests,
level ground around the mountains and many beautiful rivers.
Cranes and *chakravaka*s wandered around the riverbanks. There
were lakes with lotuses and many kinds of aquatic birds. There

were herds of antelopes, crazy and horned buffaloes and boars and
elephants that treated trees like enemies. After they had travelled a
long distance along the way, the sun became elongated. They saw a
beautiful lake that was one yojana in expanse. It was full of red and
white lotuses and ornamented with herds of elephants. There were
cranes, swans, kadambas[49] and other aquatic birds. In the sparkling
water of that beautiful lake, the sounds of singing and the playing
of musical instruments could be heard, but no one could be seen.
Because of their curiosity, Rama and maharatha Lakshmana asked
the sage named Dharmabhrita. Raghava, with dharma in his soul,
asked the sage, 'O great sage! All these wonderful sounds can be
heard. A curiosity has been generated. You should tell us about the
auspicious account.'

He started to tell them about the powers of the lake. 'O Rama!
This perennial lake, named Panchapsara[50] has been constructed
by the sage Mandakarni through his austerities. The great sage,
Mandakarni, tormented himself through fierce austerities for ten
thousand years, lying down in the water and surviving only on air.
All the gods, with Agni at the forefront, came together. Having
assembled together, they addressed each other in these words. "The
sage desires to obtain one of our positions." All the gods instructed
five foremost apsaras, with forms as radiant as the lightning, to
cause impediments to his austerities. The sage possessed insight
about this world and the next. However, to accomplish the task of
the gods, the apsaras brought him under the subjugation of desire.
Those five apsaras became the wives of the sage. Inside the lake,
he built an invisible house for them. The five apsaras dwell there
happily. They pleasure themselves with the sage, who became young
because of his austerities and yoga. As they sport, the sounds of the
musical instruments can be heard. The beautiful sounds of singing
can be heard, mingling with the tinkling of ornaments.' Hearing the
words of the one with the cleansed soul, Raghava and his immensely
illustrious brother said that this was indeed wonderful.

---

[49] Kind of goose.
[50] Literally, five apsaras.

As they conversed, they saw a circle of hermitages. There were many kinds of trees, and kusha grass and bark were strewn around. With Vaidehi and Lakshmana, Raghava Kakutstha entered that beautiful circle of hermitages. Honoured by the maharshis, they happily resided there, progressively going from the hermitage of one ascetic to that of another. When the cycle was over, the one who knew about all the great weapons went back to one he had dwelt with earlier. He resided for ten months in one place and for one year in another. He resided for four months in one place and five months in another. There were some places where he resided for more than one month and others where he resided for more than one-and-a-half months. In some places, Raghava happily dwelt for three months and for eight months in others. As he happily dwelt in the hermitages of the sages, through their favours, ten years passed. With Sita, Raghava, who knew about dharma, took their leave. The handsome one again went to Suteekshna's hermitage. When he arrived at the hermitage, he was honoured by the sages. Rama, destroyer of enemies, resided there for some time too.

Once, at this hermitage, Suteekshna was seated and Kakutstha humbly addressed the great sage. 'O illustrious one! I have always heard accounts that Agastya, supreme among sages, resides in this forest. Because of the vastness of the forest, I do not know where that spot is. Where is the sacred hermitage of that intelligent maharshi? With my younger brother and with Sita, I wish to obtain the favours of that illustrious one, by going and worshipping the sage Agastya. This great desire is circling around in my heart, that I should myself be able to serve that supreme sage.' Suteekshna heard the words of Rama, who possessed dharma in his soul. Delighted, the sage replied to Dasharatha's son. 'I also wished to speak to you and Lakshmana about this. O Raghava! With Sita, go to Agastya. It is good fortune that you have yourself spoken to me about this. O child! I will tell you where Agastya, the great sage, is. O son![51] If you go four yojanas from this hermitage, towards the south, you will find the great and beautiful hermitage of Agastya's brother. It

---

[51] The word used is tata.

is located on flat ground within the forest and is ornamented with groves of *pippala* trees.[52] There are many kinds of beautiful flowers and fruit and the sounds of many kinds of birds. In the sparkling and auspicious waters, there are diverse kinds of lotuses. The place is full of swans and karandavas and decorated with chakravakas. O Rama! Spend one night there and leave next morning towards the southern direction, alongside that forest region. Agastya's hermitage is one yojana from there. This is a beautiful part of the forest, with many trees. With you, Vaidehi and Lakshmana will find pleasure there. That beautiful part of the forest is full of many kinds of trees. O immensely illustrious one! If your mind has turned towards seeing Agastya, the great sage, you should make up your mind to leave today itself.'

Having heard the words of the sage, with his brother, Rama worshipped the sage. With his younger brother and Sita, he left to see Agastya. Along the path, they saw many wonderful forests and mountains that were like clouds, lakes and rivers that flowed along the path. As they cheerfully proceeded along the path indicated by Suteekshna, in supreme delight, he addressed Lakshmana in these words. 'This must indeed be the hermitage of the great-souled sage, Agastya's brother,[53] the performer of auspicious deeds. It can be seen. In this forest, along the path, thousands of trees can be discerned, bent down with the burden of fruits and flowers. Suddenly, the bitter smell of ripe pippala fruit has arisen from the forest and is being borne by the wind. Heaps of wood have been kept here and there. Along the path, cut *darbha* grass can be seen, as radiant as lapis lazuli. In the middle of the forest, from the hermitage, a crest of smoke can be seen to arise from the fire, dark like the top of a cloud. Having had their baths in the fords, the brahmanas wish to collect offerings of flowers themselves.[54] O amiable one! I have heard Suteekshna's words. This must certainly be the hermitage of Agastya's brother.

---

[52] The sacred fig tree.

[53] Agastya's brother's name was Sudarshana, but the name is not mentioned here.

[54] It is preferable that flowers meant for worshipping are collected by the worshipper himself. If obtained from someone else, half of the merit goes to the person who originally gathered the flowers and only half goes to the worshipper.

His brother,[55] auspicious in his deeds, is the refuge of this direction. In a desire to ensure the welfare of the worlds, he quickly controlled death. Once upon a time, there were the cruel brothers, Vatapi and Ilvala.[56] Together, those two great *asuras* used to kill brahmanas. The cruel Ilvala would assume the form of a brahmana and with polished words, would invite brahmanas to a funeral ceremony.[57] Following the rites prescribed for a funeral ceremony, he would cook his brother, who would assume the form of a ram, and feed this to the brahmanas. Once the brahmanas had eaten, Ilvala would shout in a loud voice, "O Vatapi! Come out." Hearing his brother's words, Vatapi would roar like a ram and emerge, tearing through and mangling the bodies of the brahmanas. Subsisting on human flesh and assuming whatever form they willed, they always destroyed and killed thousands of brahmanas.[58] The gods prayed to maharshi Agastya and in a funeral ceremony, he ate the great asura.[59] Ilvala said that the ceremony was over and giving him[60] water to wash his hands, asked his brother to come out. The slayer of brahmanas spoke in this way to his brother. The intelligent Agastya, supreme among sages, laughed and said, "I have digested the rakshasa and he no longer possesses the strength to come out. In the form of a ram, your brother has gone to Yama's abode." On hearing the words that his brother had indeed been killed, the one who roamed in the night was enraged and started to attack the sage. He attacked the Indra among brahmanas. However, blazing in his energy, the sage burnt him down with the fire in his sight and he came by his death. Because of his compassion, the brahmana performed this extremely difficult deed. Adorned with lakes and groves, this is his brother's hermitage.' As Rama was conversing in this way with Soumitri, the sun set and

[55] Meaning Agastya.

[56] Vatapi was Viprachitti's son and Hiranyakashipu's nephew.

[57] The text uses the phrase *samskritam vadan*. This means—with polished words. It can also mean—speaking Sanskrit. The latter seems unlikely, since the word Sanskrit (which means polished) was used for the language much later. Earlier, the language was simply referred to as *bhasha*.

[58] They ate the flesh of the brahmanas who had been killed.

[59] Ilvala invited Agastya to a funeral ceremony and Agastya digested Vatapi.

[60] Agastya.

evening arrived. With his brother, he followed the prescribed rites
and worshipped the western sandhya. He entered the hermitage and
greeted the rishi. The sage welcomed Raghava in the proper way.
He spent a night there and subsisted on roots and fruits. When night
was over and the solar disc became sparkling, Raghava took his
leave from Agastya's brother. 'O illustrious one! We worship you.
We have happily spent the night here. We seek your leave to see
your senior, your elder brother. When the permission to leave was
granted, the descendant of the Raghu lineage departed.

He followed the indicated path and saw the forests. There was
wild grain and *sala*, jackfruit, *ashoka*, *tinisha*, *dhava*, young *bilva*,
bilva, *madhuka* and *tinduka* trees. They had blossoms and flowering
creepers on their tops. Rama saw hundreds of such beautiful trees
there. They had been crushed by the trunks of elephants and were
adorned with apes. Flocks of hundreds of maddened birds chirped.
The brave Lakshmana, the extender of prosperity, was following
at the rear and was nearby. The lotus-eyed Rama spoke to him.
'The trees possess gentle leaves. The animals and birds are quiet.
The hermitage of the maharshi with the cleansed soul can't be far
away. Because of his own deeds, Agastya is famous in this world.
His hermitage can be seen and it destroys the tiredness of those
who are exhausted. The forest is enveloped in smoke.[61] The place
is clean, with garlands of bark. The herds of deer are quiet. Nor
are the birds calling. For the welfare of the worlds, he swiftly
controlled death. That performer of auspicious deeds is a refuge
and he cleaned the southern direction. This is his sacred hermitage.
Because of his powers, the rakshasas are terrified and are not seen
to frequent the southern direction. Ever since the performer of
auspicious deeds came to the southern direction, those who roam in
the night have become pacified and have stopped all enmity.[62] The
southern direction is named after that illustrious and accomplished
one.[63] He is famous in the three worlds and the perpetrators of

---

[61] From sacrificial fires.
[62] Probably enmity among themselves.
[63] There is a pun. The south is known as *dakshina* and the word *daksha*/dakshina
means someone who is accomplished.

cruel deeds found him difficult to assail. The excellent mountain, Vindhya, always obstructed the sun's path. It is because of his command that the mountain did not increase.[64] The one with the long lifespan is famous in the worlds because of his deeds. Agastya's beautiful hermitage is served by gentle deer. The virtuous one is worshipped in the world and is always engaged in the welfare of the righteous. When we approach him, he will do what is best for us. We will worship the great sage, Agastya, here. O amiable one! O lord! I will spend the rest of the exile in the forest here. The gods, the gandharvas, the siddhas and the supreme rishis always worship Agastya, who is restrained in diet, here. No one who lives here is a liar, cruel, deceitful, violent or addicted to desire. The sage ensures that. The gods, the *yakshas*,[65] the serpents and the birds dwell here together, restrained in diet and worshipping dharma. The supreme rishis cast aside their bodies here. Having become siddhas, without bodies, those great-souled ones go to heaven on celestial vehicles that are like the sun. The gods confer the status of being a yaksha, immortality and many kinds of kingdoms to the auspicious creatures who worship here. We have arrived at the sacred hermitage. O Soumitri! You enter first and tell the rishi that I have come with Sita.'[66]

Chapter 3(11)

Lakshmana, Raghava's younger brother, entered the sacred hermitage. He approached Agastya's disciple and spoke these

[64] Mount Meru was the tallest mountain and Mount Vindhya was jealous. Vindhya grew taller and obstructed the sun's path. Agastya interceded and asked Vindhya to lower itself, so that he and his wife (Lopamudra) could travel southwards. Once he returned from the south, Vindhya could increase its height again. However, Agastya never returned from the south. The name Agastya is derived from mountain (*aga*), stay (*stha*).

[65] Yakshas are semi-divine species, described as companions of Kubera, the lord of riches.

[66] This is a departure from their practice of entering a hermitage together and is worth noting.

words. 'There was a king named Dasharatha. His eldest son, the powerful Rama, has come here with his wife, Sita, and wishes to see the sage. My name is Lakshmana. I am his brother and am engaged in the welfare of my elder brother. If you have heard of us, you know that I am devoted and faithful to him. We have entered this terrible forest on the instructions of our father. All of us wish to see the illustrious one. Please tell him.' Hearing Lakshmana's words, the store of austerities agreed. He entered the place where the sacrificial fire was kept to pass on the information. He quickly entered the place where the unassailable one, foremost among sages, was engaged in austerities. Joining his hands in salutation, he conveyed the news about Rama's arrival. 'Dasharatha's two sons, Rama and Lakshmana have entered the sacred hermitage. His wife, Sita, is also with him. The destroyers of enemies have come here to see you and serve you. You should instruct us about what needs to be done next.' He heard from his disciple about Rama and Lakshmana's arrival and also about the extremely fortunate Vaidehi. He spoke these words. 'It is good fortune that Rama has come here to see me, after a long time. My mind was hoping for his arrival here, to meet me. Go and receive Rama, his wife and Lakshmana properly. Make them enter and come here. Why have they not entered already?' The great-souled sage, who knew about dharma, spoke in this way. The disciple joined his hands in salutation, honoured him and agreed to what he had said. Concerned,[67] the disciple emerged and told Lakshmana, 'Where is Rama? He should himself enter and see the sage.' With the disciple, Lakshmana went to the entrance to the hermitage and pointed out Kakutstha and Sita, Janaka's daughter, to him. The disciple honoured him and repeated Agastya's words. He welcomed them hospitably, following the proper rites, and made the deserving ones enter. Rama entered, with Sita and Lakshmana, and saw the hermitage, which was full of truculent deer.

They progressively passed through Brahma's place, Agni's place, Vishnu's place, the great Indra's place, Vivasvat's[68] place,

---

[67] Probably because he had not ushered them in immediately.
[68] The sun god.

Soma's place, Bhaga's place, Kubera's place, Dhatri–Vidhatri's place and Vayu's place.[69] Surrounded by his disciples, the sage emerged. In front of him, Rama saw the sage, blazing in his energy. The brave one[70] spoke these words to Lakshmana, the extender of prosperity. 'O Lakshmana! The illustrious rishi, Agastya, is emerging. I can recognize him from his eminence and store of austerities.' Having said this, the mighty-armed scorcher of enemies prostrated himself and seized the feet of Agastya, resplendent like the sun. Honouring him, Rama, with dharma in his soul, joined his hands in salutation. Rama, Lakshmana and Vaidehi Sita stood there. He[71] received Kakutstha and offered him a seat and water. Having asked about his welfare, he asked him to be seated. He rendered oblations into the fire and honoured the guest with *arghya*.[72] Following the dharma of those who are in vanaprastha, he offered them food.[73] The bull among sages, who knew about dharma, sat down first. Rama, who knew about dharma, sat down and joined his hands in salutation. He[74] said, 'O Kakutstha! If an ascetic acts contrary to this,[75] in the world hereafter, he will be treated as one who indulged in perjury and will be made to eat his own flesh. You are a king of all the worlds and a maharatha. You follow dharma. You must be worshipped and revered and you have come here as my beloved guest.' Having said this, he honoured Raghava with fruits, roots and all the other objects of desire. He then added, 'This is a great and divine bow, decorated with gold and diamonds. O tiger among men! This belonged to Vishnu[76] and was constructed by Vishvakarma. These excellent arrows are invincible and are like the sun. They were

---

[69] To this list of ten, non-Critical versions add the names of other gods too, such as Varuna, Vasu, Garuda, Kartikeya, Dharma and so on.

[70] Rama.

[71] Agastya.

[72] These are objects always offered to a guest—*padya* (water to wash the feet), *achamaniya* (water to wash the mouth/face), arghya (a gift) and *asana* (a seat).

[73] The food offered was appropriate for vanaprastha.

[74] Agastya.

[75] The practice of honouring a guest.

[76] The text says Vaishnava. Strictly speaking, this means associated with Vishnu.

given by Brahma. The great Indra gave me two quivers with an inexhaustible supply of arrows. They are filled with sharp arrows that blaze like a raging fire. There is this large sheath made of silver, with a sword decorated with gold.[77] O Rama! In ancient times, Vishnu used this bow to slay the great asuras in a battle and brought back blazing prosperity to the residents of heaven. O one who deserves honours! For the sake of victory, accept this bow, the two quivers, the arrows and the sword, just as the wielder of the vajra accepted the vajra.' Having said this, the immensely energetic illustrious Agastya gave all those supreme weapons to Rama and spoke again.

Chapter 3(12)

'O Rama! I am delighted. May you be fortunate. O Lakshmana! I am satisfied with you. You have come here with Sita to show me respect. You are exhausted from your journey. You are suffering from great exhaustion and sweating. Your anxiety[78] is evident, especially for Maithilee, Janaka's daughter. She is delicate and has not suffered from such exhaustion earlier. Out of love for her husband, she has accepted this hardship in the forest. O Rama! Act so that Sita can find some pleasure. She has performed the extremely difficult task of following you to the forest. O descendant of the Raghu lineage! Since creation, the natural trait of women is to be devoted in times of prosperity and to forsake in times of adversity. They are as fickle as lightning and as sharp as a weapon. Women are quick to follow,[79] like Garuda or the wind. This wife of yours is free from such taints. She is as praiseworthy as the goddess Arundhati.[80] O destroyer of enemies! O Rama! Whichever

---

[77] By implication, also given by Indra.

[78] The word used is *utkantha*, which means anxiety. However, it is possible to translate the word utkantha as above the neck, that is, they were sweating above their necks.

[79] Those in prosperity.

[80] Vasishtha's wife.

region you reside in, with Soumitri and Vaidehi, that part will be ornamented.' The sage spoke in this way.

The self-controlled Raghava joined his hands in salutation and addressed these gentle words to the rishi who blazed like a fire. 'O bull among sages! I am blessed that you have shown me your favours. I am content that I have received the boon of a brother and a wife with such qualities. Please tell me about a region that has water and many groves, so that we can construct a hermitage there and always reside happily.' Having heard what Rama had said, the best among sages replied. The one with dharma in his soul thought for a while. Then he patiently spoke these penetrating words. 'O son![81] Two yojanas from here, there is a spot with a lot of roots, fruits and water. There are a lot of deer there and the beautiful region is famous as Panchavatee. Go there and construct a sacred hermitage with Soumitri. Find pleasure there and follow exactly the instructions you received from your father. O unblemished one! I know everything about you, because of the power of my austerities and because of my affection towards Dasharatha. Through my austerities, I also know the desire in your heart. You wish to live here in this hermitage with me. However, I am asking you to go to Panchavatee.[82] That part of the forest is beautiful and Maithilee will enjoy herself there. O Raghava! That part is praiseworthy and is not very far from here. It is near the Godavari and Maithilee will enjoy herself there. There are plenty of roots and fruits and numerous birds of diverse kinds. O mighty-armed one! It is isolated, but is also sacred and beautiful. O Rama! You are good in conduct and are capable of protecting. If you reside there, you will be able to protect the ascetics who are there. O brave one! You can see this great forest of madhuka trees. Go northwards past this until you reach a *nyagrodha* tree.[83] Ascend the mountain that is not very far from there. The perennial flowering grove there is known as Panchavatee.' When Agastya said this, together with Soumitri, Rama honoured

[81] The word used is tata.

[82] Agastya doesn't want Rama to live in his hermitage because he wants the destruction of the rakshasas.

[83] The Indian fig tree.

him and sought the permission of the rishi who was truthful in speech. Having obtained his permission, they worshipped at his feet. With Sita, they left for the hermitage of Panchavatee. The two sons of the king seized their bows. Undaunted in battle, they girded their quivers. Controlling themselves, as instructed by the maharshi, they left for Panchavatee.

Chapter 3(13)

As they proceeded towards Panchavatee, the descendant of the Raghu lineage came across an eagle that was giant in form and terrible in valour. In the forest, the immensely fortunate Rama and Lakshmana saw him. Thinking that the bird was a rakshasa, they asked, 'Who are you?' As if he was delighted, he replied in sweet and amiable words. 'O child! Know me to be your father's friend.' Realizing that he was his father's friend, Raghava worshipped him. Composed, he asked him about his name and his lineage. Hearing Rama's words, the bird told him about his own lineage and also about the origin of all beings.

'O Raghava! O mighty-armed one! Listen. In earlier times, there were the Prajapatis.[84] From the beginning, hear about all of them. Kardama was the first and Vikrita came after him. There were Shepa, Samshraya and the valiant Bahuputra.[85] There were Sthanu, Marichi, Atri, the immensely strong Kratu, Pulastya, Angira, Pracheta and Pulaha. O Raghava! After them, there were Daksha, Vivasvat and Arishtanemi. The immensely energetic Kashyapa was the last among them. O Rama! We have heard that the immensely illustrious Prajapati Daksha had sixty famous daughters. Kashyapa accepted eight of them and they possessed excellent waists—Aditi, Diti, Danu, Kalaka, Tamra, Krodhavasha, Manu and Anala. Delighted, Kashyapa spoke

---

[84] Literally, lords of beings. They were the creators of beings. The number of Prajapatis varies from text to text, though the usual number is ten. We are given a list of seventeen here, unless Bahuputra is an adjective. Then the number becomes sixteen.

[85] This can also mean that Samshraya had many sons.

to those maidens. "You will give me sons who are like me and can be the lords of the three worlds." O Rama! O mighty-armed one! Aditi, Diti, Danu and Kalaka agreed to this, but the remaining ones paid no heed. O scorcher of enemies! Aditi gave birth to the thirty-three gods—the Adityas, the Vasus, the Rudras and the Ashvins.[86] O son![87] Diti gave birth to illustrious sons, the *daitya*s.[88] Earlier, the entire earth, with its forests and oceans, belonged to them. O destroyer of enemies! Danu gave birth to a son named Ashvagreeva. Kalaka gave birth to Naraka and Kalaka.[89] Tamra gave birth to five daughters who are famous in the worlds—Krounchee, Bhasee, Shyenee, Dhritarashtree and Shukee.[90] Krounchee gave birth to owls and Bhasee gave birth to vultures. Shyenee gave birth to extremely energetic eagles and hawks. Dhritarashtree gave birth to swans and all the aquatic birds. Know that the beautiful one[91] gave birth to fortunate chakravakas. Know that Shukee gave birth to Nata and Nata's daughter was Vinata. O Rama! Know that Krodhavasha had ten daughters from her own self[92]— Mrigee, Mrigamanda, Haree, Bhadramada, Matangee, Shardulee, Shveta, Surabhee, Surasa and Kadruka. O supreme among the best of men! Mrigee's offspring are all the deer and Mrigamanda's are bears, *srimara*s[93] and yaks. Bhadramada gave birth to a daughter named Iravatee. Her son is the gigantic elephant Airavata, the protector of the world. Haree's offspring were lions, tawny apes, the monkeys that look like ascetics and *golangula*s.[94] Shardulee's sons were tigers. O bull among men! Matangee's offspring were elephants. O Kakutstha! Shveta gave birth to sons who are the white *dishagaja*s.[95] O Rama!

---

[86] Twelve Adityas, eight Vasus, eleven Rudras and two Ashvins.

[87] The word used is tata.

[88] Demons who are descendants of Diti.

[89] The mother is Kaalakaa and the son is Kaalaka.

[90] Tamra didn't agree to have sons.

[91] It is unclear whether this is a reference to Dhritarashtree or Shukee, probably the former.

[92] That is, Krodhavasha didn't have sons either.

[93] Kind of animal that is found in marshy places, similar to deer.

[94] With a tail like that of a cow, langur.

[95] Four (sometimes eight) elephants are believed to hold up the four (or eight) directions.

Surabhee gave birth to two daughters—the fortunate Rohini and the illustrious Gandharvee. Rohini gave birth to cows and Gandharvee's sons were the horses. Surasa gave birth to *naga*s and Kadru[96] to *pannaga*s.[97] O bull among men! Through the great-souled Kashyapa, Manu gave birth to humans—brahmanas, kshatriyas, *vaishya*s and *shudra*s. It has been heard that the brahmanas were born from the mouth, the kshatriyas from the chest, the vaishyas from the thighs and the shudras from the feet. All the trees with auspicious fruit were born from Anala. Vinata was Shukee's granddaughter and Surasa and Kadru were sisters. Kadru gave birth to the thousand-headed serpent who holds up the earth.[98] Vinata had two sons—Garuda and Aruna.[99] I have been born from Aruna and Sampati is my elder brother. Know me to be Jatayu and I am descended from Shyenee. If you so wish, I can help you find a residence. O son![100] I can also protect Sita when you and Lakshmana go out.'

Raghava honoured Jatayu. Delighted, he embraced him and lowered his head. He had heard Jatayu repeatedly say that he had been his father's friend. He took Sita Maithilee with him and that extremely strong bird. With Lakshmana, he went to Panchavatee to burn down his enemies, like a fire to insects.

Chapter 3(14)

They went to Panchavatee, which was full of many predatory beasts and herds of deer. Rama spoke to his brother Lakshmana, who blazed in his energy. 'We have come to the place that the

---

[96] The same as Kadruka.

[97] Throughout the translation, we have generally used serpents for nagas and snakes for *sarpa*s. Nagas are not quite snakes. They are semi-divine, can assume human forms and live in specific regions. All these traits are uncharacteristic of snakes. The word naga is usually used as a synonym for pannaga. But a distinction is being drawn here. With that distinction, a naga is a many-hooded serpent, while a pannaga is an ordinary one.

[98] Ananta, also known as Shesha.

[99] Aruna is the sun's charioteer.

[100] The word used is tata.

maharshi told us about. O amiable one! With groves in blossom, this is the region of Panchavatee. You are accomplished. Cast your eye around everywhere in this forest. In which spot can we construct an excellent hermitage? O Lakshmana! Look for a spot that is near a waterbody, where Vaidehi, you and I can find pleasure. The forest must be agreeable and the water must be agreeable. It must be a spot where flowers, kusha grass and water are nearby.' Thus addressed by Rama, Lakshmana joined his hands in salutation. In Sita's presence, he spoke these words to Kakutstha. 'O Kakutstha! I will be dependent on you for one hundred years. You yourself tell me the agreeable spot where I should construct it.' The immensely radiant one was extremely pleased at Lakshmana's words. He sought out an agreeable spot that possessed all the qualities. Rama measured out the agreeable spot where the hermitage could be constructed. Holding Soumitri's hand in his hand, he said, 'This spot is flat and beautiful. It is surrounded by trees in bloom. O amiable one! You should construct an auspicious hermitage here. Not far away, one can see a beautiful lake that is full of lotuses. The lotuses have a fragrant scent and bear the complexion of the sun. This is exactly as the sage Agastya, cleansed in his soul, had recounted. This Godavari is surrounded by beautiful and blossoming trees. It is full of and adorned with swans, karandavas and chakravakas. There are herds of deer, not too far away and not too close. Peacocks are calling in agreeable tones. The slopes have many caves. O amiable one! Beautiful mountains can be seen, covered with flowering trees. In this place and in that place ores of gold, silver and copper can be seen. They are as radiant as windows, or excellent *bhakti* on elephants.[101] There are sala, *tala*, *tamala*,[102] *kharjura*[103] and *panasa*[104] trees. The place is decorated with wild grain, *tinisha* and *punnaga*.[105] There are mango trees,

---

[101] The word used is *gavaksha*. This literally translates as the eye of a cow, but means a window. Bhakti means ceremonial and auspicious marks made on the body of an elephant.

[102] Tree with dark bark.

[103] Date palm.

[104] Jackfruit.

[105] This can mean either nutmeg or a white lotus. Nutmeg fits better here.

ashokas,[106] *tilaka*s,[107] *champaka*s[108] and *ketaka*s.[109] Flowering creepers and vines have covered the trees from all sides. There is sandalwood, *syandana*,[110] *neepa*,[111] jackfruit, *lokucha*,[112] dhava,[113] *ashvakarna*,[114] *khadira*,[115] *shami*,[116] *kimshuka*[117] and *patala*.[118] This auspicious spot is delightful and is full of many animals and bird. O Soumitri! With this bird, let us reside here.'

Lakshmana, the slayer of enemy heroes, was thus addressed by Rama. Without any delay, the extremely strong one started to fashion a hermitage for his brother. He levelled out the earth there and constructed an extremely large cottage made out of leaves. It was adorned well with excellent pillars that were made out of hollow bamboo cane from long bamboos. The handsome Lakshmana then went to the river Godavari. Having bathed, he collected lotuses and fruits and returned. Following the prescribed rites, he rendered offerings of flowers for pacification. He then showed Rama the auspicious hermitage that he had constructed. With Sita, Raghava saw the hermitage that the amiable one had constructed. He was overcome with great delight at this cottage made out of leaves. Extremely happy, he embraced Lakshmana in his arms. He addressed him in these extremely gentle and profound words. 'O lord! I am delighted at this great task that you have performed. That is the reason why I have embraced you. O Lakshmana! You know about sentiments. You are grateful.

---

[106] Tree with red flowers.
[107] Tree with beautiful flowers.
[108] The champaka tree.
[109] The crew pine.
[110] The sandana tree.
[111] Kind of ashoka tree.
[112] Kind of breadfruit tree.
[113] Dhava is the axle-wood tree.
[114] Another name for the sala tree, literally like the ear of a horse. Here ashvakarna is the name of the tree. Elsewhere, *ashva* and *karna* are sometimes referred to as separate trees.
[115] Kind of tree.
[116] Name of a large tree.
[117] Tree with red blossoms.
[118] The trumpet flower.

You know about dharma. You possess dharma in your soul. Through you, my father has obtained a son and lives through him.' Raghava, the extender of prosperity, spoke to Lakshmana in this way. Delighted and happy, he dwelt in the region that had many kinds of fruits. The one with dharma in his soul comfortably resided there for some time, with Sita and Lakshmana, like the immortals in the world of heaven.

Chapter 3(15)

The great-souled Raghava dwelt there happily. *Sharat* season was over and the pleasant *hemanta* presented itself.[119] On one occasion, when night became morning, the descendant of the Raghu lineage went to the beautiful river Godavari, with Sita, to have a bath. His valiant brother, Soumitri, followed him at the rear, with a pot in his hand. He[120] said, 'O beloved one! O one who is pleasant in speech! This is the time when everything is decorated and radiant, suggesting that the year is going to be auspicious.[121] The dew is harsh on people. The earth is full of grain. The water is no longer agreeable and the fire is extremely agreeable. At the time of the new solstice,[122] virtuous ones who worship and render offerings to

[119] The cold season is hemanta, between autumn and winter. Winter proper is *shishira*. Hemanta is the months of Margashirsha (also known as Agrahayana) and Pousha. Margashirsha is roughly mid-November to mid-December, while Pousha is mid-December to mid-January. Sharat is the months of Ashvina (mid-September to mid-October) and Kartika (mid-October to mid-November).

[120] Lakshmana.

[121] This naturally suggests that at the time, the year began in November or December. At the time, the month could have ended with the day of the new moon or the day of the full moon. If it is the former, the new year probably began with the first day of *shukla paksha* in Pousha. If it is the latter, the new year probably began with the first day of *krishna paksha* in Margashirsha.

[122] This solstice means the winter solstice (say December). *Uttarayana* is the movement of the sun to the north of the equator, the period from the winter to the summer solstice (say June). *Dakshinayana* is the movement of the sun to the south of the equator, the period from the summer solstice to the winter solstice.

gods and ancestors, appropriate to the solstice,[123] are cleansed of all sins. The desires of the countryside are met because the cows are full of milk. Kings wander around, setting out on journeys, wishing to be victorious and earn wealth. Having steadily served Yama's direction,[124] the sun still doesn't radiate towards the north, like a woman without a mark on her forehead.[125] The Himalayas are naturally a store of snow. However, since the sun is still far away, it is evident that they have been appropriately named. Those mountains are full of snow. However, at midday, the movement of the sun brings joy and its touch is pleasant and agreeable. The shadow and water are unpleasant. Because of dew, the sun is mild. Because of the wind, the cold is bitter. Devastated by ice, the forest is deserted. That is what days are like now. One can no longer sleep under the open sky. Pushya nakshatra brings a brownish-grey mist. The night[126] is now such that each yama seems to be cold and longer. Though the sun has passed over into a period of good fortune, the solar disc is covered with mist.[127] The moon can no longer be seen, like a mirror rendered blind by the breath. Because of the mist, the moonlight is faded and the day of the full moon is not radiant, like Sita who seems to have become dark because of the heat and no longer seems to be that beautiful. Nature is cold to the touch and is now pierced by the ice. The west wind is blowing and at this time, it seems to be twice as cold. The forest is covered with dew and so are the barley and the wheat. But now that the sun has arisen, it is beautiful and curlews and cranes are calling. The dazzling paddy is bent down slightly, the heads full of rice. The complexion is golden

[123] The sacrifice in question is known as *agrayana*, observed either on the day of the new moon or the day of the full moon.

[124] Yama's direction is the south.

[125] The sky is being compared to a woman's forehead. In the morning, when the sun shines properly, the rising sun will be like the mark on a woman's forehead. But since it is still the cold season, this hasn't yet happened.

[126] *Triyama*. A *yama* consists of three hours. Night is called triyama because it lasts for nine hours.

[127] We have taken some liberties with the text. Otherwise, the meaning is not clear. The text uses the word *samkranta*, meaning 'passed over'. This may well be a reference to *makara samkranti*, a harvest festival celebrated on the day after the winter solstice.

and the form is like that of date flowers. As the sun rises in the distance, it seems to be like the moon. Though the rays radiate, they are enveloped in mist and snow. Even though its[128] energy cannot be felt in the morning, the touch is pleasant at midday. The redness is pale, but the heat makes the earth beautiful. The grass is somewhat wet with the fall of dew. The forests are beautiful and the young sun's heat is permeating the earth. The forest region is enveloped in darkness, shrouded in dew and mist. Bereft of flowers, it seems to be sleeping. The water is covered in mist and the cranes can be discerned only because they are calling. The sand along the banks is wet because of the ice. That is what the river looks like now. The sun is mild because of the fall of snow. The water is generally tasty, but cannot be touched now because of the cold. The lotuses in the lakes are no longer radiant. Their leaves have become old with age. The stalks and filaments have withered away. What is left of the stalks has been destroyed by the snow. O tiger among men! This is the time when Bharata is overcome by sorrow. Out of devotion towards you, the one with dharma in his soul will be observing austerities in the city. He has cast aside the kingdom, his pride and many kinds of objects of pleasure. He is restrained in diet, like an ascetic, and sleeps while lying down on the ground. This is the time of the day when he will certainly wake to perform his ablutions. Surrounded by the ordinary people, he will always go to the river Sarayu. He has been reared in a great deal of happiness. The delicate one will be afflicted by the cold. When night is over, how can he possibly bathe in the Sarayu? He is lotus-eyed and dark. He is handsome and great, with a flat stomach. He knows about dharma and is truthful in speech. His humility is unrestrained and he has conquered his senses. He is pleasant in speech and sweet. The destroyer of enemies is mighty-armed. The noble one has given up all the objects of pleasure in every way and has sought refuge with you. Your brother, the great-souled Bharata, has conquered heaven. Though you are in the forest, he is following you in your austerities. "Human beings do not follow their fathers, but follow their mothers

---

[128] The sun's.

instead." This is a saying that is famous in the world, but Bharata has acted contrary to this. Kaikeyee's husband was Dasharatha and Bharata is her virtuous son. How can a mother like that be so cruel in her foresight?'

Out of affection, Lakshmana was speaking these words to the one who followed dharma. However, Raghava could not tolerate this censure of their mother and said, 'O son![129] Your medium mother[130] must never be censured. You can continue to speak about the lord of the Ikshvaku lineage[131] and Bharata. My mind is firm in its vow of dwelling in the forest. However, tormented and out of affection, Bharata has committed a childish act.'[132] While he lamented in this way, they reached the river Godavari. With his younger brother and with Sita, Kakutstha performed his ablutions. They worshipped the ancestors and the gods with water. Controlling themselves, they prayed to the rising sun and the gods. Having performed his ablutions, Rama was radiant. With Lakshmana, Sita was the second. Having performed her ablutions, the princess was like the daughter of the mountain,[133] with the illustrious Rudra Isha and Nandi.[134]

Chapter 3(16)

With Sita and Soumitri, Rama had his bath and returned to his own hermitage from the banks of the Godavari. Having returned to the hermitage with Lakshmana, Raghava went to the cottage and performed the morning ablutions. Rama was seated in that cottage made of leaves with Sita. The mighty-armed one

---

[129] The word used is tata.

[130] We have already commented on Kaikeyee being the medium.

[131] Dasharatha.

[132] Of refusing the kingdom.

[133] Parvati.

[134] Sita is being compared with Parvati, Rama with Shiva and Lakshmana with Nandi.

was like the moon, with the nakshatra Chitra. With his brother, Lakshmana, he talked about various things.

While Rama was seated and attentively speaking in this way, a *rakshasi*[135] roamed around as she willed and arrived at the spot. Her name was Shurpanakha and she was the rakshasa Dashagriva's sister. She approached Rama and saw someone who resembled a god. The mighty-armed one's chest was like that of a lion and his eyes were like the petals of a lotus. He was delicate and great in spirit, with all the signs of being a king. Rama was dark, like a blue lotus. His radiance was like Kandarpa.[136] On seeing someone who was like Indra, the rakshasi was flooded with desire. The one with the disagreeable face faced Rama, the one with the agreeable face. The one with a giant stomach faced the slender-waisted one, the one with malformed eyes faced the one with large eyes, the one with copper-coloured hair faced the one with excellent hair, the one with an ugly form faced the one with a handsome form, the one with a horrible voice faced the one with a pleasant voice, the hideous and ugly one faced the young one, the one who was harsh in speech faced the one who was sweet in speech, the one who was extremely wicked in conduct faced the one who was good in conduct, the ugly one faced the handsome one. With her body thus suffused, the rakshasi spoke to Rama. 'You are in the form of an ascetic, with matted hair. But you wield bow and arrows and are with your wife. Why have you come to a region that is frequented by rakshasas?' Thus addressed by the rakshasi Shurpanakha, the scorcher of enemies, who was upright in his intelligence, started to tell her everything. 'There was a king named Dasharatha and he was like a god in his valour. I am his eldest son. People have heard of me under the name of Rama. This is my younger brother, Lakshmana, who follows me. This is my wife Vaidehi, famous as Sita. To follow dharma and desiring dharma, I followed the instructions of my mother and the king, my father, and came here, to reside in the forest. I wish to know about your account. Who

---

[135] Rakshasa lady.
[136] Kama, the god of love.

are you and whom do you belong to? Why have you come here? Tell me the truth about this.' Hearing these words, the rakshasi was afflicted by desire. 'O Rama! I will tell you the truth. Hear my words. My name is Shurpanakha. I am a rakshasi who can assume any form at will. I roam around alone in this forest and create fear in all beings. The rakshasa Ravana is my brother and he is the lord of the rakshasas. So is[137] the extremely strong Kumbhakarna, who sleeps all the time. So is Vibhishana. Though he acts like a rakshasa, he possesses dharma in his soul. Khara and Dushana, famous for their valour in battle, are my brothers. I can surpass all of them. O Rama! O Purushottama![138] As soon as I first saw you and approached you, I was overcome by the thought that you should be my husband. Be my husband for a long time. What will you do with Sita? She is malformed and disagreeable and is not your equal.[139] I am your equal. Look upon me in the form of a wife. This one is vile and malformed. She is terrible in appearance and has a flat stomach. I will devour this woman and your brother. After that, as you desire, you can roam around with me in Dandakaranya, on the summits of mountains and the many kinds of forests.' The one with intoxicated eyes laughed and told Kakutstha this. Addressed in these words, the one who was eloquent in the use of words started to reply.

Chapter 3(17)

Shurpanakha was in the throngs of desire. Rama smiled first. Then, as he willed, he addressed her in gentle words. 'I am married and this is my beloved wife. Therefore, for women like you, it will be extremely distressing to have a co-wife. This younger brother of mine is good in conduct and handsome and pleasant.

[137] That is, the ones who are hereafter mentioned are also brothers.

[138] Literally, excellent man. But we have retained Purushottama, as it is also one of Vishnu's names.

[139] Non-Critical versions have shlokas where Shurpanakha assumes a beautiful form.

The valiant one's name is Lakshmana and he doesn't have a wife.[140] He is without a wife and desires one.[141] He is young and handsome. Given your beauty, he is the right husband for you. O large-eyed one! Seek my brother as your husband. O beautiful one! Without a co-wife, you will then be like Meru, with the radiance of the sun.'[142]

Addressed by Rama in this way, the rakshasi was overcome by desire. She instantly abandoned Rama and spoke to Lakshmana. 'I am lovely. I am beautiful and can be your wife. With me, happily roam around, everywhere in Dandakaranya.' Soumitri was thus addressed by the rakshasi. Lakshmana, accomplished in the use of words, smiled and addressed Shurpanakha in words that were full of reason. 'Why do you desire to be a wife and a servant to someone who is a servant? O one with the complexion of a lotus! I am my noble brother's servant. He is the prosperous one! O one with the unblemished complexion! O lotus-eyed one! You will accomplish your objective if you become the noble one's younger wife. O one with the distended stomach! She is malformed, wicked, cruel and aged. He will abandon such a wife and serve you.[143] O one who is beautiful in complexion! Who will abandon someone who is supreme in beauty? O beautiful one! The one who is accomplished will know what it means to be a human woman.' The hideous one, with the distended stomach, heard what Lakshmana said. She did not know

[140] The word used for Lakshmana is *akritadara* and there has been a lot of speculation about the use of this word. On the face of it, this means unmarried and is therefore a lie, lies being justified under certain circumstances. However, the word akritadara is also capable of being interpreted as someone who has not brought his wife with him, but has left her behind.

[141] This entire section is full of puns that are impossible to translate. Each statement has a double meaning. Rama has one meaning in mind, but Shurpanakha interprets it in a different sense. Rama says, he has been without a wife for a long time, Shurpanakha takes it to mean that he has never had a wife. Rama says, he desires his wife, Shurpanakha takes it to mean that he desires a wife. Rama says, he has not seen his wife for a long time, Shurpanakha takes it to mean that he is handsome. Rama says, he can never be your husband, Shurpanakha takes it to mean that he can be your husband.

[142] Lakshmana being the radiance of the sun.

[143] Lakshmana's words are also full of innuendo, impossible to translate. Shurpanakha takes this to mean that Rama will abandon Sita and serve her. The alternative meaning is that Rama will abandon Shurpanakha and serve Sita.

about jesting and took those words to be the truth. Rama, scorcher of enemies and invincible, was seated in the cottage made out of leaves with Sita. The one who was overcome by desire addressed him. 'She is malformed and wicked. She is ugly and possesses a flat stomach. By clinging on and not abandoning this old and decayed wife, you are not exhibiting a great deal of respect for me. While you look on, I will now devour this human female. Without a co-wife, I will happily roam around with you.' The one with eyes like a burnt-out torch said this. Extremely angry, she then dashed towards the deer-eyed one, like a giant meteor towards Rohini. She descended like the noose of death. However, the extremely strong Rama, became enraged and restrained her. He told Lakshmana, 'O Soumitri! One should never jest with a cruel and ignoble woman. O amiable one! Behold Vaidehi. She is barely able to remain alive. This one is malformed and wicked. She is extremely intoxicated and possesses a distended stomach. O tiger among men! You should disfigure this rakshasi.'

Lakshmana was thus addressed and became wrathful. While Rama looked on, the immensely strong one unsheathed his sword and sliced off her ears and nose.[144] With her ears and nose severed, she screamed in a loud voice. The terrible Shurpanakha rushed away to the forest, where she had come from. The extremely terrible rakshasi was disfigured and blood began to flow. She roared in many kinds of tones, like a cloud that is about to rain down. The one who was hideous to see started to exude many flows of blood. She roared. Clasping her arms, she entered the great forest.[145] The disfigured one went to Janasthana, where Khara was surrounded by a large number of rakshasas. She reached her fiercely energetic brother and fell down on the ground, like a bolt of thunder from the sky. Senseless with fear and with blood flowing, Khara's sister told him everything about how she had been disfigured and about Raghava's arrival in the forest with his wife and Lakshmana.

---

[144] It is believed that the city of Nashika (Nasika) got its name from this incident.
[145] This probably means that she used her arms to cover her ears and nose.

Chapter 3(18)

She fell down there, disfigured and exuding blood. On seeing her, the rakshasa Khara raged with anger and told her, 'You possess strength and valour. You can go wherever you want. You can assume any form at will. You are Death's equal. Who has reduced you to this state? Which god, gandharva, creature or great-souled rishi possesses the great energy to disfigure you in this way? I do not see anyone in the world who can cause displeasure to me in this way, with the exception of the thousand-eyed great Indra, the chastiser of Paka. Today, I will use my arrows, which can take away lives, to take away life from his body, just as a swan drinks milk from water.[146] I will slay him in a battle and mangle his inner organs with arrows. Whose red blood, mixed with froth, will the earth drink? When I cheerfully slay him in a battle, whose flesh will predatory birds gather around and tear apart and eat? When I make the miserable one suffer in a great battle, the gods, the gandharvas, the *pishacha*s[147] and the rakshasas will not be able to save him. You should gradually regain your senses and tell me. Which rash person has vanquished your valour in the forest?'

She heard her brother's words, which were especially laced with rage. Choking with tears, Shurpanakha addressed him in these words. 'They are young and handsome. They are delicate, but immensely strong. Their eyes are as large as lotuses. Their garments are made out of bark and antelope skin. They are like the king of the gandharvas and possess the signs of being kings. I am not interested in debating whether they are gods, *danavas*[148] or humans. There, I saw a woman in between them. She was slender-waisted. She was young and beautiful and was adorned in all kinds of ornaments. I have been reduced to this state because of them, primarily because of the woman. It is as if I do not have a protector. She is deceitful in conduct. When those two are killed, I will remain in the forefront of

---

[146] When milk is mixed with water, a swan has the reputation of being able to drink the milk, while leaving the water untouched.

[147] Malevolent beings.

[148] Demons.

the battle and drink their blood, together with that of the one who is wicked in conduct.[149] O father![150] My first wish is that you should accomplish this. I wish to drink their blood in a battle.'

When she said this, Khara became angry. He instructed fourteen extremely strong rakshasas who were like Death. 'There are two men with weapons, though their garments are made of bark and antelope skin. With a woman, they have entered this terrible Dandakaranya. They are wicked in conduct and you will return only after you have killed them and this sister of mine has drunk their blood. O rakshasas! Without delay, let my sister's wish be accomplished. Crush them with your own energies.' Those fourteen rakshasas were commanded in this way. They left with her, like dense clouds blown by the wind.

Chapter 3(19)

The terrible Shurpanakha went to Raghava's hermitage. She showed the rakshasas the two brothers and Sita. They saw the immensely strong Rama seated in that cottage made of leaves, with Sita and served by Lakshmana. The handsome Raghava saw them and the rakshasi arriving. Rama spoke to his brother Lakshmana, blazing in energy. 'O Soumitri! Immediately remain close to Sita. I will kill the ones who are following in her[151] footsteps.' Rama, who knew about his soul, spoke in this way. Hearing Rama's words, Lakshmana honoured them and signified his assent.

Raghava strung the great bow that was decorated with gold. The one with dharma in his soul addressed the rakshasas. 'We are Dasharatha's sons, the brothers Rama and Lakshmana. With Sita, we have entered this impenetrable Dandaka forest. We are self-controlled and survive on fruits and roots. We follow the dharma of

---

[149] Meaning Sita.

[150] The word used is tata. However, we don't know whether Khara was younger or older.

[151] Shurpanakha's.

ascetics. We dwell in Dandakaranya. Why do you wish to cause us injury? I have been engaged by the rishis and have come here with a bow and arrows. In a great encounter, I will kill evil-souled ones like you who cause injuries. If you are satisfied with this, remain here and do not retreat. O ones who roam around in the night! If you value your lives on this earth, you should return.' Hearing his words, the fourteen rakshasas, the slayers of brahmanas and with spears in their hands, became extremely angry. They were terrible and their eyes were red with rage. The ends of their eyes turned red. Though the valiant Rama spoke pleasantly, they spoke harshly and disagreeably, not having witnessed his valour. 'You have made our lord, the extremely great-souled Khara, angry. We will slay you in a battle today and rob you of your lives. Who has the strength to single-handedly withstand many in the field of battle? Since you are standing in front of me, why mention your prowess in a battle?[152] We will release clubs, spears and battleaxes from our arms. You will lose your life, your valour and the bow that you are holding in your hand.' Saying this, the fourteen rakshasas became angry. They raised their sharp weapons and rushed towards Rama. They hurled their spears towards the invincible Raghava. Using fourteen arrows that were decorated with gold, Kakutstha sliced down those fourteen spears. After this, the immensely energetic one became extremely angry and picked up fourteen iron arrows that had been sharpened on stone and were as dazzling as the sun. He seized his bow, stretched it and aimed towards the rakshasas. Raghava released the arrows, like Shatakratu releasing the vajra. Those arrows were gold-tufted and decorated with gold. They blazed through the sky like giant meteors and were as radiant as the sun. With great force, they struck the chests of the rakshasas. Covered with blood, they fell down on the ground, as if shattered by a bolt of thunder. With their hearts shattered, they were like trees severed at the roots. They fell down, bathed in blood and disfigured, robbed of their lives.

On seeing that they had fallen down on the ground, the rakshasi became senseless with rage. Having regained her senses, she emitted

---

[152] That is, demonstrate it, instead of talking about it.

a terrible roar. Shrieking loudly, Shurpanakha again went to Khara, the blood on her having dried somewhat. Afflicted, she again fell down there, like a juicy creeper. On seeing that the rakshasas had been brought down in the battle, Shurpanakha rushed there again. Khara's sister informed him that all the rakshasas had been killed.

Chapter 3(20)

Khara saw Shurpanakha fall down before him. Though she had come as a calamity,[153] it was evident she desired something. He angrily addressed her. 'I have just commanded brave and flesh-eating rakshasas to accomplish your objective. Why are you weeping again? They are faithful and devoted to me, always engaged in my welfare. Even if they are struck, they cannot be killed. There is no doubt about their not acting in accordance with my words. I wish to hear the reason why you have come here again. Why are you shrieking 'Alas, protector'? Why are you writhing around on the ground, like a snake? Why are you lamenting that you do not have a protector? Indeed, there is a protector in me. Arise. Do not be frightened. Arise. Cast aside this lassitude.' The invincible Khara said this and comforted her.

She wiped away the tears from her eyes and spoke to her brother, Khara. 'You sent fourteen brave and terrible rakshasas to bring me pleasure and slay Raghava and Lakshmana. They were intolerant and wielded spears and battleaxes in their hands. However, Rama has killed all of them in an encounter, using arrows that penetrated the inner organs. I saw those immensely strong ones fall down on the ground in an instant. Witnessing Rama's great deed, I am filled with great fright. O one who roams around in the night! I am scared, anxious and distressed. I can see terror everywhere and have again come to you for refuge. I am submerged in a great ocean of grief, with misery in the form of crocodiles. There is great terror in the

---

[153] The harbinger of destruction for the rakshasas.

form of garlands of waves. Why don't you save me? They have been slain and have been made to fall down on the ground by Rama's sharp arrows. Those flesh-eating rakshasas have been reduced to this state because of me. O one who roams around in the night! If you have compassion for me and for those rakshasas and if you possess strength and energy, kill Rama, who has made an abode in Dandakaranya and is a thorn for the rakshasas. If you do not slay the enemy Rama today, since I have been ashamed, I will cast aside my life in front of you. Using my intelligence, I can see that you are incapable of standing before Rama in an encounter, when he wields his bow in a great battle. You are proud of your valour, but you are not brave. The bravery that is ascribed to you is false, since you are incapable of killing Rama and Lakshmana, who are mere humans. Quickly abandon Janasthana with your relatives. Lacking spirit and limited in valour, why should those like you reside here? Rama's energy will quickly overcome and destroy you. Rama, Dasharatha's son, is full of energy. I possess an immensely valorous brother, yet I have been disfigured.'

Chapter 3(21)

Shurpanakha taunted the brave Khara in this way. In the midst of the rakshasas, Khara spoke these harsher words. 'Because of the insult that has been inflicted on you, my rage is infinite. I am incapable of bearing it and am like the turbulent salty ocean. I do not reckon Rama as valiant. Humans have limited spans of life. Because of the wicked things that he himself has done, he will be slain and be robbed of his life today. Control your tears and cast aside your fear. With his brother, I will convey Rama to Yama's abode. O rakshasi! He will be slain with a battleaxe today. When Rama, weak in life, lies down on the ground, you can drink his warm blood.' She was delighted to hear the words that issued out of Khara's mouth. In her foolishness, she again praised her brother, supreme among rakshasas. Though she had used harsh words earlier, she praised him again.

Khara addressed his general, named Dushana. 'Instruct fourteen thousand terrible and forceful rakshasas, those whose minds are devoted to me and those who do not retreat from the field of battle. Let them be like dark clouds in complexion, horrible and the perpetrators of cruel deeds. Let them be strong, foremost among those with energy, those who take delight in causing violence to creatures. Let them be as proud as tigers, with large mouths and great in energy. O amiable one! Instruct those rakshasas and arm them with all kinds of weapons. O amiable one! Swiftly equip my chariot with bows, arrows, colourful swords and many kinds of sharp spears. To slay the insolent Rama, accomplished in battle, I wish to advance ahead of the great-souled Poulastyas.'[154] Thus addressed, Dushana arranged a great chariot that had the complexion of the sun. Once it had been yoked to well-trained and speckled horses, he informed that this had been done. It was like the summit of Meru and was decorated with molten gold. The wheels and bumpers were made out of gold and the pole[155] was made out of lapis lazuli. The auspicious signs and decorations were made out of gold and were in the form of fish, flowers, trees, the sun, the moon, flocks of birds and stars. It was filled with standards and swords and ornamented with the best of bells. The intolerant Khara ascended the chariot, yoked to well-trained horses. On seeing that he was astride the chariot, those rakshasas, terrible in valour, surrounded him and the immensely strong Dushana.

All the rakshasas saw Khara, the great archer, march out, with his chariot, shield, weapons and standards and spoke about it. The terrible rakshasa soldiers also emerged, with shields, weapons and standards. They emerged from Janasthana with great speed, emitting a loud roar. They held clubs, swords, spears, extremely sharp battleaxes, broad swords and blazing javelins in their hands. Terrible to behold, they seized spikes, fearful maces, extremely long bows, bludgeons, clubs and vajras. There were fourteen thousand extremely terrible rakshasas. Following Khara's wishes, they

---

[154] These rakshasas were descended from the sage Pulastya.
[155] *Kubara*, the pole for attaching the yoke.

emerged from Janasthana. On seeing that those rakshasas, terrible to behold, were rushing forward, Khara's chariot held back and followed at some distance. The harnesses of those speckled horses were decorated with gold. Ascertaining Khara's intentions, the charioteer urged them on. Khara was the slayer of enemies. When his chariot was urged on swiftly, it filled the directions and the sub-directions with its roar. Khara's intolerance waxed. To slay the enemy, he advanced hurriedly, like the Destroyer. He roared again and urged the charioteer in a harsh voice. The immensely strong one was like a cloud about to shower down rocks.

Chapter 3(22)

As the inauspicious and terrible army departed, a large and tumultuous cloud, in the shape of a red ass, showered down blood.[156] Though the immensely swift horses yoked to the chariot[157] were proceeding, as they willed, along the flat terrain of the royal road where flowers had been strewn, this made them fall down. A disc that was in the shape of a circle of fire seized the sun and surrounded it, dark in the centre and red at the edges. The standard was raised on a golden pole. An extremely terrible and large vulture came and sat atop this. Many kinds of animals and birds that feed on flesh, with harsh voices, approached Janasthana and surrounded it, shrieking in many kinds of unmelodious tones. Facing the blazing directions, jackals howled in loud tones and these terrible and loud sounds were inauspicious for the demons.[158] Terrible clouds that were like shattered elephants,[159] and were full of blood instead of water, made the sky no longer look like the sky. There was a horrible darkness that made the body hair stand up. The directions and the sub-directions could no longer be clearly distinguished. The

---

[156] These are evil omens.
[157] Khara's chariot.
[158] The word used is *yatudhana*. A yatudhana is an evil spirit or demon.
[159] Elephants in musth.

sandhya was without radiance and had the complexion of blood flowing from wounds. Facing Khara, animals and birds shrieked in fierce voices. In a battle, jackals always signify the inauspicious and the horrible. They howled in front of the army and their mouths seemed to blaze with flames. Clubs that resembled headless torsos could be seen near the sun. Though it was not the right time, the giant planet, Svarbhanu,[160] seized the sun. As swift winds started to blow, the sun lost its radiance. Though it wasn't night, stars could be seen, and they were like fireflies in radiance. In the lakes, fish and aquatic birds stood still and the lotuses dried up. At that time, the trees were without flowers and fruits. Though there was no wind, dust and red clouds arose. Mynahs[161] chirped. Meteors that were terrible to see fell down with a roar. The earth, and the mountains and forests, started to quake. Astride his chariot, the intelligent Khara was roaring. However, his left arm trembled and his voice turned harsh. While he glanced around in every direction, his eyes filled with tears. His head started to ache. However, because of his confusion, he did not retreat.

There were these ominous portents and they made the body hair stand up. But Khara laughed and spoke to all the rakshasas. 'All these great and terrible portents have arisen and they are terrible to behold. However, because of my valour and strength, unlike a weak person, I do not think about them. Using my sharp arrows, I can bring down stars from the firmament. When enraged, with death as my dharma, I can take on Death.[162] I am not interested in retreating without using my sharp arrows to kill Raghava, who has been agitated by his strength, or his brother, Lakshmana. My sister will satisfy her desire and I will drink their blood. It is because of Rama and Lakshmana that the catastrophe has resulted. Earlier, I have not faced defeat in any battle. I do not utter a falsehood and that is evident to all of you. Even if the king of the gods is angry

---

[160] Svarbhanu is another name for Rahu. An eclipse occurs when Rahu swallows the sun (or the moon).

[161] *Sharika*, the bird *Turdus salica*.

[162] The god of death.

and advances in a battle astride Airavata[163] and with the vajra in his hand, I can kill him, not to speak of mere humans.' That large army of rakshasas heard him roar in this way. Entangled in the noose of death, they obtained great delight from this.

Desiring to witness the battle, the great-souled ones, rishis, gods, gandharvas, siddhas and *charana*s,[164] assembled. Those performers of auspicious deeds assembled and spoke to each other. 'May cattle, brahmanas and those who are revered by the worlds be fortunate. In the battle, let Raghava be victorious over the descendants of Pulastya who roam around in the night, like the one with the *chakra* in his hand[165] acted in an encounter against all the bulls among the asuras.' Those supreme rishis said many other things, having seen that the army consisted of rakshasas who had exhausted their lifespans.

Ahead of the soldiers, Khara speedily emerged on his chariot. On seeing the rakshasa, many other rakshasas also emerged— Shyenagami, Prithugriva, Yajnashatru, Vihamgama, Durjaya, Karaviraksha, Parusha, Kalakarmuka, Meghamali, Mahamali, Sarpasya and Rudhirashana. Immensely valorous, these twelve advanced, around Khara. Mahakapala, Sthulaksha, Pramathi and Trishira—these four were ahead of the soldiers, following Dushana at the rear. Desiring a battle, they were terrible in force. The brave rakshasa soldiers were extremely fierce. They suddenly advanced against the two princes, like a garland of evil planets towards the moon and the sun.

Chapter 3(23)

Khara, terrible in his valour, advanced towards the hermitage. With his brother, Rama also saw those portents, the extremely inauspicious and terrible omens that made the body hair stand up and signified misfortune to beings. On seeing these, he addressed

[163] Indra's elephant.
[164] Celestial bards.
[165] Vishnu.

Lakshmana in these words. 'O mighty-armed one! Behold. These great portents have arisen and they signify the end of all creatures. However, they will destroy all the rakshasas. The clouds are circling around in the sky, showering down blood and thundering in a harsh tone. Red donkeys are braying harshly. All my arrows are delighted at the prospect of a battle and seem to be smoking. O Lakshmana! The bow with the golden handle seems to be itching. The birds that roam around in the forest are calling, suggesting that fear lies ahead. There is a doubt about remaining alive. There is no doubt that there will be a great encounter. My arm is repeatedly twitching. O brave one! Our victory and the defeat of the enemy are imminent. It is manifest that your face has turned extremely radiant. O Lakshmana! When the faces of those who are headed for battle turn pale, that signifies their lifespans have become exhausted. But a learned man who desires welfare must take precautionary measures when he suspects a calamity. Therefore, take arrows and a bow in your hand. Take Vaidehi and find refuge in a cave that is covered with trees within the mountain. O child! Even if you wish to act contrary to my desires, pledge on my feet that you will leave without any delay.'[166]

Thus addressed by Rama, with Sita, Lakshmana took his bow and arrows and sought refuge inside an impenetrable cave. When Lakshmana listened and entered the cave with Sita, as he had been asked to, Rama donned his armour. In dazzling armour that was like the fire, Rama was resplendent, like a great fire that has arisen in the darkness. The valiant one seized his arrows and raised his great bow, twanging the bowstring with a sound that filled the directions. The gods, the gandharvas, the siddhas, the charanas and the *guhyakas*[167] were terrified and spoke to each other. 'There are fourteen thousand rakshasas who are terrible in their deeds. Rama, with dharma in his soul, is alone. What will the encounter be like?'

---

[166] Because Rama is capable of taking on the rakshasas alone. Safety may not have been the only reason for sending Sita away. Sita was against the idea of killing rakshasas. Perhaps Rama did not want her to witness the destruction.

[167] Semi-divine species, companions of Kubera, similar to yakshas.

The army of the yatudhanas[168] could be seen in every direction, with a deep and terrible roar, full of shields, weapons and standards. They roared like lions and growled at each other. They stretched their bows and jumped around a lot. The sounds of their roaring mingled with the beating of drums and that tumultuous sound filled the forest. The carnivorous beasts who resided in the forest were frightened at this sound. They fled towards the parts that were silent and did not look back. That extremely powerful army rushed against Rama, wielding many kinds of weapons and looking like the unfathomable ocean. Rama, skilled in war, cast his eye in every direction and saw that Khara's soldiers were advancing for the battle. He stretched his terrible bow and took arrows out of his quiver. He was overcome by great rage and wished to destroy all the rakshasas. Enraged,[169] he was like the blazing fire of destruction and was impossible to look at. On seeing him filled with energy, the divinities of the forest were distressed. Rama's wrathful form was like that of the wielder of the *pinaka*, when he was ready to slay Daksha at the time of the sacrifice.[170]

Chapter 3(24)

Khara reached the hermitage in advance of his troops and saw Rama, the slayer of enemies, there, holding the bow in his hand. On seeing him, Khara raised his strung bow, which made a harsh noise. Raising it, he urged his charioteer to drive towards Rama. At Khara's command, the charioteer urged the horses towards where the mighty-armed Rama was standing alone, wielding his bow. Seeing that he[171] was descending, all the roamers in the night

---

[168] Evil demons.

[169] Rama was not normally prone to anger.

[170] The pinaka is Shiva's weapon. It is sometimes described as a bow and sometimes as a spear/trident. Daksha had not invited Shiva to the sacrifice. When Sati/Parvati immolated herself, Shiva destroyed the sacrifice.

[171] Khara.

emitted a loud roar and his advisers surrounded him. Khara's chariot was in the middle of all those yatudhanas. He dazzled, like the red-limbed one[172] arising in the middle of the stars. Rama was invincible and wielded a terrible bow. Angrily, all the roamers in the night showered down many kinds of weapons on him. The angry rakshasas wished to kill Rama in the battle and used iron clubs, spears, javelins, swords and battleaxes. They were immensely large and immensely strong and were like clouds. Wishing to kill Kakutstha Rama in the battle, they attacked him. The large number of rakshasas showered arrows on Rama. It was like gigantic clouds showering down on an Indra among mountains. Raghava was surrounded by a large number of terrible rakshasas. It was like Mahadeva being surrounded on an auspicious occasion by a large number of his companions.

The yatudhanas released weapons on Raghava. However, he received them the way the ocean receives the rivers and countered them with his arrows. Though his body was mangled by those terrible weapons, he was not pained. He was like a giant mountain against the onslaught of many blazing vajras. Raghava was pierced throughout his body and there were wounds. Rama was as radiant as the sun, enveloped by clouds during evening. Seeing that the single one was enveloped by many thousands, the gods, the gandharvas, the siddhas and the supreme rishis were distressed. Rama became extremely angry and stretched his bow out, in the form of a circle. He released hundreds and thousands of sharp arrows. They were impossible to stop and impossible to withstand. In the battle, they were like nooses of Death. As if playing, Rama released arrows tufted with heron feathers. As if playing, Rama released these arrows towards the enemy soldiers. Like nooses of Death, they robbed the rakshasas of their lives. With the energy of the fire, those arrows blazed through the sky and penetrated the bodies of the rakshasas, becoming covered with blood. Innumerable extremely fierce arrows were released from the circle of Rama's bow. They descended and robbed the rakshasas of their lives. In the

---

[172] Mars.

battle, Rama severed hundreds and thousands of bows, the tops of
standards, shields, heads, many hands, ornaments and thighs that
were like the trunks of elephants. There were hollow arrows and
iron arrows, sharp at the tip and tufted. Thus severed, the roamers
in the night wailed in terrible tones. The soldiers were afflicted by
sharp arrows that penetrated the inner organs, like a dry forest
consumed by a fire. Rama did not give them any peace. Some brave
roamers in the night, terrible in strength, became extremely angry
and released javelins, spears and battleaxes towards Rama. The
mighty-armed Raghava used arrows to counter those weapons. In
the encounter, he sliced off their heads and took away their lives.
The remaining roamers in the night became distressed. Afflicted by
arrows, they rushed towards Khara to find refuge.

Seizing his bow, Dushana comforted all of them. Like an angry
Rudra or angry Death, he rushed towards Kakutstha. Fearless
because of the refuge Dushana had granted, all of them returned.
With sala trees, tala trees and rocks as weapons, they attacked
Rama. There was an extraordinary and tumultuous battle that
made the body hair stand up. Yet again, there was an extremely
terrible engagement between Rama and the rakshasas.

Chapter 3(25)

A shower of trees and rocks rained down, capable of taking one's
life away. Raghava, with dharma in his soul, used sharp arrows
to receive them. He was like a bull that closes its eyes and receives
the rain. With the objective of slaying all the rakshasas, Rama
invoked great rage. Immersed in rage, he blazed in his energy. From
every direction, he shrouded the soldiers and Dushana with arrows.
The commander, Dushana, the destroyer of enemies, became angry.
He seized a club that possessed the complexion of the summit of a
mountain and this made the body hair stand up. It was encased in
golden cloth and had crushed the soldiers of the gods. It was made
of iron, with sharp spikes that were covered with the fat of enemies.

Its touch was like that of thunder or the vajra. It could break down the ramparts of enemies. It was like a giant serpent. Dushana, the roamer in the night who performed cruel deeds, seized that club in the battle and attacked Rama. When Dushana descended on him, Raghava used two arrows to severe his two arms, bedecked as they were with ornaments on the hands. Thus severed, that gigantic one fell down in the field of battle. The severed club in the hand lay down in the front, like Shakra's standard when it is brought down. With his arms spread around, Dushana fell down on the ground. He was like a spirited and giant elephant when the two tusks have been severed. On seeing that Dushana had been killed in the battle and had fallen down on the ground, all the creatures praised Kakutstha.

Meanwhile, there were three foremost warriors ahead of the soldiers. They too had come under the subjugation of Death's noose. Angrily, they attacked Rama together. They were Mahakapala, Sthulaksha and the immensely strong Pramathi. The rakshasa Mahakapala held aloft a giant spear. Sthulaksha used a sword and Pramathi a battleaxe. On seeing them descend, Raghava used arrows that were sharp at the tip to receive them, just as one welcomes guests who have arrived. The descendant of the Raghu lineage severed Mahakapala's head. He used a torrent of innumerable arrows to crush Pramathi. He stuffed Sthulaksha's large eyeballs with arrows, and slain, he fell down on the ground, like a large tree with branches. The spirited one[173] then used arrows that were like the fire, decorated with gold and diamonds, to kill the remaining soldiers.[174] The arrows were gold-tufted and were like flames with trails of smoke. He slew the rakshasas with those, like a bolt of thunder brings down a large tree. In the field of battle, Rama used one hundred barbed arrows to kill one hundred rakshasas and one thousand to kill one thousand. Their armour and ornaments were shattered. Their bows and arrows were severed and scattered. Covered with blood, the roamers in the night fell down on the ground. In the battle, they fell down with dishevelled

---

[173] Rama.

[174] Rather inexplicably, the Critical Edition excises shlokas that specifically mention the slaying of Dushana.

hair, drenched in blood. The entire earth was strewn with them, like a giant altar spread with kusha grass. In a short while, when the rakshasas were slain, the forest was covered with mud from their flesh and blood and looked extremely terrible, like hell. There were fourteen thousand rakshasas who were the performers of horrible deeds. Rama, a human who was on foot, slew all of them alone. Among all those soldiers, the only ones who were left were maharatha Khara, the rakshasa Trishira and Rama, the slayer of enemies.[175] That terrible army was destroyed in the battle by Rama, whose strength was superior. On seeing this, Khara resorted to a giant chariot and rushed towards Rama, like Indra with an upraised vajra.

Chapter 3(26)

Khara advanced towards Rama. However, the commander of the army was the rakshasa Trishira. He approached and spoke these words. 'Refrain from this rashness and engage me to show my valour. You will see that I will bring down the mighty-armed Rama in the battle. I know that I am speaking the truth when I touch my weapon and pledge that I will slay Rama. He deserves to be killed by all the rakshasas. Restrain your eagerness to do battle for a while. Instead, examine whether I will ensure his death in battle, or whether he will ensure mine. If Rama is killed, you can happily go to Janasthana. If I am killed, you can advance and fight Rama.' Khara was thus persuaded by Trishira to test his love of death and said, 'Go and fight.' He[176] advanced towards Raghava.

Trishira was on a chariot that was yoked to radiant horses. He rushed towards Rama, like a mountain with three peaks.[177]

---

[175] The structure of the sentence is such that Rama is mentioned along with the rakshasa soldiers. However, a few more were left, the ones who carried the news to Ravana. Those were ordinary rakshasas, not the main ones.

[176] Trishira.

[177] Trishira means three heads and Trishira possessed three heads.

He released a torrent of arrows that was like a giant cloud. These created a noise similar to the sound from a drum that is wet with water. Raghava saw that the rakshasa Trishira was approaching. He grasped and twanged his bow and picked up sharp arrows. There was a tumultuous encounter between Rama and Trishira. It was between two extremely strong ones, like that between a lion and an elephant. Trishira struck Rama on the forehead with three arrows. Angry, enraged and intolerant, he said, 'Such is the valour and strength of this brave rakshasa! He wounds me on the forehead with arrows that are like flowers. Also accept the arrows that are released from my bow.' Saying this, he angrily used fourteen arrows that were like virulent serpents and in rage, struck Trishira on his chest. With four swift arrows with drooping tufts, the spirited one brought down his four skilled horses. With eight arrows, he brought down the charioteer from the seat on the chariot. Using another arrow, Rama severed the standard raised aloft. With the chariot destroyed, the roamer in the night descended. Rama pierced his heart with arrows and he was rendered immobile. The one with the immeasurable soul then used three forceful and sharp arrows. Intolerantly, he brought down the three heads of that rakshasa. Afflicted by Rama's arrows, the roamer in the night fell down on the ground, where his heads had fallen down in the battle earlier, spouting blood. When he was killed, the remaining rakshasas were in disarray and sought refuge with Khara. They didn't stay, but fled, like frightened deer before a tiger. On seeing them run away and retreat, Khara became quickly enraged. He himself rushed towards Rama, like Rahu towards the moon.

Chapter 3(27)

On seeing that Dushana had been slain in the battle, together with Trishira, Khara was terrified, having witnessed Rama's valour. The army of the rakshasas was immensely strong and impossible to withstand. However, Rama destroyed them single-

handedly, even Dushana and Trishira. Seeing that the army was
entirely destroyed, the rakshasa Khara was distressed and attacked
Rama, like Namuchi against Vasava.[178] Khara forcefully stretched
his bow and angrily released iron arrows that fed on blood and were
like virulent serpents towards Rama. He twanged the bowstring
in many different ways and displayed his learning with weapons.
As he roamed around in the battle on his chariot, Khara shot his
arrows along many paths. The maharatha filled all the directions
and sub-directions with his arrows. On seeing this, Rama also
released arrows that were extremely difficult to withstand from
his extremely large bow. They were like flames with sparks and
incessantly coursed through the sky, like Parjanya showering down
rain. Because of those sharp arrows released by Khara and Rama,
everything was shrouded in arrows and not a single bit of the sky
remained to be seen. The sun was enveloped in a net of arrows and
could not be seen. They angrily fought, seeking to kill each other. In
the encounter, he struck Rama, who was like a giant elephant, with
hollow arrows, iron arrows and barbed arrows that were sharp at
the tip. Astride the chariot, the rakshasa presented himself, with the
bow in his hand. He was like Yama, with a noose in his hand, and all
the creatures saw him. He was like a lion in his valour and his stride
was like that of a brave lion. However, like a lion against an inferior
animal,[179] Rama was not agitated on seeing him. Khara was on a
large chariot that was as radiant as the sun. Like an insect towards
a fire, he approached Rama on that. Khara affixed an arrow and
displaying the dexterity of his hands, severed the bow held in the
hands of the great-souled Rama. Wrathfully, he again seized seven
arrows that were like Shakra's vajra in radiance. With these, in that
battle, he struck the armour.[180] In the encounter, Khara struck the
infinitely energetic Rama with one thousand arrows and roared
extremely loudly. Rama's armour dazzled like the sun. However,
struck by the arrows with excellent tufts released by Khara, it was
severed and fell down on the ground. Raghava was struck by arrows

[178] Namuchi was a demon killed by Indra.
[179] Which could also be an inferior lion.
[180] Rama's armour.

all over his body and became angry. Rama dazzled in the battle, like a blazing fire without any smoke. Wishing to kill the foe, Rama, the destroyer of enemies, strung another large bow that emitted a deep roar. This was the Vaishnava bow that had been given by the maharshi.[181] Raising that supreme bow, he rushed towards Khara. In that encounter, Rama angrily used gold-feathered arrows with straight tufts to sever Khara's standard. That golden standard was worth seeing and it was fragmented in many ways. It fell down on the ground, like the sun falling down on the instructions of the gods. The angry Khara, who knew about striking the inner organs, struck Rama on the body, like striking an elephant with a goad, with four arrows that pierced the chest. Rama was struck by many arrows that were released from Khara's bow. He was pierced and blood started to flow from his limbs. He became extremely angry. In that supreme encounter, he seized the bow that was the best among bows. From that foremost bow, he released six arrows that were aimed at the target. He struck the head with one arrow and the two arms with two others. He struck his chest with three crescent-shaped arrows. After that, wishing to kill the rakshasa, the immensely energetic one wrathfully used thirteen arrows that were as radiant as the sun and had been whetted on stone. The yoke was severed with one and the four speckled horses with four. In the battle, the sixth was used to sever the head of Khara's charioteer. With three, the valiant one severed the *trivenu*.[182] With two, the immensely strong one shattered the two wheels. With the twelfth, he severed Khara's bow, with an arrow affixed to it. In that encounter, Raghava, Indra's equal, seemed to laugh, as he used a thirteenth that was like the vajra to pierce Khara. Khara's bow was shattered. He was without a chariot. His horses had been slain. His charioteer was dead. He seized a club in his hands and leapt down on the ground. The assembled gods and maharshis witnessed maharatha Rama's deed. Delighted, they joined their hands in salutation and

---

[181] Agastya.

[182] Trivenu means three bamboo poles. One doesn't know what part of the chariot this is, except that it is clearly a joint.

worshipped him, astride their celestial vehicles on which they had assembled.

Chapter 3(28)

Khara was without a chariot. He stood there, with a club in his hand. Gently initially, and harshly later, the immensely energetic Rama addressed him in these words.[183] 'You possessed a huge army with elephants, horses and chariots. Using these, you committed extremely terrible deeds of obstruction that were censured by all the worlds. Someone who agitates creatures performs cruel and wicked deeds. Even if he is the lord of the three worlds, he will not be able to maintain his position. He is like a fierce and evil snake that has turned up and all the people should kill him. If a person does not understand and commits wicked deeds out of greed or desire, his end will be seen, like that of a lizard that eats hail stones.[184] The ascetics follow dharma and dwell in Dandakaranya. O rakshasa! If you slay those immensely fortunate ones, why will you not reap the fruits? Cruel ones who perform wicked deeds are condemned by the worlds. Even if they obtain prosperity, that does not remain for a long time, like a tree that has decayed at the roots. A performer of wicked deeds will certainly reap the consequences. At the right time, he will come to a terrible end, like seasonal flowers falling down from trees. In this world, a performer of wicked deeds suffers the consequences within a short space of time. O one who walks around in the night! It is like eating food mixed with poison. O one who roams around in the night! I am the king who has come here and my task is to slay those who perform wicked and terrible deeds and desire to cause unpleasantness to the worlds. I will release arrows that are decorated with gold. They are like serpents emerging from termite hills. They

[183] These also answer the questions Sita had posed earlier.

[184] Specifically, a type of lizard. The text refers to this type of lizard by name. It is a red-tailed lizard, called a *brahmani* lizard. The belief is that if this lizard eats hail stones, it dies.

will descend on you and pierce you and shatter you. You have eaten those who followed dharma in Dandakaranya. In the battle today, I will slay you and the soldiers who follow you. The supreme rishis, whom you injured earlier, are astride their celestial vehicles and will see you slain with arrows and conveyed to hell. O worst of your lineage! Strike me as you will. Today, I will bring down your head, like a palm fruit.' Eyes red with rage, Rama spoke in this way.

However, senseless with anger, he laughed and replied to Rama in this way. 'O Dasharatha's son! You have slain some ordinary rakshasas in the battle and are praising yourself, for something that does not deserve any praise. Bulls among men who are valiant and powerful pride themselves on their energy and do not indulge in self-praise. In this world, it is only the worst among kshatriyas, ordinary ones who have not cleansed their souls, who futilely indulge in self-praise. O Rama! That is the way you are praising yourself. When the time for battle presents itself, when the time for death has arrived, which brave one will praise himself? In every way, this self-praise demonstrates your inferiority. This is just like the blade of kusha grass, which, when on fire, seems to be like gold. You have not seen me standing here, wielding a club in my hand. I am like a mountain that does not tremble, with minerals in its core, held aloft by the earth. With the club in my hand, I am sufficient to rob you of your life in the battle, like Yama, with the noose in his hand, takes away the lives of all those in the three worlds. Though I wish to say many more things, I will not tell you anything more. The sun is about to set and that causes an obstruction in the way of the encounter.[185] You have slain fourteen thousand rakshasas. Therefore, I will kill you now and wipe away their tears.'

Saying this, the extremely enraged Khara flung the supreme club, encrusted with ornaments, towards Rama, like a blazing bolt of thunder. That giant and blazing club was released from Khara's hand. Having consumed the trees and the creepers, it approached him. The giant club descended like Death's noose. However, while it was still in the sky, Rama shattered it with many arrows. Shattered

---

[185] No fighting took place during the night.

and fragmented by those arrows, the club fell down on the ground,
like a female serpent is brought down through mantras and herbs.

Chapter 3(29)

Raghava, devoted to dharma, shattered the club with his arrows.
Delighted, he addressed the enraged Khara in these words. 'O
worst among rakshasas! Is this the entire strength of your army
that you can display? Your strength is inferior. You are roaring in
vain. The club has been shattered by these arrows and has fallen
down on the ground. You spoke and boasted a lot. But your faith
has also been destroyed. You said that you would wipe the tears
of the rakshasas who had been destroyed. Those words of yours
have also turned out to be false. You are an inferior rakshasa.
You are lowly in conduct and your behaviour is full of falsehood.
I will take away your life, like Garuda took the *amrita* away.[186] I
will sever your throat today, mangle it with my arrows. The earth
will drink the blood and foam that gushes out. Your limbs will be
decorated with dust. You will stretch out your arms and lie down,
as if sleeping while embracing a woman who is extremely difficult
to obtain. O worst among rakshasas! While you lie down in that
sleep, this Dandaka, which is no longer a refuge today, will actually
become a refuge. O rakshasa! My arrows will destroy Janasthana,
and fearlessly, the sages will roam around everywhere in the forest.
With their relatives slain, the rakshasis who are causing terror today
will run away. They will be distressed and terrified, their faces
covered with tears. As a husband, you have wives who are equal to
you in lineage and have revelled in the misery of others. Their lives
will be rendered futile today. You are cruel in conduct and inferior.
You yourself have always been a thorn to brahmanas. It is because
of you that sages have been reluctant to light sacrificial fires and
offer oblations into them.'

[186] Garuda took amrita away from heaven.

In the battle, Raghava spoke in this way to the enraged Khara. Censured, Khara became more angry and used harsher words. 'Indeed, though you will be destroyed, you are firm. Though there is reason for fear, you are fearless. You have said what should not be said. Though you do not comprehend it, you have come under the subjugation of death. When men are ensnared in the noose of destiny, their six senses[187] are disabled and they cannot distinguish between what should be done and what should not be done.' Angry and frowning, he spoke to Rama in this way. Not very far away, the roamer in the night then saw a giant sala tree. Looking around here and there for something that could be used as a weapon in the battle, he bit his lips and uprooted it. Having uprooted it with his arms, the immensely strong one roared and hurled it towards Rama, saying, 'You have been killed.' As it descended, the powerful Rama sliced it down with his arrows. To slay Khara in the battle, he invoked a fierce rage. Rama was sweating and the ends of his eyes were red with rage. In that encounter, he pierced Khara with one thousand arrows. From the gaps left by the arrows,[188] froth and blood issued, like water flowing down a waterfall on a mountain.[189] In the battle with Rama, Khara suffered from those arrows. As if intoxicated with the smell of blood, he rushed forward impetuously. He descended angrily, covered with blood. Accomplished in the use of weapons and swift in valour, he stepped back two or three steps.[190] To slay Khara in the battle, Rama picked up an arrow that was like the fire and was only second to Brahma's staff. This was given to him by Maghavan, the intelligent king of the gods.[191] The one with dharma in his soul affixed it and released it towards Khara. Rama stretched his bow and released that great arrow, with a sound like that of a storm. It struck Khara in the chest. Consumed by the fire in the arrow, Khara fell down on the ground. It was as

---

[187] The five senses and the mind.

[188] The body was covered by arrows and there were gaps left on the body.

[189] Alternatively, the mountain named Prasravana.

[190] Rama is the one who is accomplished in the use of weapons. He stepped back two or three steps so as to strike better.

[191] Through Agastya.

if Andhaka had been burnt down by Rudra in Shvetaranya.[192] Just as Indra killed Vritra with the vajra, Namuchi with foam and Bala with the vajra, Khara was slain and brought down.[193]

At this time, all the *rajarshi*s and supreme rishis assembled. Delighted, they worshipped Rama and spoke these words. 'It was for this reason that the immensely energetic and great Indra, Purandara, the chastiser of Paka, came to Sharabhanga's sacred hermitage once. The maharshis thought of a means to bring you to this region, so that these cruel rakshasas, the perpetrators of wicked deeds, could be killed. O Dasharatha's son! You have accomplished this task for us. The maharshis can now happily roam around in Dandaka and pursue dharma.'

Meanwhile, with Sita, the brave Lakshmana emerged from the cave in the mountain and happily entered the hermitage. Rama was victorious and was worshipped by the maharshis. The brave one entered the hermitage and was honoured by Lakshmana. Vaidehi was delighted to see her husband, the slayer of the enemy and the one who had brought happiness to the maharshis. She embraced him.

Chapter 3(30)

Shurpanakha saw that Rama had single-handedly slain fourteen thousand rakshasas who were the performers of terrible deeds. In the battle, he had also killed Dushana, Khara and Trishira. On seeing this, she again uttered a mighty roar, like the thunder of a cloud full of water. She witnessed Rama's deed, which others would have regarded as extremely difficult. Extremely anxious, she went to Lanka, ruled over by Ravana. Astride the foremost of *vimana*s,[194] she saw the seated Ravana, blazing in his energy. He was with

[192] Literally, *shvetaranya* means 'white forest'. Andhaka was a demon killed by Shiva.

[193] The demon Namuchi had a boon that he could not be killed by anything wet or dry. Therefore, Indra killed with foam from the water.

[194] This was the Pushpaka vimana. However, the text only uses the word vimana and this could simply mean a palace.

his advisers, like Vasava amidst the Maruts. He was seated on a supreme and golden throne that was like the sun. He was like the fire of a sacrificial altar, when oblations of ghee had been poured on to it. He was terrible and could not be vanquished in battle by the gods, the gandharvas and the great-souled rishis. He was like Death with a gaping mouth. He had crushed the gods and the asuras and there were scars left by the vajra. There were scars on his chest, when Airavata had gored him with his sharp tusks. With his twenty arms and ten heads[195] and his accoutrements, he was a sight to behold. The brave one's broad chest bore all the signs of his being a king. His earrings were made out of molten gold and were decorated with shining lapis lazuli. His arms were excellent. His teeth were white and his mouth was large.[196] He was like a mountain. In hundreds of battles with the gods, his body had been marked by Vishnu's chakra.[197] All his limbs had been struck by the weapons of the gods. Like the ocean, he could not be agitated. However, he was swift in his action and himself caused agitation. He was the one who hurled the summits of mountains and crushed the gods. He was the one who destroyed dharma and oppressed the wives of other people. He possessed all the divine weapons and always caused impediments to sacrifices. He went to the city of Bhogavati and defeated Vasuki.[198] He defeated Takshaka and abducted his beloved wife. He went to Mount Kailasa and vanquished Naravahana.[199] He seized his Pushpaka vimana, which can travel anywhere at will. In his rage, the valiant one destroyed the groves of the gods, the divine grove of Chaitraratha and the grove of Nandana, filled with lotuses.[200] His

[195] Literally, ten necks or throats.

[196] The mouth is mentioned in the singular.

[197] This doesn't mean the famous *sudarshana chakra*, used by Vishnu alone. Presumably, other gods used chakras that were similar to the sudarshana chakra.

[198] Bhogavati was the capital city of the nagas and Vasuki was the king of the nagas. Takshaka was a naga and Takshashila is named after him. In the Mahabharata, Takshaka's wife was killed by Arjuna.

[199] Naravahana is Kubera's name. Literally, the word means someone whose mount is a man.

[200] Chaitraratha is the name of Kubera's pleasure garden, while Nandana is the name of Indra's pleasure garden.

arms were like the summits of mountains and with those, he was capable of restraining the two scorchers of enemies, the immensely fortunate sun and the moon, when they were about to rise. In ancient times, in the great forest, he had tormented himself with austerities for ten thousand years. The patient one had then offered his heads to Svayambhu.[201] He had then obtained the boon that he would not suffer fear in any battle with gods, danavas, gandharvas, pishachas, birds and serpents and would not meet his death through them, with the exception of humans.[202] Consecrated by mantras, brahmanas kept oblations of soma in sacrificial vessels and the immensely strong one seized this. When sacrifices were about to be completed, the cruel one stole them.[203] He was wicked in conduct and killed brahmanas. He was incessantly harsh and engaged in causing harm to subjects. Such was Ravana, fearful to all creatures and to all the worlds. The rakshasi saw her cruel and immensely strong brother. He was attired in divine garments, with celestial ornaments. He was decorated with divine garlands. This was the immensely fortunate Indra among rakshasas, the delight of the lineage of Pulastya.

Senseless with fear and delusion, the large-eyed one displayed these to the blazing one and spoke to him. Fearless in action, Shurpanakha, who had been disfigured by the great-souled one, spoke these extremely terrible words.

Chapter 3(31)

Ravana was one who made the worlds wail.[204] He was in the midst of his advisers. Distressed and angry, Shurpanakha

---

[201] Brahma.

[202] Because he thought so lightly of humans, Ravana forgot to mention humans in the boon he got.

[203] The personifications of those sacrifices.

[204] There is a pun, based on the derivation of the word Ravana. The word *rava* means to wail, so Ravana means someone who causes wailing. There is a different story about how Shiva made Ravana wail, which explains the derivation of the word Ravana. That story will be told later.

addressed him in these harsh words. 'You are intoxicated because of your addiction to desire and objects of pleasure. You do what you will, without any restraints. A terrible fear has arisen and one should know about it. However, you don't realize it. If a king is addicted to carnal desire and conducts himself in accordance with that desire, the subjects do not respect such an avaricious person, but regard him like the fire of a cremation ground. At the right time, if a king does not himself undertake the tasks that need to be done, he will be destroyed, with his kingdom and with those tasks. If a king cannot control himself and spies find it extremely difficult to meet him, men abhor him from a distance, like elephants avoid mud in a river. If a king cannot control himself and does not protect the kingdom, his prosperity will not manifest itself, like a mountain that is submerged in the ocean. Engaging with gods, gandharvas and danavas, you are apparently enhancing your own prosperity. However, you are fickle and do not engage with spies. How can you be a king? O supreme among victorious ones! If kings do not control themselves and don't possess spies, treasuries and proper policies, they are the equals of ordinary people. From the words spoken by spies, from a distance, kings can discern everything about the pursuit of artha. Such kings are far-sighted. I think that you do not interact with your spies and therefore only consult ordinary advisers. Despite your own relatives having been killed in Janasthana, you do not know about it. There were fourteen thousand rakshasas, terrible in their deeds. Rama has single-handedly slain them, along with Khara and Dushana. He has granted safety to the rishis and brought peace to Dandaka. Rama, unblemished in his deeds, has thus oppressed Janasthana. O Ravana! You are avaricious and intoxicated. You are under the control of others. A fear has arisen within your own dominion, but you do not understand this. If a king is fierce, does not give generously, is intoxicated, proud and deceitful, at times of hardship, creatures do not approach him. If a king is extremely vain, impossible to approach, indulging in self-praise and prone to anger, at times of hardship, his own relatives will kill him. If he does not swiftly perform the required tasks, and is scared even though there is no reason to be frightened, he will be dislodged from his kingdom and, in his distress, he will become like an ordinary blade of grass. Dried wood, stones and even dust serve some purpose. But kings who have been dislodged from their positions have no utility. A king who has been dislodged from his kingdom may be capable. However, he serves no purpose, like a garment that has been worn, or a garland that has been crushed. If a king is not distracted, knows everything, has conquered his senses, is grateful and is devoted to dharma, such a king remains for a long time. If the eyes of good policy are awake even when the eyes are sleeping, and if anger and favours manifest themselves, it is only then that a king is worshipped by people. O Ravana! You are evil in intelligence. You are devoid of these qualities. After all, through your spies, you have not been informed about the great destruction of rakshasas that has occurred. You disrespect others. Though you rule over a kingdom, you do not know the truth about the apportioning of time and space.[205] You do not possess the intelligence to distinguish between qualities and sins. The kingdom is in danger. Within a short span of time, you will be brought down.'

She recounted his own taints in this way. Using his own intelligence, the lord of those who roam around in the night reflected on them. Possessing riches, insolence and strength, Ravana thought for a long time.

Chapter 3(32)

In the midst of the advisers, Ravana spoke these harsh words to the angry one. Enraged, Ravana asked her. 'Who is Rama? What is his valour like? What is his appearance? How brave is he? Dandakaranya is extremely difficult to penetrate. Why has he come here? What are the weapons Rama used to slay the rakshasas and kill Khara, Dushana and Trishira in the battle?'

---

[205] The idea is that a king must apportion out time between dharma, artha and kama, and not spend all of his time on one, at the expense of the others.

Thus addressed by the Indra among rakshasas, the rakshasi became senseless with rage. She started to describe Rama properly. 'His arms are long and his eyes are large. His garments are made out of bark and dark antelope skin. Rama is Dasharatha's son and his beauty is like Kandarpa.[206] He stretches a bow that is decorated with gold and is like Shakra's bow. He shoots blazing iron arrows that are like serpents with virulent poison. In the battle, I could not see when the immensely strong Rama took out those terrible arrows, released them, or stretched his bow.[207] I saw those soldiers slaughtered by the shower of arrows. It was like an excellent crop of grain devastated by Indra's shower of hail stones. There were fourteen thousand rakshasas who were terrible in their valour. A single one on foot slew them with sharp arrows, together with Khara and Dushana, within the space of one-and-a-half *muhurta*s.[208] He granted safety to the rishis and brought peace to Dandaka. Somehow, I alone managed to escape from being vanquished by that great-souled one. Rama, who knows about his soul, hesitated to kill a woman.[209] His brother is immensely energetic and is his equal in qualities and valour. The valiant one is faithful and devoted to him and his name is Lakshmana. He is intolerant and impossible to defeat. He is victorious, brave, intelligent and strong. He is always like Rama's right arm, as is his[210] breath of life, moving around outside. Rama possesses an illustrious and large-eyed wife.[211] The beautiful and slender-waisted one has the name of Sita Vaidehi. Earlier, I have never seen a woman with her kind of beauty on this earth, be it a goddess, or a gandharva,

---

[206] Kama, Manmatha or Madana, the god of love.

[207] The action was too fast.

[208] Though it is sometimes used in the sense of an instant, a muhurta is a measure of time, equal to forty-eight minutes. The encounter lasted for just over an hour.

[209] Oddly, the Critical Edition excises some shlokas. In one of these, Ravana asks about Shurpanakha's disfigurement, which he was certain to notice. Though Shurpanakha distorted the story to suit herself, the reply doesn't mention the disfigurement either, at least not directly. In passing, non-Critical versions also have an account about a rakshasa named Akampana informing Ravana about the incident before Shurpanakha does.

[210] Rama's.

[211] Literally, wife according to dharma.

yaksha or *kinnara* lady.[212] If Sita becomes the wife of a person and cheerfully embraces him, he truly lives in all the worlds, even more than Purandara. She is good in conduct. Her form is praiseworthy. Her beauty is unmatched on earth. She is the appropriate wife for you and you are the right husband for her. Her hips are wide. Her breasts are full and peaked. I wished to bring that beautiful one here as your wife. Vaidehi's face is like the full moon. If you see her now, you will also have to seek refuge with Manmatha. If you have intentions of accomplishing the objective of obtaining her as your wife, you should act quickly. Stretch out your right foot for the sake of victory.[213] O lord of rakshasas! Do what will bring pleasure to the rakshasas. Slay the cruel Rama who lives in a hermitage. Slay maharatha Lakshmana with your sharp arrows. When her protectors have been slain, you will be able to happily enjoy Sita. O lord of the rakshasas! O Ravana! If my words appeal to you, without any doubts, act in accordance with my words. You have heard that Rama used straight-flying arrows to slay the roamers of the night who had gone to Janasthana. You have also learnt that Khara and Dushana have been killed. You should now arise and do what needs to be done.'

Chapter 3(33)

He heard Shurpanakha's words and they made the body hair stand up. He made up his mind about what should be done. Taking his leave of his advisers, he departed. He thought about the appropriate course of action that should be followed. He weighed the pros and cons and thought about the strengths and weaknesses. He then made up his mind about what should be done. Having decided this, he went to the beautiful quarter[214] where all the vehicles were kept. The lord of the rakshasas secretly went to

---

[212] Kinnara, also known as *kimpurusha*, is a semi-divine species, described as Kubera's companions.

[213] The left foot is inauspicious.

[214] That is, a garage.

the garage and instructed the charioteer, 'Yoke the chariot.'[215] In a short while, the charioteer, quick in his valour, yoked the excellent and favourite chariot. The golden chariot could travel, as it willed, through the sky. It was adorned with jewels. It was yoked to mules, with faces like pishachas, and with golden harnesses. The lord of the rakshasas, Dhanada's prosperous younger brother,[216] went to the lord of the male and female rivers.[217] Dashanana[218] was fanned with whisks made of white yak hair and a white umbrella was held aloft his head. His ornaments were made out of molten gold and had the complexion of mild lapis lazuli. With ten faces and twenty arms, his garments deserved to be seen. He was the enemy of the gods and the one who killed sages. With ten heads, he was like a king of the mountains. Astride a chariot that could travel at will, the lord of the rakshasas was radiant. It[219] looked like a cloud in the sky, encircled with lightning and with flying cranes.

The valiant one looked at the shoreline of the ocean, with mountains and full of thousands of trees with many kinds of flowers and fruits. In every direction, there were lakes with lotuses, full of auspicious and cool water. There were large hermitages, with decorated sacrificial altars. It was ornamented with coconut trees and plantain trees were like a dam. There were blossoming sala, tala and *tamala*[220] trees. It was ornamented with supreme rishis who were extremely restrained in their diet. There were thousands of nagas, birds, gandharvas and kinnaras. The place was beautiful with siddhas and charanas who had conquered desire. There were *aaja*s, vaikhanasas, *masha*s, valakhilyas and marichipas.[221] There

---

[215] The reason for Ravana going secretly and not asking someone else to convey the command to the charioteer remains a matter of speculation.

[216] Dhanada is one who bestows riches and is Kubera's name. Ravana was Kubera's younger brother.

[217] The ocean.

[218] Meaning one with ten faces, Ravana's name.

[219] The chariot.

[220] Tree with dark bark.

[221] Aajas are those without birth, so they mean Brahma's mental children; vaikhanasas are hermits; and mashas are difficult to pin down, probably meaning sages who subsist only on beans.

were thousands of apsaras who knew about the techniques of sexual pastimes, wearing divine ornaments and garlands and enveloped in celestial forms. The beautiful wives of the gods frequented the place and loved it. Large numbers of gods and danavas wandered around, desiring amrita.[222] The place was filled with swans, curlews and frogs. There were the sounds of cranes. It was spread over with mild and beautiful lapis lazuli and the ocean's energy. In every direction, there were vimanas, large and white, decorated with divine garlands and filled with the sound of trumpets and singing. They could travel at will and such worlds could be won[223] by those who practised austerities. Dhanada's younger brother saw them,[224] served by gandharvas and apsaras. He saw thousands of gentle forests, filled with roots that exuded the juices of sandalwood. These satisfied the sense of smell. There were the best of forests and groves, filled with aloe. There were fragrant fruits from nutmeg and bay rum trees.[225] There were blossoming tamala trees and clumps of pepper. Large numbers of oysters were drying along the shore. There were conch shells, rocks and heaps of coral. There were gold and silver hills in every direction. There were waterfalls pleasing to the mind and sparkling lakes. The place was filled with riches and grain and gems among women. He also saw cities, with sheds for elephants, horses and chariots. It was level and pleasant in every direction. The breeze was mild to the touch. He saw the shore of the lord of the rivers and it was like heaven.

He saw a nyagrodha tree there.[226] It had the complexion of a cloud and was surrounded by rishis. In every direction, its branches stretched out for a hundred yojanas. The immensely strong Garuda seized the elephant and the extremely large tortoise as food and sat down on its branch to eat them.[227] When the

---

[222] Amrita emerged from the churning of the ocean.

[223] With such vimanas.

[224] The vimanas.

[225] *Takkola,* meaning the bay rum tree.

[226] These shlokas about Garuda are a bit of a digression.

[227] The story is about a giant elephant and tortoise who were fighting. While they fought, Garuda seized them both and ate them.

supreme among birds suddenly sat down on the branch, covered
with many leaves, because of the burden caused by the immensely
strong Suparna, it broke. The supreme rishis, the vaikhanasas,
the mashas, the valakhilyas, the marichipas, the aajas and the
dhumras[228] were collectively attached to the branch.[229] Garuda
was overcome with compassion for them. With great force, he
seized the broken branch that was one hundred yojanas long
and the elephant and the tortoise. The one with dharma in his
soul used one talon to devour the flesh. The supreme among
birds used the branch to destroy the dominion of the *nishadas*.[230]
Having been freed, the great sages were infinitely delighted.
Their delight was doubled when the intelligent one turned his
intelligence towards bringing the amrita and performed an
act of valour. He shattered the mesh made of iron and broke
into the excellent vault meant for treasures. He penetrated the
protected residence of the great Indra and carried the amrita
away. Dhanada's younger brother saw the nyagrodha named
Subhadra, frequented by large numbers of maharshis and with
Suparna's marks on it.

He passed over to the other shore of the ocean, the lord of the
rivers. At the end of a beautiful and sacred forest there, he saw
a lonely hermitage. He saw the rakshasa named Maricha there,
restrained in his food. He was attired in black antelope skin and bark
and sported matted hair. In the proper way, Ravana approached
the rakshasa. After this, the one who was eloquent in the use of
words[231] addressed him in these words.

---

[228] Sages who subsist on smoke.

[229] They were performing austerities on the branch.

[230] This requires explanation. Garuda seized the elephant in one talon and the
tortoise in the other talon. He then settled down on the branch to eat them, noticing the
sages in the process. When the branch broke, Garuda took off. While still in flight, he
ate the elephant and caught the tortoise with one talon. After the sages escaped, Garuda
flung the branch away. This descended on the dominion of the nishadas and destroyed
them.

[231] Ravana.

Chapter 3(34)

'O Maricha! O son![232] Listen to the words I am going to speak. I am afflicted. You are the supreme refuge in my state of affliction. You know about Janasthana. My brother, Khara, the mighty-armed Dushana, my sister, Shurpanakha, the immensely energetic rakshasa, Trishira, who survived on human flesh, and many other brave roamers in the night who were successful in their objectives followed by counsel and resided there. Those rakshasas dwelt there. In that great forest, they obstructed the sages who sought to follow dharma. There were fourteen thousand rakshasas who were terrible in their deeds. They were brave and successful in their objectives. They followed Khara's wishes. Those immensely strong ones used to reside in Janasthana now. In a battle, they had a supreme engagement with Rama. In the field of battle, Rama's rage was ignited by this. Though he did not utter anything harsh, he affixed arrows to his bow. There were fourteen thousand rakshasas who were fierce in their energy. A man on foot used sharp arrows to slay them. In the battle, Khara was slain and Dushana was brought down. Trishira was killed and he rendered Dandaka free from fear. With his wife, his father exiled him in his rage and he possesses a limited lifespan. That Rama, the worst among kshatriyas, has killed those soldiers. He is wicked in conduct and harsh. He is fierce, stupid and greedy and has not conquered his senses. He has abandoned dharma and has adharma in his soul. He is engaged in causing injury to creatures. There was no reason for enmity in the forest. Yet, he resorted to his spirited nature and disfigured my sister by slicing off her nose and ears. His wife is Sita and she is like a daughter of the gods. She is in Janasthana. With you as my aide, I will use my valour to bring her away. O immensely strong one. With you by my side as my aide and with my brothers, I will not worry about fighting against the assembled gods in a battle. O rakshasa! Become my aide. You are capable. With your valour and your pride, there is no one who is your equal in a battle. O one who

---

[232] The word used is tata.

roams around in the night! This is the reason why I have come here and approached you. Listen to me about what you have to do to help me. My words will spell out your task. Assume the form of a golden deer, with colourful silver spots. Roam around in Rama's hermitage, in front of Sita. On seeing you in the form of a deer, there is no doubt that Sita will ask her husband and Lakshmana to seize you. When they are away and Sita is alone, without any impediments, I will cheerfully abduct her, like Rahu robs the moon of its radiance. After that, Rama will be miserable and afflicted because his wife has been abducted. I will strike him if he retaliates and thus accomplish the inner desire of my heart.'

The great-souled Maricha heard this about Rama. His mouth turned dry and he was terrified. He knew about Rama's valour in the great forest. He was scared and miserable in his mind. He joined his hands in salutation and addressed Ravana in the following words, knowing what would be good and what would be bad for his own self.

Chapter 3(35)

The one who was eloquent in the use of words heard the words spoken by the Indra among the rakshasas. The immensely wise Maricha replied to the lord of the rakshasas. 'O king! It is always easy to get men who are pleasant in speech. It is extremely difficult to find a speaker and a listener for disagreeable medication. There is no doubt that you do not know about Rama's great valour and superior qualities. You are fickle and do not engage with your spies. He is like the great Indra and Varuna. O father![233] Will there be safety for all the rakshasas on earth? Or will Rama be enraged and render the world devoid of rakshasas? Has Janaka's daughter been born to bring an end to your life? Is Sita going to be the reason behind a great catastrophe for us? If you completely follow this

---

[233] The word used is tata.

conduct engendered by desire and she obtains you as her lord, will
the city of Lanka, with you and the rakshasas, be destroyed? If an
evil-minded king like you engages in conduct that is engendered by
desire and follows wicked conduct and evil counsel, he destroys his
own self, the people and the kingdom. He has not been abandoned
by his father and no disrespect has been shown to him. He is not
greedy. He is not wicked in conduct. Nor is he the worst among
kshatriyas. The extender of Kousalya's delight is not devoid
of the qualities of dharma. He is engaged in the welfare of all
creatures and is not violent towards them. His father was truthful
in speech and was deceived by Kaikeyee. On seeing this, the one
with dharma in his soul agreed to exile in the forest. He wished
to do what would bring pleasure to Kaikeyee and to his father,
Dasharatha. He abandoned the kingdom and objects of pleasure
and entered the Dandaka forest. O father![234] Rama is not harsh.
He is not devoid of learning. It is not that he has not conquered
his senses. He is not false. He is not bereft of learning. You should
not speak in this way. Rama is the personification of dharma. He
is virtuous. Truth is his valour. He is the king of all the worlds,
like Vasava among the gods. He can protect Vaidehi through his
own energy. Like robbing the sun of its radiance,[235] how can you
wish to rob him of his resplendence? In a battle, the rays of his
arrows are invincible and his bow and arrows are like kindling.
When the fire that is Rama blazes suddenly, you should not enter
it. The flaming mouth of the bow will gape. The rays of arrows
cannot be tolerated. The brave one will wield bow and arrows that
will destroy the enemy soldiers. O father! If you desire your own
welfare and do not wish to give up your kingdom, your happiness
and your life, you should not test Rama. He is like Death. His
energy is immeasurable and Janaka's daughter is his wife. When
she is under the protection of Rama's bow in the forest, you are
incapable of abducting her. He loves the wife more than his own
life and she is always devoted to him. The slender-waisted Sita is

---

[234] The word used is tata.
[235] The word used is *prabha*, referring to the sun's radiance. However, there is another
related meaning too. Prabha is the sun's wife.

like the flames of a sacrificial fire into which oblations have been offered. O lord of the rakshasas! Why do you wish to undertake a futile endeavour? Even if he glances at you in a battle, your life will come to an end. Life, happiness and the kingdom are extremely difficult to obtain. Make up your mind and consult with all the advisers and those who follow dharma, with Vibhishana at the forefront. Reflect on the pros and the cons and the strengths and the weaknesses. Determine the truth about your own strength and that of Raghava's. You should make up your mind about what is most beneficial and act accordingly. I do not think that you should embark on this battle and encounter with the son of the king of Kosala.[236] O lord of those who roam around in the night! Listen yet again to these excellent and desirable words.'

Chapter 3(36)

'With my great valour, I was once travelling around this earth. I possessed the strength of thousands of elephants and was like a mountain. I was like a dark blue cloud and wore golden earrings. Wearing a crown and with a club as a weapon, I generated fear in the worlds. I wandered around Dandakaranya, devouring the flesh of rishis. The great sage, Vishvamitra, with dharma in his soul, was terrified of me. He himself went to King Dasharatha and spoke these words. "The right time has come and let this Rama protect me. O lord of men! A terrible fear has arisen on account of Maricha." Thus addressed, King Dasharatha, with dharma in his soul, replied to the immensely fortunate and great sage, Vishvamitra. "Raghava is less than sixteen years old and is unskilled in the use of weapons. If you wish, I and all my soldiers will go with you. O best among sages! As you wish, I will slay your enemy." Thus addressed, the sage spoke to the king. "With the exception of Rama, no other force will

---

[236] We have earlier remarked that this reference to Dasharatha as the king of Kosala is odd.

be sufficient for that rakshasa. Though he is a child, he is immensely energetic and is capable of restraining him. O scorcher of enemies! May you be fortunate. Let me take Rama and go." Saying this, the sage took the prince. Extremely delighted, Vishvamitra went to his own hermitage and consecrated himself for a sacrifice. Rama was there, twanging his colourful bow. At that time, the handsome one still didn't have a beard on his face. He was dark and with excellent eyes. He was attired in a single garment, with a bow, crested hair and a golden garland. He rendered Dandakaranya beautiful with the radiance of his own energy. At that time, Rama was seen to be like the young moon when it has arisen.

'I was like a cloud, with earrings made out of molten gold. Strong and insolent because of the boon I had obtained,[237] I went to that hermitage. With an upraised weapon, I entered violently. On seeing me, he was not scared and strung his bow. Because of my delusion, I took Raghava to be a child and did not show him any respect. I quickly rushed towards Vishvamitra's sacrificial altar. He released a sharp arrow that was capable of killing the enemy. Struck by it, I was flung one hundred yojanas away, into the ocean. Because of the force of Rama's arrow, I became unstable and my senses were in a whirl. I was then submerged into the deep waters of the ocean. O father! After having regained my senses after a long time, I went to the city of Lanka. I escaped in this way, though my aides were slain. Though Rama was still a child and not skilled in the use of weapons, he was unblemished in his deeds. Therefore, I will restrain you from a clash with Rama. If you do so, there will be a great catastrophe and you will quickly be destroyed. The rakshasas know about sporting and satisfying desire. Their assemblies are engaged in festivities. You will rob them of those and bring about torment and calamity. The city of Lanka has mansions, palaces and ramparts. It is decorated with many jewels. Because of Maithilee, you will witness its destruction. Like fish in a lake where there is a serpent, even if virtuous people do not engage in wicked acts, but consort with those who are wicked, they are destroyed

[237] Boon obtained from Brahma.

because of the sins of others. The rakshasas are smeared with divine sandalwood paste and celestial unguents. They are adorned with divine ornaments. Because of your sins, you will see them slain and fallen down on the ground. You will see the remaining roamers in the night flee in the ten directions, with their wives and without their wives, without a refuge. There is no doubt that you will see the houses in Lanka burn, surrounded by a circle of fire and enveloped in a net of arrows. O king! You have already married one thousand women. O rakshasa! Be devoted to your own wives and save your own lineage. Make efforts to enhance your respect, the prosperity of the kingdom and your own life. If you desire to enjoy these for a long time, do not do anything disagreeable towards Rama. Despite being restrained by your well-wishers, if you still engage in this terrible act of oppressing Sita, your soldiers and relatives will decay. With your life taken away by Rama's arrows, you will go to Yama's eternal abode.'

Chapter 3(37)

'In an encounter with him, I escaped in this way. Now listen to what happened thereafter. Though I had been shamed by him in this way, with two other rakshasas, I entered the Dandaka forest. They were in the forms of animals. I also roamed around in Dandakaranya in the form of a giant animal that fed on flesh. My tongue was ablaze and I had large tusks. I had sharp horns and was immensely strong. O Ravana! I roamed around in that extremely terrible form and oppressed the ascetics, in the agnihotra sacrifices, in tirthas and chaityas[238] and amidst the trees. In Dandakaranya, I killed the ascetics who followed dharma. I drank their blood and ate their flesh. Acting in this cruel way, I ate the flesh of rishis and terrified those who resided in the forest. Intoxicated by the blood,

---

[238] A tirtha is a sacred place of pilgrimage with water where one can have a bath. The word chaitya has several meanings—sacrificial shed, temple, altar, sanctuary and a tree that grows along the road.

I roamed around in the forest of Dandaka. I thus roamed around in Dandakaranya, abusing dharma. At that time, I approached Rama, who was following the dharma of ascetics, the immensely fortunate Vaidehi and maharatha Lakshmana. He was in the form of an ascetic, restrained in diet and engaged in the welfare of all creatures. Remembering the former enmity and knowing that Rama had come to the forest in the form of an ascetic, I wished to vanquish the extremely strong one. Extremely angry, not capable of discrimination, but remembering the former chastisement, I rushed against him, wishing to kill him, in the form of an animal with sharp horns. He forcefully stretched his bow and released three sharp arrows that could slay the enemy. They were as swift as Suparna[239] and the wind. Those three extremely terrible arrows were like the vajra and fed on blood. They possessed straight tufts and together, they rushed towards us. Earlier, I had known about his valour and the fear he could cause. I deceived him and escaped.[240] But the other two rakshasas were killed. I somehow managed to escape from the arrow released by Rama with my life. I came here, renounced everything and became an ascetic. Attired in bark and black antelope skin, I can see Rama in each and every tree, wielding the bow, like Yama with the noose in his hand. O Ravana! I am scared and can see thousands of Ramas. It seems to me that this entire forest is full of Rama. O lord of the rakshasas! I do not see anything that is without Rama. Rama appears in my dreams and my senses are whirled around. O Ravana! Because of my terror of Rama, all words that begin with the letter "R", like *ratna* and *ratha*,[241] generate fear in me. I know of his powers and you are not his equal in a battle. O Ravana! You can pardon him[242] or fight with Rama. If you wish to see me,[243] you should not mention anything about Rama. I have spoken these words with a view to ensuring the welfare of my relatives. If you do not like what I have spoken, with

---

[239] Garuda.

[240] Rama's arrow chased Maricha to the shores of the ocean and retreated.

[241] Respectively, gem and chariot.

[242] The slaughter of Khara, Dushana, Trishira and the other rakshasas.

[243] Alive.

your relatives, you will give up your life in a battle. Rama's straight-flying arrows will kill you today.'

Chapter 3(38)

Maricha's words were full of what was beneficial. However, like a person wishing to die does not accept medicines, Ravana did not accept what he said. Maricha spoke words that were like a medicament. However, goaded by destiny, the lord of the rakshasas addressed him in harsh and inappropriate words. 'O Maricha! You have addressed me in inappropriate and futile words. These are extremely pointless words, like seeds sown in a barren spot. With these words, you are incapable of frightening me against taking on Rama in a battle. He is wicked in conduct and foolish. Moreover, he is human. Rama has abandoned his well-wishers, his kingdom, his mother and his father. Hearing the ordinary words of a woman, he went to the forest alone, on foot. He killed Khara in a battle. In your presence, I should certainly abduct Sita, whom he loves more than his own life. O Maricha! This resolution of my heart has been determined. Even if Indra is there, with the gods and the asuras, I am incapable of withdrawing from it. Had I asked you about the pros and cons and about the appropriate and inappropriate means, it would indeed have been your task to determine that and speak to me in this way. A skilled adviser who desires his own prosperity should speak, with hands joined in salutation, only when he has been asked by the king. If one wishes to address disagreeable words, appropriate and beneficial, to a lord of the earth, they should be properly spoken, displaying mildness first. O Maricha! A king who deserves respect does not take delight in disrespectful and insulting words, even if they are uttered for the sake of benefit. Infinitely energetic kings embody the five forms of Agni, Indra, Soma, Yama and Varuna[244] and the respective attributes of fierceness, valour, gentleness,

[244] Respectively identified with the five elements—fire, wind, earth, space and water.

chastisement and suppleness. Therefore, under all circumstances,
kings must be respected and worshipped. You have ignored dharma
and are only immersed in delusion. I have come to you, but because
of the wickedness of your soul, you have spoken in this harsh way
to me. O rakshasa! I did not ask you about the pros and the cons,
or about what is beneficial for my own self. You should help me in
this task. Assume the form of a wonderful golden deer, with silver
spots. After having tempted Vaidehi, you can go wherever you
wish to. On seeing your golden form, full of *maya*, Maithilee will
be filled with wonder. She will tell Rama, "Bring it here quickly."
When Kakutstha and Lakshmana have withdrawn, I will cheerfully
abduct Vaidehi, like the one with the one thousand eyes taking away
Shachi.[245] O rakshasa! After having performed this task, you can
go away wherever you want. O Maricha! O one with the excellent
vows! I will give you half of my kingdom. O amiable one! Follow the
auspicious path of accomplishing this task. I will deprive Raghava
and obtain Sita without a battle. Having accomplished the task, with
you, I will leave for Lanka. You will accomplish this task, even if
I have to force you to do it. A person who acts against his king
does not obtain happiness. When you approach him, there may be a
doubt about your remaining alive. However, if you act against me,
your death now is certain. You must make your intelligence realize
that doing this here and that there, is beneficial for you.'

Chapter 3(39)

The roamer in the night heard the contrary command spoken by
the king. Maricha addressed these harsh words to the lord of
the rakshasas. 'O roamer in the night! Who has instructed you about
this wicked deed that leads to your destruction, with your sons, your
kingdom and your advisers? O king! Who is the evil-acting one who

---

[245] Shachi was the daughter of the asura Puloma. Indra killed Puloma and took
Shachi away.

does not rejoice in your happiness? Who has urged you towards a means that will convey you to death's door? O roamer in the night! It is sufficiently clear that they are your enemies, desiring a reduction in your valour and your destruction by urging you against someone who is stronger. Who is the inferior one, disastrous in intelligence, who has instructed you in this way? O roamer in the night! He desires that you should be destroyed because of your own deeds. O Ravana! It is evident that your advisers are not restraining you from killing yourself. Even if their status is elevated, they should be restrained in every way. If a king follows desire and conducts himself, resorting to an inappropriate path, virtuous advisers must restrain him in every way. But though you should be restrained, they are not restraining you. O supreme among victorious ones! O roamer in the night! Advisers obtain dharma, artha, kama and fame through the favours of their master. O Ravana! When there is a catastrophe, all those become futile. The calamity a master reaps because of his evil qualities also devolves on inferior people. O supreme among victorious ones! The king is the foundation for dharma and victory. Therefore, in every situation, kings must be protected. O roamer in the night! O rakshasa! It is impossible to protect a kingdom through ferocity, contrariness and lack of humility. There are advisers who worship you and give you ferocious counsel. Like a wicked charioteer, they will swiftly drive you down an uneven road. In this world, there are many virtuous people who follow dharma. However, because of the crimes of others, they are destroyed, with their followers. O Ravana! When the master is contrary and ferocious, the protection and prosperity of the subjects is not enhanced, like sheep who are protected by a jackal. O Ravana! All the rakshasas will certainly be destroyed, since they have a harsh and evil-minded king like you, who has been unable to conquer his senses. Like a coincidence, you are bringing about this terrible calamity.[246] When you are going to

---

[246] Coincidence doesn't capture the nuance. The word used is *kakataliya*, *kaka* means a crow and *tala* means a palm tree. An injured fox sought refuge under a palm tree. A crow came and sat down on the tree, dislodging a ripe palm fruit, which fell on the fox's head, increasing its misery. The fox sitting there, the crow sitting there and the palm fruit falling occur at the same point in time. But one is not responsible for the other. To attribute causation to one is fallacious. This analogy is used extensively in the *nyaya* school of philosophy (*darshana*).

be destroyed, with your soldiers, what is admirable? After I have
been slain, Rama will soon kill you. I will act so that the act is done
by him. My death will come about through an enemy.[247] Know that
as soon as Rama sees me, my death is certain. Know that you and
your relatives will also be killed when you abduct Sita. If you go with
me to the hermitage and bring Sita, you will not remain. I will not
remain, nor will Lanka and the rakshasas remain. O one who roams
in the night! I am restraining you because I seek your welfare. Do
not be intolerant about these words. When the lifespans of men are
over and they are like those who are dead, they do not accept the
beneficial words spoken by their well-wishers.'

Chapter 3(40)

The distressed Maricha addressed these harsh words to Ravana.
However, scared of the lord of those who roam around in
the night, he agreed to go. 'He is the one who wields arrows, a
bow and a sword. If he sees me, and doesn't even raise a weapon,
my life will be destroyed. But since you are so evil-souled, what
am I capable of doing? O father![248] O one who roams around in
the night! May you be fortunate. I will go.' The rakshasa[249] was
delighted at these words. He embraced him extremely tightly and
spoke these words. 'Despite being under my subjugation, you have
uttered these rash and obstinate words.[250] You are Maricha now.
But formerly, you used to be another roamer in the night.[251] With
me, swiftly ascend this chariot, decorated with jewels, that travels
through the sky. It is yoked to mules that have faces like pishachas.'
Ravana and Maricha ascended the chariot that was like a vimana.
They swiftly travelled towards the circle of hermitages. They saw

[247] Rather than suffer death at your hands.

[248] The word used is tata.

[249] Ravana.

[250] The sense seems to be the following. Maricha is under Ravana's protection.
Despite this, he has spoken about Rama killing him. That is rash and obstinate.

[251] You are no longer the Maricha you used to be.

all the habitations, forests, mountains, rivers, kingdoms and cities.
They reached Dandakaranya, where Raghava's hermitage was, and
with Maricha, Ravana, the lord of the rakshasas, saw it. Ravana
descended from the chariot that was decorated with gold. Taking
Maricha's hand in his, he spoke these words. 'Rama's hermitage
can be seen. It is surrounded with plantain trees. O friend! Quickly
do what we have come here for.'

Hearing Ravana's words, the rakshasa Maricha assumed the
form of a deer and roamed around near the entrance to Rama's
hermitage. The tips of his horns had the best of jewels. His face
was partly white and partly dark. His mouth was like a red lotus.
His ears were like blue lotuses. His neck was elevated and his
stomach had the complexion of a blue diamond. His flanks were
partly of the hue of madhuka flowers and partly like the filaments
of lotuses. His hooves were like lapis lazuli. His body and calves
were formed well. The radiant tail was raised up and had the
complexion of Indra's weapon.[252] His complexion was pleasant
and mild, decorated with many kinds of jewels. In an instant,
the rakshasa assumed the form of this extremely beautiful deer.
He seemed to make the forest and Rama's hermitage blaze. The
rakshasa created this beautiful form that was a sight to behold.
To tempt Vaidehi, there were many kinds of wonderful minerals
on his body. He went there and roamed around, grazing on the
grass that was there in every direction. He was pleasant to see and
there were hundreds of colourful silver spots on him. He grazed
on grass and the leaves of trees and wandered around. Here and
there, he went into the groves of plantain and *karnikara* trees. He
resorted to a gentle pace, so that Sita could see him. The large
deer was resplendent, with the marks of red lotuses on his back.
At ease and cheerfully, he roamed around in Rama's hermitage.
That excellent deer wandered around, entering and retreating.
He would swiftly enter and withdraw in an instant. He played
around and sometimes sat down on the ground. He went to the
hermitage's entrance and then joined a herd of deer. Having

[252] The rainbow.

followed that herd of deer, he returned again. The rakshasa had assumed the form of a deer so as to show himself to Sita. He wandered around in wonderful circles and jumped around. All the others who roam around in the forest saw this deer. They approached him, inhaled his smell and fled in the ten directions. Those wild deer recognized him to be a rakshasa, engaged in the killing of deer. However, he disguised those sentiments and did not touch them or eat them.

At that time, Vaidehi, with the beautiful eyes, approached the trees, eager to collect some flowers. The one with the beautiful eyes and beautiful face wandered around, collecting flowers from karnikara, ashoka and mango trees. She did not deserve to live in the forest. The supreme lady saw the deer, covered with jewels and with wonderful pearls and gems decorating his limbs. His teeth and lips were beautiful. The hair on the body seemed to be made out of silver. As she gazed affectionately at him, her eyes dilated in wonder. Rama's beloved saw the deer that was full of maya. He was wandering around there, as if setting the forest on fire. She had not seen anything like this earlier, a deer decorated with jewels. Sita, Janaka's daughter, was filled with great wonder.

Chapter 3(41)

While she was collecting flowers, the one with the beautiful hips saw him. His flanks were decorated in colours of silver and gold. The one with the unblemished limbs and with a golden complexion was delighted. She called out to her husband and to Lakshmana, who was armed. Rama and Lakshmana, tigers among men, were summoned there by Vaidehi. They glanced around that spot and saw the deer. On seeing him, Lakshmana was suspicious and told Rama, 'I think this is the rakshasa Maricha in the form of a deer. O Rama! When kings came to the forest on a hunt, this wicked one, who can assume any form at will, disguised himself and killed them. He is skilled in the use of maya and has used maya to

create the form of a deer. O tiger among men! This is like a dazzling
city of the gandharvas.[253] O Raghava! A deer with these kinds of
wonderful jewels does not exist. O lord of the world! There is no
doubt that this is a maya in this world.'

When he spoke in this way to Kakutstha, Sita, the one with the
beautiful smiles, restrained him. Her senses confused by the deceit,
she cheerfully said, 'O son of a noble person! This delightful deer
has stolen my heart. O mighty-armed one! Bring him here. We will
play with him. There are many kinds of auspicious deer that can
be seen to wander around in this hermitage, like *chamara*s and
*srimara*s.[254] There are large numbers of bears, spotted deer, apes
and *kinara*s.[255] O mighty-armed one! Those immensely strong ones
assume the best of forms and roam around. O king! But I have not
seen a deer like this earlier. In energy, mildness and radiance, this is
supreme among deer. His limbs have many wonderful hues and he
is dotted with gems. Completely at ease, he beautifies and radiates
the forest, like the moon. Look at his form. Look at his radiance.
He is calling in a beautiful tone. This extraordinary and wonderful
deer is stealing my heart. If this deer allows you to capture him
alive, that will be extraordinary and will generate great wonder.
When our residence in the forest is over and we return to the royal
palace again, this deer will be an ornament in the inner quarters.
O lord! This divine form of the deer will generate great wonder in
Bharata, in the son of the noble one[256] and in my mothers-in-law.
O tiger among men! If you are unable to capture this excellent deer
alive, its hide will still be beautiful. Even if the spirited one is killed,
I wish to be humbly seated on its golden skin, spread with tender
darbha grass. It has been said that this kind of ferocity and conduct
driven by desire is unseemly in women. But the form of the spirited
one has generated great wonder in me. His body hair is golden.
His horns are adorned with the best of jewels. His complexion

---

[253] Which is not real.

[254] Chamara is a yak. Srimara is a kind of small deer. In general it also means an
animal that frequents marshy places and has been identified as nilgai.

[255] Kinara is a kind of deer, not to be confused with kinnaras.

[256] Probably meaning Shatrughna.

is like that of the rising sun and is as radiant as the path of the nakshatras.'[257]

Raghava's mind was also filled with wonder. He heard Sita's words and saw the extraordinary deer. Happily, Raghava addressed his brother, Lakshmana, in these words. 'O Lakshmana! Behold what has caused desire and delight in Vaidehi. This is the best among deer and his like does not exist today in the forest, in the region of Nandana, or in the refuge of Chaitraratha. O Soumitri! Where on earth is there a deer that is his equal? The beautiful hair on his body grows up at some places and down in others. With colourful spots of gold, this deer is splendid. Look at him yawn, with his tongue emerging from his mouth like the blazing flame of a fire, as if a cloud is tinged with lightning. His curved mouth has sapphires and his stomach has the complexion of a conch shell. Can you name anyone whose mind will not be tempted by this deer? His form has the complexion of molten gold. There are many kinds of celestial jewels. On seeing him, whose mind will not be filled with wonder? On hunts, kings roam around in the great forest. O Lakshmana! Wielding bows, they kill deer for the sake of their flesh. They exert themselves in the great forest and collect many kinds of minerals, gems, jewels and gold. All those riches make men prosper. O Lakshmana! Everything thought of in the mind enhances Shukra's treasure house.[258] O Lakshmana! If a person desires artha and goes around unhesitatingly collecting that artha, those who know the sacred texts about artha say that this artha is true artha. With me, the slender-waisted Vaidehi will be seated on half of this deer's golden and gem-encrusted hide. It is my view that nothing will be equal to that touch—not *kadali*, not *priyaki*, not *praveni*, not *aviki*.[259] There are only two deer that

[257] The Milky Way.

[258] Shukra possessed the power that if he thought of anything, it was added to his store of treasures. Similarly, everything in the forest is something that kings can aspire to and accumulate.

[259] These are the names of different kinds of deer prized for their skin. Kadali has white stripes on the neck, priyaki has thick brown and black hair and aviki is sheep. Praveni may be a different species of deer, but may also be a composite expression standing for the hide of the buck and the doe.

are so beautiful and divine. There is this one that is wandering around on earth. There is also the divine one that roams around in the sky, following the path of the stars.[260] O Lakshmana! Even if what you have said is correct, that it is the rakshasa's maya, it is my task to kill him. This is the cruel Maricha who is unclean in his soul. He used to wander around in the forest earlier, causing violence to the bulls among the sages. There were many kings, supreme archers, who came here on hunts and he arose against them and killed them. Therefore, this deer should be slain. On an earlier occasion, Vatapi vanquished the ascetics. When he was in the stomachs of the brahmanas, he slew them, like a mare.[261] After some time, because of his great greed, he ate the great sage, Agastya, whose great energy meant that he[262] was the one who came to be eaten. The illustrious one saw that Vatapi desired to rise up and assume his own form. He smiled and told him, "O Vatapi! Using your energy, you indiscriminately vanquished the best of brahmanas in the world of the living. Therefore, I have digested you." O Lakshmana! There will never be another rakshasa like Vatapi. Even if he is always devoted to dharma and has conquered his senses, if he shows me disrespect, he will be slain, just as Vatapi was devastated by Agastya. Remain here. Arm yourself and attentively protect Maithilee. O descendant of the Raghu lineage! Everything that we wish to do is based on her. I will kill or capture this deer. O Soumitri! I will go and quickly bring the deer back. O Lakshmana! Look at Vaidehi and see how she desires the deerskin. The deer's skin is his remarkable feature and he will no longer remain today. Without any distraction in sentiments, remain in the hermitage with Sita. I will slay the spotted deer with a single arrow. O Lakshmana! I will kill him and quickly come back with the hide.[263] O Lakshmana! The extremely

---

[260] The one in the sky is the constellation of Orion, with *mrigashira* as the head.

[261] Vatapi's story has already been mentioned. It is the belief that when a mare is about to give birth, the offspring is born after tearing apart the mare's womb, thereby killing it.

[262] Vatapi.

[263] Under the assumption that the deer is not captured.

strong and intelligent bird, Jatayu is circling around. Take care of
Maithilee without any distraction. In every instant, be suspicious.'

Chapter 3(42)

The descendant of the Raghu lineage instructed his brother
in this way. The immensely energetic one girded the sword
with a handle made out of molten gold. He grasped the bow with
the three arches that marked him out.[264] Fierce in his valour, he
fastened the two quivers and proceeded. The deer saw that the
Indra among kings was descending and sought to deceive him.
Because of his terror, he disappeared and then showed himself
again. With girded sword and seizing his bow, he rushed towards
wherever he could see his radiant form in front of him. In the great
forest, with the bow in his hand, he rushed to wherever he could
be seen. Sometimes, he ran away, far from the reach of the arrow
and sometimes, he tempted him. Sometimes, he seemed to be
scared and leapt up and down, as if in the sky. Sometimes, he was
visible in parts of the forest and sometimes, he became invisible.
Sometimes, he appeared like scattered clouds around the lunar
disc in the autumn. He could be seen in an instant and disappeared
in an instant. Showing himself and hiding himself, he dragged
Raghava away. Kakutstha was angry, confused and powerless at
the same time. After some time, as if greatly exhausted, he sought
out some shade amidst the grass. Surrounding himself with other
wild animals, he showed himself from a distance. Having seen
him, the immensely energetic Rama made up his mind to kill him.
The powerful one stretched his bow, firmly and forcefully. He
released a blazing and flaming weapon, that had been constructed
by Brahma and dazzled like a serpent. That excellent arrow pierced
the body of the one who was in the form of a deer. Like the vajra,
it penetrated Maricha's heart. Severely afflicted, he leapt up the

---

[264] Rama's bow was special. It had three arches, instead of the standard two.

distance of a tala tree and fell down. With a little bit of life left in him, he fell down on the ground and roared in a terrible tone. As he died, Maricha cast aside that artificial body. Knowing that his time was near, he exclaimed in a voice that was like Raghava's, 'Alas, Sita! Alas, Lakshmana!' The unmatched arrow penetrated his inner organs. He abandoned the form of a deer and adopted his own form of a rakshasa. As he gave up his life, Maricha assumed that extremely gigantic form. Rama saw that the rakshasa, terrible to see, had fallen down on the ground. His crown was wonderful and he was adorned with all kinds of ornaments. He possessed large teeth and was decorated with golden garlands. The rakshasa was struck by the arrow. In his mind, he[265] remembered Lakshmana's words to Sita.[266] As the rakshasa was dying, he had loudly shrieked, 'Alas, Sita! Alas, Lakshmana!' On hearing this, how would Sita be? What state would the mighty-armed Lakshmana be in? With his body hair standing up, Rama, with dharma in his soul, thought about this. Rama was immersed in a terrible fear and sorrow. When the rakshasa in the form of a deer had been slain, that voice had been heard. Raghava killed another spotted deer and gathered its flesh. He then quickly hurried in the direction of Janasthana.

Chapter 3(43)

Sita heard an afflicted voice in the forest and knew that it was like that of her husband's. She told Lakshmana, 'Go and find out about Raghava. The breath of life is disturbed in my heart. I have heard that terrible sound of someone screaming extremely grievously. Your brother is screaming in the forest and you should save him. Rush to your brother. He is looking towards you as refuge. He may be distressed, under the subjugation of rakshasas,

[265] Rama.
[266] About the maya of a rakshasa.

like a bull amidst lions.' Though he was addressed in this way, he abided by his brother's instructions and did not leave. At this, Janaka's daughter angrily told him, 'O Soumitri! In the disguise of being a friend to your brother, you are his enemy. Even though your brother is in such a state, you are not going towards him. O Lakshmana! Because of me, you desire Rama's destruction. I think you love the idea of his facing a difficulty. You have no affection for your brother. Therefore, you are not considering the immensely radiant one and remain here, nonchalant. Since you remain here with me, do you doubt that he is facing a difficulty? He is the leader who has brought you here. How can it be your duty to remain here?'

Her voice choking with tears of torment, Vaidehi said this. Sita was like a terrified she-deer and Lakshmana told her, 'O queen! In an encounter, Rama is like Vasava. Among gods, men, gandharvas, birds, rakshasas, pishachas, kinnaras, animals and terrible danavas, there is no one who can stand up to him. Rama cannot be killed in a battle. You should not speak in this way. In Raghava's absence, I am not interested in leaving you here in this forest. His strength is invincible and he is stronger than the strongest, even if the three worlds, with the lords and the immortals, arise against him. You should cast aside the torment that is there in your heart. Having slain the supreme among deer, your husband will arrive soon. It is evident that it wasn't his voice, or that of a divinity. The rakshasas are foremost among those who use maya, like a city of the gandharvas.[267] O Vaidehi! You have been left as a trust. The great-souled Rama has left you as a trust. O beautiful lady! I am not interested in leaving you here. O fortunate one! We have performed an act of enmity against those who roam around in the night. O queen! We did that through Khara's death and the destruction of Janasthana. In the great forest, the rakshasas speak in many kinds of voices. O Vaidehi! They find sport in violence. You should not think about this.'

[267] City of the gandharvas is an expression used for something that is illusory and not real.

Addressed by Lakshmana in this way, her eyes turned red with rage. She spoke these harsh words to Lakshmana, who was truthful in speech. 'O ignoble one! O one who lacks compassion! O cruel one! O worst of your lineage! I think that you love me and that is the reason you have spoken in this way. O Lakshmana! Wicked and cruel ones always act in a colourful way towards their rivals and hide their true character. Since you have alone followed Rama into the forest, you are extremely wicked. You have disguised this for my sake, or perhaps you have been engaged by Bharata. Rama is as dark as a blue lotus and his eyes are like lotuses. With such a person as my husband, how can I desire an ordinary person? O Soumitri! There is no doubt that I will give up my life in your presence. Without Rama, I will not remain alive on this earth even for an instant.'

Sita spoke these harsh words that made the body hair stand up. Lakshmana, who had conquered his senses, joined his hands in salutation and addressed Sita. 'I am not interested in giving you a reply. You are like a divinity to me. O Maithilee! It is not surprising that women should use such contrary words. It can be seen in the worlds that this is the innate nature of women. They are separated from dharma. They are fickle. They are fierce. Women cause dissension. All those who roam around in the forest are witnesses to what I have heard. Though I spoke to you in words that were appropriate, you addressed me harshly. Shame on you now. Since you have suspected me in this way, because of the wicked nature of women, you will be ruined. I have only followed the commands of my senior. O one with the beautiful face! May you be fortunate. I will go where Kakutstha is. O large-eyed one! Let all the divinities of the forest collectively protect you. I can see terrible portents manifesting themselves. When I return again with Rama, I hope I can see you.'

Addressed by Lakshmana in this way, Janaka's daughter started to weep. Her voice choking with tears, she replied in these fierce words. 'O Lakshmana! Without Rama, I will bind myself and enter the waters of the Godavari. Or I will fling my body down from a high place. I will consume terrible poison, or I will enter the fire. Other than Raghava, I will never touch another man with my foot.'[268] Sita, full of sorrow, spoke to Lakshmana in this way. Weeping and miserable, she struck her stomach with her hands. Her form was afflicted and distressed. She was crying. Soumitri glanced at the wide-eyed one. He tried to reassure her about her husband and his brother, but Sita did not say anything. Lakshmana then greeted Sita. He joined his hands in salutation and bowed down a little.[269] The one who was in control of his soul glanced several times towards Maithilee and then left towards Rama.

Chapter 3(44)

Raghava's younger brother was angry at these harsh words. Though he was extremely eager to see Rama, there was no hurry for that. However, he left. Dashagriva swiftly seized the opportunity and approached. Adopting the form of a wandering mendicant,[270] he came towards Vaidehi. He was dressed in a soft ochre garment, with a tuft of hair on his hand. He was clad in sandals and held an umbrella. The sacred staff was on his left shoulder and a water pot dangled from the staff. The extremely strong one approached Vaidehi in the forest in the form of a mendicant, when the two brothers were absent. It was like evening being enveloped by a great darkness when the sun and the moon are missing. He saw the young and illustrious princess, as if an extremely terrible planet was looking at Rohini when the moon was not present. On seeing the fierce perpetrator of wicked deeds, the trees of Janasthana stopped swaying and the wind ceased to blow. On seeing the one with the red eyes, the swift-flowing river Godavari was terrified and its flow became less. Dashagriva desired a weakness to get at Rama. Finding the opportunity, Ravana presented himself before

---

[268] The touching with the foot requires an explanation. This refers to a wedding custom, where the couple touch each other's feet.

[269] Signifying that this was half-hearted.

[270] *Parivrajaka.*

Vaidehi, in the form of a mendicant. When she was sorrowing over her husband, the ignoble one approached Vaidehi in a noble form, like Saturn approaching Chitra.[271] The wicked one assumed a noble form, like a well covered with grass. Stationed there, he glanced at Vaidehi, Rama's illustrious wife. Standing there, Ravana looked at Rama's wife. She was pure and her teeth and lips were beautiful. Her face was like the full moon. She was seated in that cottage made of leaves, tears of sorrow flowing down. The lotus-eyed one was attired in an ochre silken garment. The evil-minded roamer in the night went to Vaidehi.

As soon as he saw her, he was struck by Manmatha's arrows. She was alone. The lord of the rakshasas uttered hymns to the brahman and addressed her in cultured words. She was supreme in the three worlds and was like Shri[272] without the lotus. Ravana praised her radiant form. 'With the golden complexion and radiance and attired in ochre silken garments, who are you? You are like a garland made out of lotus flowers, as radiant as a lake full of lotuses. O one with the beautiful face! O beautiful one! Are you Hri, Shri, Kirti, auspicious Lakshmi, an apsara, Bhuti, Rati, or someone who acts on her own?[273] The tips of your teeth are smooth and white. Your large eyes sparkle and are red at the ends. Your pupils are black. Your hips are broad. Your thighs are thick and like the trunks of elephants. Your beautiful and rounded breasts are rising up, rubbing against each other. The nipples are peaked and lovely. They are like gentle palm fruits. They are decorated with ornaments that have the best of pearls. O one with the beautiful smiles! O one with the beautiful teeth! O one with the beautiful eyes! O temptress! O beautiful one! You have stolen my heart, like water eroding the banks of a river. Your slender waist can be grasped by the hands. O one with the beautiful hair and with breasts that are close together! I have never seen such a beautiful woman on

[271] The nakshatra Chitra.

[272] Lakshmi.

[273] Hri is the personified form of modesty, Kirti of deeds and Bhuti of one who bestows fortune. Rati is Manmatha's wife. 'Acts on her own' delinks her from being associated with a male divinity.

earth earlier, nor among goddesses, gandharva, yaksha or kinnara ladies. In this world, your beauty is overpowering and so are your gentleness and youth. Why are you residing in this desolate spot, agitating my consciousness? O fortunate one! Return, you should not reside here. Terrible rakshasas are here and they can assume any form at will. There are the best of places and beautiful cities and groves. They are prosperous and full of fragrances. That is where you should roam around. O beautiful one! O dark-eyed one! I think that you should have the best of garlands, the best of fragrances, the best of garments and the best of husbands. O one with the beautiful smiles! Who are you? Do you belong to the Rudras, the Maruts or the Vasus! O beautiful one! You look like a goddess to me. The rakshasas dwell here and gandharvas, gods and kinnaras do not come here. How have you come here? Monkeys,[274] lions, leopards, tigers, animals, bears, hyenas and herons exist here. How come you are not terrified of them? There are terrible and spirited elephants, intoxicated by musth. O one with the beautiful face! You are alone in this great forest. Why are you not scared? Who are you? Whom do you belong to? Where have you come from? Why have you come to Dandaka? O fortunate one! You are roaming around alone in this terrible place, frequented by rakshasas.'

The evil-souled Ravana praised Vaidehi in this way. She saw Ravana, who had arrived in the attire of a brahmana. Maithilee honoured him with everything that should be offered to a guest.[275] She first offered him a seat and then invited him with padya. He was amiable in appearance and looked like a siddha. Maithilee saw the one who had arrived in the attire of a brahmana, holding a vessel meant for alms. On seeing his appearance, she saw no reason to suspect anything. Taking him to be a brahmana who had come, she invited him. She said, 'O brahmana! Here is darbha grass, a desired seat for you. Here is padya. Please accept it. Here is excellent forest fare that has been cooked for your sake. Comfortably partake of it.'

[274] The word used is *shakhamriga*. While this is a monkey, it literally means an arboreal animal.

[275] The word used is *atithi*. Atithi doesn't mean any guest, it means a guest who has arrived unannounced, *a-tithi*, without occasion.

Maithilee, the king's wife, invited him wholeheartedly. Ravana looked at her. Dedicated to the cause of his own destruction, he firmly made up his mind to forcibly abduct her.

Her excellently attired husband had gone out on the hunt. She waited for him and Lakshmana. As she looked around that great forest, she only saw greenery and no Rama or Lakshmana.

Chapter 3(45)

Ravana wished to abduct her. However, asked by him, who was in the form of a mendicant, Vaidehi told him about herself. She reflected for an instant. 'He is a brahmana and a guest. If I do not tell him, he will curse me.' Therefore, Sita addressed him in these words. 'I am the daughter of the great-souled Janaka of Mithila. O fortunate one! O supreme among brahmanas! My name is Sita and I am Rama's wife. I spent one year in Raghava's residence.[276] I enjoyed all the desired objects of prosperity and everything that humans crave after. After one year was over, the king consulted an assembly of his ministers and honoured my husband, Rama, by deciding to instate him as the heir apparent. Arrangements were being made for Raghava's consecration. At that time, the noble Kaikeyee sought a boon from her husband. Because of a good deed she had done for my father-in-law earlier, she sought the boon that my husband should be exiled and Bharata should be consecrated. These were the two boons she sought from her husband, the excellent king who was firm in adherence to the truth. "If Rama is consecrated, from today, I will never eat, sleep or drink, until my life comes to an end." This is what Kaikeyee told my father-in-law, the one who deserves honours. She was asked to refrain from seeking something undesirable. But she persisted in seeking that undesirable end. My immensely energetic husband was twenty-five years old

---

[276] That is, after marriage, they spent one year in Ayodhya. Since Rama was sixteen at the time of marriage, he was seventeen when he was exiled.

then.[277] Rama is famous in the worlds. He possesses the qualities. He is pure and good in conduct. The large-eyed and mighty-armed one is devoted to the welfare of all creatures. When Rama approached his father for the sake of the consecration, Kaikeyee swiftly addressed my husband in these words. "O Raghava! Hear from me what your father has instructed. Without any thorns, this kingdom must be given to Bharata. O Kakutstha! To save your father from uttering a falsehood, you must indeed be exiled to the forest for fourteen years." Rama fearlessly agreed to what Kaikeyee had said. My husband is firm in his vows and acted in accordance with her words. He gives and does not receive. He speaks the truth, not a falsehood. O brahmana! This is Rama's excellent and unwavering vow. His valiant stepbrother is named Lakshmana. That tiger among men doesn't leave an enemy in a battle and is Rama's aide. The brother named Lakshmana follows dharma and is firm in his vows. With the bow in his hand, and with me, he followed him on the exile. Because of what Kaikeyee did, the three of us were dislodged from the kingdom. O best among brahmanas! Resorting to our energy, we are wandering around in this dense forest. You can be comfortable and stay here for some time. My husband will bring everything[278] from the forest. Tell me the truth about your name and your *gotra*.[279] O brahmana! Why are you roaming around in Dandakaranya alone?'

Sita, Rama's wife, spoke in this way. Thereafter, the immensely strong Ravana, lord of rakshasas, replied harshly. 'O Sita! My name is Ravana and I am the lord of large numbers of rakshasas. I am the one who terrifies the worlds and gods, asuras and men. I saw your golden complexion and ochre garments. O unblemished one! I do not find any pleasure in my own wives. I have abducted many excellent women from here and there. O fortunate one! Among all of them, you will be my chief queen. My great city of Lanka is in the midst of the ocean. It is located on the summit of a mountain and is

[277] Across different versions of the Ramayana and even across different versions of the Valmiki Ramayana, this inconsistency in Rama's age is impossible to reconcile. The Critical Edition excises a shloka where Sita says she was eighteen at the time.

[278] Forest fare.

[279] Family name, denoting common lineage.

protected by the ocean. O Sita! With me, you will roam around in the forests there. O beautiful one! Then, you will no longer desire to reside in this forest. O Sita! If you become my wife, five thousand servant maids, adorned with all the ornaments, will tend to you.'

Addressed in this way by Ravana, Janaka's daughter became angry. Ignoring what the rakshasa had said, the one with the unblemished limbs replied. 'My husband is like the great Indra. Like a great mountain, he does not quake. Like the great ocean, he is not agitated. This is the Rama whom I follow. He is mighty-armed and possesses a broad chest. His stride is like that of a valiant lion. He is like a lion and is a lion among men. This is the Rama whom I follow. The brave one's face is like the full moon. The king's son has conquered his senses. The mighty-armed one is extensive in his deeds. This is the Rama whom I follow. You desire me, but I am extremely difficult to obtain. You are like a jackal, desiring a lioness. Like the radiance of the sun, I am incapable of being touched by you. O unfortunate one! O rakshasa! You desire Raghava's beloved wife, as if you have seen many trees made out of gold.[280] You wish to grasp something from the jaws of a hungry lion, the spirited enemy of deer, though that mouth is filled with virulent poison. You wish to seize the excellent Mount Mandara. You wish to consume lethal poison and remain safe. By approaching Raghava's beloved wife, you desire to wipe your eyes with a needle and lick the blade of a razor with your tongue. With a boulder around your neck, you wish to swim across the ocean. Since you wish to oppress Rama's beloved wife, you desire to seize the sun and the moon in both your hands. Since you desire to abduct Rama's beloved wife, who is enveloped in auspicious conduct, you wish to seize a raging fire wrapped in a piece of cloth. Since you wish to approach a wife who is Rama's equal, you desire to walk on the tips of an excellent spear. In the forest, there is a difference between a lion and a jackal. There is a difference between a stream and the ocean. There is a difference between the best of liquor and sour gruel. That is the difference between you and Dasharatha's son. There is a difference

---

[280] The image of an unrealistic wish.

between gold and lead or iron. There is a difference between water
mixed with sandalwood and muddy water. In the forest, there is a
difference between an elephant and a wildcat. That is the difference
between you and Dasharatha's son. There is a difference between a
crow and Vinata's son.[281] There is a difference between a waterbird
and a peacock. In the forest, there is a difference between a crane
and a vulture. That is the difference between you and Dasharatha's
son. He is like the one with the one thousand eyes in his power.
Even if you abduct me, you will not be able to digest me, like a fly or
a diamond that has been swallowed.[282] With the bow and arrow in
his hands, Rama will be stationed and will kill you.' He was wicked
in his sentiments. She addressed these words to the extremely wicked
one who roamed around in the night. She was distressed and her
body trembled, like a delicate plantain tree swaying in the wind.
He saw that Sita was trembling. Ravana, who was like Death in his
powers, told her about his own self, about his lineage, strength and
name. That was the reason for the fear.

Chapter 3(46)

When Sita spoke in this way, Ravana became angry. With his
forehead furrowed, he replied in these harsh words. 'O one
who is beautiful in complexion! I am Vaishravana's[283] stepbrother.
O fortunate one! My name is Ravana and I am the powerful
Dashagriva. Just as all beings are scared of Death, the gods, the
gandharvas, the pishachas, the birds and the serpents are terrified
of me and flee. Vaishravana is my stepbrother. Because of a certain
reason, I angrily challenged him to a duel and in that encounter,
vanquished him with my valour. Because he was afflicted by his fear
of me, Naravahana abandoned his own seat of prosperity and sought

[281] Garuda.
[282] The diamond tears the stomach and the foul fly has to be vomited out.
[283] Kubera's.

refuge on the excellent Kailasa, supreme among mountains.[284] He possessed an auspicious vimana named Pushpaka that could travel anywhere at will. O fortunate one! I obtained this through my valour and use it to travel through the sky. O Maithilee! When they glance at my face, once my rage has been ignited, the gods, with Shakra at the forefront, are terrified and run away. Wherever I am present, the wind is scared to blow. Scared of me, the sun turns his fierce rays into gentle rays. Wherever I am present or roam around, the leaves on the trees do not flutter and the water in the rivers is quiet. My auspicious city of Lanka is on the other shore of the ocean. It is like Indra's Amaravati and is full of terrible rakshasas. It is decorated and protected by white ramparts. The beautiful city has golden chambers and gates of lapis lazuli. The place is full of elephants, horses and chariots and there is the blaring of trumpets. The gardens are ornamented with trees and these are laden with fruits that yield all the objects of desire. O Sita! O princess! Reside there with me. O spirited one! You will no longer remember that you are a human lady. O one who is supreme in complexion! Enjoy human and divine objects of pleasure. You will no longer remember Rama. As a human, his lifespan is over. King Dasharatha instated his beloved son. But the eldest son was limited in valour. That is the reason he left for the forest. O large-eyed one! Rama has been dislodged from his kingdom. Bereft of his senses, he has become an ascetic. Why should you practise austerities with him? I am the lord of all the rakshasas. However, overcome by desire, I have come here myself. You should not refuse a person who has been afflicted by Manmatha's arrows. O timid one! If you refuse me, you will have to repent, like Urvashi did when she struck Pururava with her foot.'[285]

Thus addressed, Vaidehi became angry and her eyes turned red with rage. In that lonely place, she addressed the lord of the rakshasas in these harsh words. 'You wish to perform an inauspicious deed. How can you say that the god Vaishravana, worshipped by all the

[284] The sense is that Ravana won't attack him in Kailasa.

[285] There are many stories about Urvashi and Pururava, but none where Urvashi struck Pururava with her foot. This must therefore be metaphorical, in the sense of Urvashi having spurned Pururava.

gods, is your brother? O Ravana! All the rakshasas will certainly be destroyed. They have a cruel and evil-minded king like you, who has not been able to conquer his senses. After abducting Shachi, Indra's wife, it is possible to remain alive. However, it is impossible to remain alive after abducting me, Rama's wife. Shachi's beauty has no parallel. After oppressing her, even though the wielder of the vajra holds the weapon in his hand, it is possible to remain alive for a long time. O rakshasa! However, after oppressing someone like me, there can be no emancipation, even if one has drunk amrita.'

Chapter 3(47)

Hearing Sita's words, the powerful Dashagriva struck the palm of one hand with the other and assumed an extremely gigantic form. He again addressed Maithilee in severe words. 'I think that in your madness, you have not heard about my valour and prowess. Using my two arms, I can raise the earth up into the sky. I can drink up the ocean. Stationed in a battle, I can slay Death. Using my sharp arrows, I can shatter the sun and fragment the earth. I can assume any form at will. O mad one! Behold the form of the lord who can grant everything.' When Ravana said this, in the light of the torch, his angry eyes turned red and seemed to be tawny at the edges. Ravana abandoned the agreeable form of a mendicant. Vaishravana's younger brother assumed his own form, with a complexion and form that was like that of the Destroyer. His eyes were red. He was radiant, with ornaments made out of molten gold. The one who roamed around in the night assumed a form with ten heads, holding a bow and arrows. The one who was gigantic in form gave up the disguise of a mendicant. Ravana, the lord of the rakshasas, assumed his own form. Attired in red garments, he looked at Maithilee, jewel among women. Her hair was black at the tips. She was attired in ochre garments and wore ornaments. Her complexion was like the sun. Ravana spoke to Maithilee. 'O beautiful one! If you desire a husband who is famous in the three

worlds, seek refuge with me. I am a husband who is your equal.
Serve me for a long period of time. I will be a husband you can
praise. O fortunate one! I will never do anything that you find to
be disagreeable. Abandon your human sentiments and turn your
mind towards me. Rama has been dislodged from the kingdom and
he will not be successful in his objective. His lifespan is limited.
O foolish one who prides herself on her learning! What are the
qualities that you love? Because of the words of a woman, he has
abandoned the kingdom and the people who are his well-wishers.
The evil-minded one is residing in the forest, where predatory beasts
wander around.'

Maithilee was pleasant in speech and deserved to be addressed
in agreeable words. But saying this, Ravana seized Sita, the way
Mercury seizes Rohini in the sky. With his left hand, he grasped the
lotus-eyed Sita near the hair on her head. With his right hand, he
grasped her by her thighs. With his sharp teeth and mighty arms,
his complexion was like that of a mountain peak. On seeing him,
resembling Death, the divinities of the forest were afflicted by fear
and fled. Ravana's great chariot could be seen, golden in parts. It
was divine and full of maya. It was yoked to mules and harsh in its
clatter. He raised Vaidehi by her lap and placed her on the chariot.
The one with a loud voice censured her with harsh words. The
illustrious one was seized by Ravana and shrieked loudly. Rama
had gone far away into the forest. Struck by grief, Sita wailed, 'Alas,
Rama!' She did not desire this, but he was overcome by desire. She
was like the wife of an Indra among serpents, as she writhed. Seizing
her, Ravana rose up. Through the sky, the Indra among rakshasas
abducted her. With her senses awhirl and afflicted, as if she had
gone made, she shrieked loudly. 'Alas, Lakshmana! O mighty-armed
one! O one who always pleases his senior's mind! You do not know
that I am being abducted by a rakshasa who can assume any form
at will. O Raghava! Though alive, you have cast aside happiness
and prosperity for the sake of dharma. You do not see that I am
being abducted through adharma. O scorcher of enemies! This
Ravana is insolent and you are the one who subjugates those who
are insolent. Why are you not instructing the one who is committing

this kind of crime? Indeed, this insolent one will instantly reap the fruits of his deeds. Just as crops take time to ripe, time proceeds in segments. You have lost your senses and have committed this act because of destiny.[286] Rama will inflict a terrible calamity on you and that will bring an end to your life. Kaikeyee and her relatives have certainly accomplished their wishes now. Following dharma, I am the illustrious wife of one who desires dharma. Nevertheless, I am being abducted. I request the blossoming karnikara trees of Janasthana to quickly inform Rama that Sita has been abducted by Ravana. I bow down before the summit of Malyavan and Mount Prasravana and ask them to quickly inform Rama that Sita has been abducted by Ravana. I bow down before the river Godavari, full of swans and cranes, and request that Rama be quickly informed that Sita has been abducted by Ravana. There are divinities in this forest and in the many trees. I bow down before you. Tell my husband about my abduction. There are many living creatures that reside her. I seek refuge with all of them, the large numbers of birds and animals. Tell my husband that the helpless Sita, his beloved, whom he loves more than his life, has been abducted by Ravana. When the mighty-armed and immensely strong one knows that I have been taken away from here, he will use his valour to bring me back, even if that abduction is done by Vaivasvata.[287] O Jatayu! Tell Rama the truth about my abduction. Without leaving anything out, tell Lakshmana everything.'

Chapter 3(48)

Jatayu was asleep. Hearing the sound, he quickly awoke and saw Ravana and Vaidehi. The excellent bird possessed a sharp beak and his complexion was like that of the summit of a mountain. While seated on a tree, the handsome one uttered these auspicious

[286] Addressing Ravana.
[287] Yama.

words. 'O Dashagriva! I am established in the ancient dharma and
am devoted to the truth. My name is Jatayu and I am the extremely
strong king of the eagles. Rama, Dasharatha's son, is the king of all
the worlds and is like the great Indra and Varuna. He is engaged
in the welfare of the worlds. He is the protector of the worlds and
this is his illustrious wife. This beautiful one is named Sita and she
is the one you wish to abduct. If a king is established in dharma,
how can he touch another person's wife? O immensely strong one!
Specifically, if she is a king's wife, she must be protected. Refrain
from this inferior conduct of touching another person's wife. A
patient person does not indulge in an act that is condemned by
others. Just as one's own wife is protected from being touched,
another person's wife must be protected in that way. O Poulastya's
descendant! If kings do not follow dharma and do not follow the
sacred texts in obtaining artha or kama, virtuous people do not
follow them. The king is the supreme foundation for dharma,
kama and objects.[288] The king is the source for auspicious dharma
or wickedness. O supreme among rakshasas! How can you be
wicked in conduct and fickle? That is the way you have obtained
prosperity, like a person who is evil in conduct obtaining a vimana.
If a person's nature is based on desire, he finds it impossible to
cleanse himself. Nobility does not dwell in the residence of an evil-
souled person for a long time. The immensely strong Rama, with
dharma in his soul, has not caused any harm to your kingdom
or your city. Why are you injuring him? Earlier, Khara went to
Janasthana for Shurpanakha's sake and transgressed in his deeds.
Rama, unblemished in deeds, killed him. Tell me the truth. How
was this a transgression on Rama's part? Why are you abducting
the wife of someone who is the lord of the world? Swiftly release
Vaidehi. Otherwise, his terrible eyesight, which can burn down
beings, will consume you, just as Indra's vajra burnt down Vritra.
You do not understand that you have tied up a venomous serpent at
the end of your garment. The noose of destiny is entangled around
your throat, but you do not see it. O amiable one! A man should

---

[288] That is, artha.

pick up a burden that does not tire him out. The food that is eaten must be digestible and must not cause disease. Why should one undertake an act that does not certainly bring dharma, deeds and fame, but only brings distress to the body? O Ravana! It has been sixty thousand years since my birth. I have been properly instated in the kingdom of my fathers and grandfathers. I am aged and you are young. You have a bow, a chariot, armour and arrows. But you will not be able to take Vaidehi and go without impediment. While I bear witness, you are incapable of abducting Vaidehi forcibly. This is certainly a good enough reason, like protecting the sacred texts of the Vedas. O Ravana! If you are brave, stay for a while and fight. You will be slain and will lie down on the ground, like Khara before you. He has repeatedly slain daityas and danavas in battles. Though he is attired in rags, Rama will soon kill you in an encounter. When the two princes have gone a long distance away, what am I capable of doing? O inferior one! There is no doubt that you are scared of them and that you will quickly destroy me. However, while I am alive, you cannot take away this auspicious one. The lotus-eyed Sita is Rama's beloved wife. As long as I am alive, I must certainly do what is agreeable to the great-souled one, to Rama and to Dasharatha. Stay. O Dashagriva! Stay for a while and see. O Ravana! O one who wanders in the night! As long as I have life, I will hospitably offer you a duel. I will bring you down from your supreme chariot, like a fruit from its stem.'

Chapter 3(49)

Jatayu addressed Ravana in these appropriate words. However, all of his twenty eyes blazed with anger, like fire. Adorned in earrings made of molten gold, his eyes turned red with rage. Intolerant, the Indra among the rakshasas attacked the Indra among the birds. In the great forest, they violently struck each other. They were like two clouds in the sky and a storm seemed to arise. There was an extraordinary clash between the eagle and the rakshasa. It is as if two gigantic and winged Malyavan mountains were fighting each other.[289] The immensely strong one showered down extremely terrible hollow arrows, sharp iron arrows and piercing barbed arrows on the king of the eagles. In the encounter, the eagle Jatayu, the lord of those who use their wings as chariots, received Ravana's nets of arrows and weapons. With his sharp talons and feet, the immensely strong one, supreme among birds, caused many kinds of wounds on his[290] body. Wishing to crush the enemy, Dashagriva angrily seized ten arrows that were as terrible as the staff of Death. Those terrible arrows were sharp, with pointed heads made out of stone. They were straight-flying. The immensely valorous one stretched his bow all the way back and pierced the eagle with these. Seeing Janakee, with tears in her eyes, on the rakshasa's chariot, he[291] paid no heed to these arrows and attacked the rakshasa. With his claws, the immensely energetic one, supreme among birds, shattered the bow, adorned with pearls and gems, while arrows were still affixed to it. Using his wings, the immensely energetic lord of the birds shattered Ravana's armour, which blazed like the fire. In the encounter, the powerful one slew the mules[292] that were swift, with faces like pishachas and covered with divine and golden breastplates. The great chariot could travel anywhere at will and was like the flames of a fire. It possessed a trivenu, steps adorned with jewels and colourful parts. He shattered this too, with its whisks and an umbrella that was like the full moon. His bow was shattered. He was without a chariot. His horses were slain. His charioteer was killed. Grasping Vaidehi on his lap, Ravana fell down on the ground. When they saw that Ravana had fallen down on the ground, with his chariot destroyed, all the creatures praised this act and honoured the king of the eagles.

However, on seeing that the leader of flocks of birds was exhausted, Ravana was delighted. He seized Maithilee and leapt up again. Delighted, with Janaka's daughter on his lap, he was about

[289] It is believed that mountains once possessed wings.
[290] Ravana's.
[291] Jatayu.
[292] Yoked to Ravana's chariot.

to leave. But Jatayu, king of the eagles, also leapt up and spoke these words. 'O Ravana! O one limited in intelligence! Rama's wife is like an arrow that has the touch of the vajra. You are certainly seeking to abduct her for the destruction of the rakshasas. With your friends, relatives, advisers, soldiers and companions, you are like a thirsty person who drinks poison, taking it to be water. You do not possess discrimination and do not know the consequences that will result from this act. You will quickly be destroyed and so will they. You are bound in the noose of destiny. Where will you go to escape? You are like an aquatic creature[293] bound to a hook baited with flesh, for the sake of its destruction. O Ravana! The two invincible Raghavas, Kakutsthas, will not pardon your causing this violation of their hermitage. You have committed the act of a coward, condemned by the worlds. This is the path followed by thieves, not by those who are brave. O Ravana! If you are brave, stay for a while and fight. You will be slain and will lie down on the ground, like your brother, Khara. This act of adharma is for the sake of your own destruction. A man undertakes such an act only for the sake of going to the world hereafter. If there is wickedness associated with an act, which man undertakes it? Not even the illustrious Svayambhu, the lord of the worlds, acts in this way.' With these auspicious words, Jatayu addressed the rakshasa.

With great force, the valiant one then descended on Dashagriva's back. He was like an elephant rider astride a wicked elephant. With his sharp talons, he grasped and pierced him. He pierced him on the back with his talons and beak. With nails, wings and beak as weapons, he tore out his hair. He was thus repeatedly afflicted by the king of the eagles. The rakshasa trembled and his lips quivered in rage. Afflicted and senseless with anger, he grasped Vaidehi on his left flank and struck Jatayu with his palm.[294] When he was thus attacked, Jatayu, lord of the birds and scorcher of enemies, used his beak to sever his ten left arms. Enraged, Dashagriva released Sita. With his fists and feet, he struck the valiant king of the eagles. There

[293] The word used is general and does not necessarily mean a fish.
[294] The right palm.

was a brief clash between those two infinitely valorous ones, the foremost of rakshasas and the supreme among birds. Ravana raised his sword and severed the wings, feet and flanks of the one who was fighting for Rama's sake. The rakshasa, terrible in deeds, violently severed his wings. Slain, the eagle fell down on the ground, with only a little bit of life left in him. Jatayu fell down on the ground, wounded and wet with blood. Seeing the state her friend was in, Vaidehi was distressed and rushed towards him.

The lord of Lanka also saw Jatayu, extensive in his valour, lying down on the ground, like a conflagration that has been pacified. His form was like that of a dark blue cloud, with an extremely white chest. Crushed by Ravana's force, the one who used his wings as a chariot fell down on the ground. Sita, Janaka's daughter, with a face like a moonbeam, wept and embraced him.

Chapter 3(50)

Near Raghava's hermitage, the lord of the rakshasas saw the eagle who had fallen down on the ground, writhing and with only a little bit of life left in him. The king of the eagles had been slain by Ravana. The one with a face like the lord of the stars[295] saw this. Extremely miserable, she lamented. 'Men can certainly detect happiness and unhappiness through portents and signs seen in dreams and through the sights of harsh birds.[296] O Rama! You certainly do not know about the great catastrophe that has befallen you. O Kakutstha! For my sake, birds and animals must certainly be running towards you.[297] O Kakutstha! O Lakshmana! Save me now.' Terrified, the beautiful one screamed in this way, as if they were within range of hearing. She lamented like one without a protector and her garlands and ornaments were dishevelled. Ravana, the lord of the rakshasas, rushed towards Vaidehi. She

[295] The moon is the lord of the stars.
[296] Some birds that call harshly are regarded as evil portents.
[297] To inform you.

was like a creeper that was clinging to a large tree.[298] 'Let go. Let go.' The lord of the rakshasas said this several times. Separated from Rama in the forest, she screamed, 'O Rama! O Rama!' The one whose life had come to an end[299] and who was like Death, seized her by the hair. When Vaidehi was oppressed in this way, all the mobile and immobile objects in the world deviated from their rules[300] and everything was enveloped in a blinding darkness. The prosperous grandfather,[301] possessed divine sight and saw that Sita had been abducted. Extremely delighted, the god said, 'The task has been accomplished.' On seeing that Sita was supremely afflicted in this fashion, the supreme rishis who resided in Dandakaranya were delighted and distressed at the same time. She was weeping, 'O Rama! Alas Rama! O Lakshmana!' Ravana, the lord of the rakshasas, seized her and left through the sky.

She was attired in ochre silk garments. Her limbs had the complexion of ornaments fashioned from molten gold. The princess was as radiant as flashes of lightning in a cloud. As her ochre garments fluttered over him, Ravana looked excessively brilliant, like a blazing mountain on fire. The supremely fortunate one was adorned with lotus petals that were coppery red and fragrant.[302] As Vaidehi was seized, they covered Ravana everywhere. In the sky, her ochre garments had the complexion of gold. In the heat, this was like a coppery-red cloud, lit up by the rays of the sun.[303] In the sky, her sparkling face was in Ravana's lap. Without Rama, it was no longer resplendent, like a lotus without its stalk. Her forehead was excellent. The tips of her hair were excellent. Her sparkling teeth were white and excellent and adorned her clear face, which had the complexion of the stamen of a lotus and was without

[298] She was clinging to Jatayu.

[299] Ravana, because he was going to be destroyed.

[300] The Critical Edition excises shlokas that explain what this means. The wind did not blow, the sun lost its radiance and so on.

[301] Brahma, because the task of destroying Ravana had been accomplished. This sudden shloka breaks the continuity and doesn't seem to belong.

[302] On Sita's hair.

[303] Heat because it was midday. A red cloud is normal in the morning or the evening. But at midday, it is a bad omen.

marks. It looked as if the moon had arisen, penetrating a dark blue cloud.[304] Her face, with a golden complexion, was as pleasant to see as the moon, with an excellent nose and beautiful coppery lips. In the sky, it hung to one side, as she wept. Suffering because of the Indra among the rakshasas, her auspicious face was like the moon arising during the day, shining, but without Rama. Maithilee's complexion was golden and the lord of the rakshasas was blue in his limbs. The one with the golden complexion was like a sapphire encrusted in a golden ornament.[305] Janaka's daughter was fair, with the complexion of a golden lotus. Her ornaments were made out of molten gold. She was as radiant as a flash of lightning when it had entered the cloud that was Ravana. Vaidehi's ornaments made a sound around the lord of the rakshasas. He therefore sparkled, like a dark cloud that was roaring. As Sita was being abducted, a shower of flowers descended from the upper half of her body[306] and fell down on the ground. That shower of flowers fell down. However, because of Ravana's force, they again followed in Dashagriva's trail. Vaishravana's younger brother was shrouded in those flowers. It was as if Meru, the excellent mountain, was surrounded by an excellent garland of nakshatras. Vaidehi's anklets, decorated with gems, were dislodged. Resembling a circle of lightning, they fell down, making a pleasant sound. The lord of the rakshasas was blue in his limbs and she was as red as a coral tree. Vaidehi was as radiant as a golden harness on an elephant.[307] Because of her own radiance, she was like a giant meteor in the sky.[308] Vaishravana's younger brother had entered the sky and had seized Sita. Her ornaments, with the complexion of fire, were scattered on the ground. As they descended, like stars dislodged from the sky, they made a sound. Vaidehi wore a necklace between her breasts, with a radiance like

---

[304] Sita's face is like the moon, while Ravana is like the cloud.

[305] This requires explanation. Blue sapphire shines when it is in a silver ornament, not when it is encrusted in an ornament made out of gold. The sense is that Sita and Ravana shouldn't have been together.

[306] From her hair and from her garlands.

[307] Ravana is the elephant.

[308] A giant meteor is an evil portent, that is, for Ravana.

that of the lord of the stars. It fell down, like Ganga being dislodged
from the sky. The tops of trees, with large numbers of birds on
them, were struck by the force of the wind. The branches seemed to
stretch out and tell her, 'Do not be scared.' The lotuses in the lakes
decayed and fish and other aquatic creatures were frightened. They
sorrowed over Maithilee, as if she was their friend. Lions, tigers, deer
and other animals gathered from every direction. Because of their
anger, they followed Sita's shadow. The waterfalls on the mountains
seemed to wail and weep, as the summits stretched out like hands
at Sita's abduction. On seeing that Vaidehi was being abducted,
the sun was distressed. The handsome one's radiance diminished
and the solar disc turned pale. 'Since Rama's wife, Vaidehi, is being
abducted by Ravana, there is no dharma. Where will truth come
from? There is no uprightness. Where is non-violence?' All the large
number of creatures lamented in this way. The fawns were terrified
and wept with miserable faces. With anxious eyes, they raised their
eyes upwards and looked repeatedly. The bodies of the divinities
of the forest trembled. On seeing Sita in this miserable plight, they
lamented loudly. She screamed in a sweet voice, 'Alas, Lakshmana!
O Rama!' There were many on the ground who looked at Vaidehi.
The tips of her hair were dishevelled and the mark on her forehead
was smudged.[309] Dashagriva abducted the spirited one for the sake
of his own destruction. Maithilee's teeth were beautiful and her
smile was excellent. She had been separated from her relatives. She
could not see either Rama or Lakshmana. Her face was pale and she
suffered from the burden of fear.

Chapter 3(51)

Maithilee, Janaka's daughter, saw that he had leapt up into
the sky. She was anxious and greatly distressed and also
filled with great fear. Because of the anger and weeping, her eyes

---

[309] This could be a *tilaka* too and is not necessarily *sindoor*.

turned coppery red. As she was abducted, she wept piteously and addressed the terrible-eyed lord of the rakshasas in these words. 'O Ravana! Despite this inferior act, you are not ashamed. Knowing that I was alone, you have abducted me and are running away. You are indeed evil-souled. Like a coward, you wish to abduct me, while my husband was dragged away by maya in the form of a deer. He who tried to save me has been brought down.[310] O worst of the rakshasas! Your supreme valour has indeed been seen. I have been conquered by you only in a battle known as trust.[311] Having performed such a reprehensible deed, how is it that you are not ashamed? O one inferior in conduct! You have abducted someone else's wife when she was alone. You pride yourself on being brave, but have performed an extremely cruel act of adharma. The men in this world will talk about your wicked deed. Shame on the valour and spirit that you spoke about then. This brings ill fame to the lineage, and the world will condemn this kind of conduct. Since you are speedily running away, what are you capable of doing? Stay for a while and you will no longer remain alive. When you come within the eyesight of those two princes, with your soldiers, you will not be able to remain alive for an instant. You will never be able to bear the touch of their arrows, just as a bird is unable to bear the touch of a fire raging in the forest. O Ravana! It is better that you take the medication that is good for you. It is better that you release me. Because of my oppression, my husband and his brother will be enraged. If you do not release me, you will arrange for your own destruction. Your conduct is such that you desire to abduct me forcibly. Your conduct is inferior and will prove to be futile. I am unable to see my husband, who is like a god. When I am under the subjugation of an enemy, I am not interested in remaining alive for a long period of time. For your own self, it is indeed best that you look towards finding some medication. At the time of death, mortals consume the opposite of what is indicated.[312] All mortals who are about to die do not find medication to be agreeable. I can

---

[310] Jatayu.

[311] Because she trusted him, and not in a real battle.

[312] Ignoring the medication.

see that the noose of destiny is entwined around your throat. O Dashanana![313] Despite there being a reason for fear, you are not terrified. It is evident that you can see the golden trees.[314] The river Vaitarani is terrible and has flows of blood.[315] O Ravana! You will see the terrible sight of forests with leaves made out of swords.[316] You will see a *shalmali* tree[317] that has flowers made out of molten gold, covered with lapis lazuli. But inside, they are full of sharp and iron thorns. Like a person who has consumed poison, having done this wicked and contemptible deed towards that great-souled one, you will not be able to remain alive for a long period of time. O Ravana! You are bound in a noose of destiny that cannot be repulsed. Where will you go to find safety from my great-souled husband? Even when he was without his brother, in a battle, he killed fourteen thousand rakshasas in an instant. The powerful and brave Raghava is accomplished in the use of all weapons. Since you have wished to abduct his wife, why will he not kill you with his sharp arrows?' Stuck to Ravana's lap, Vaidehi was filled with fear and grief and lamented piteously, uttering these and other harsh words. Severely afflicted, she spoke a lot. At first, the young and beautiful one lamented piteously. Abducted in this wicked way, her body was then filled with lassitude and she writhed.

Chapter 3(52)

Abducted in this fashion, Vaidehi could not see a protector anywhere. However, on the summit of a mountain, she saw five bulls among apes. The beautiful and large-eyed one wrapped her sparkling ornaments, golden in complexion, in her silken upper garment and hurled it amidst them. Maithilee thought that if they

[313] One with ten faces, Ravana.
[314] It is believed that golden trees are seen at the time of death.
[315] Vaitarani is crossed before one reaches Yama's abode.
[316] This is a description of hell.
[317] The silk-cotton tree. Sinners have to embrace this tree.

informed Rama, he might free her. Wrapping the ornaments in the
upper garment, she threw it amidst them. Because he was hurrying,
Dashagriva did not notice that this act had been done. Those
tawny-eyed bulls among apes saw the large-eyed Sita shrieking
and did not blink. Crossing the Pampa and seizing the weeping
Maithilee, the lord of the rakshasas headed for the city of Lanka.
Extremely delighted, Ravana carried his own death, like a person
who carries a sharp-fanged and extremely virulent she-snake in
his lap. Swiftly travelling through the sky, he crossed over forests,
rivers, mountains and lakes, like an arrow that has been shot from
a bow. He reached the ocean, the abode of whales and crocodiles,
the refuge of the rivers and Varuna's eternal abode. As Vaidehi was
being abducted, Varuna's abode was terrified. The waves tossed
around and the fish and giant serpents were still. The charanas and
the siddhas who were in the sky, then spoke these words. 'This is
the end of Dashagriva.'

Ravana grasped the writhing Sita, who was like his own death,
in his lap and entered the city of Lanka. He entered the city of
Lanka, with well-laid-out large roads. He crossed through many
gated chambers and entered the inner quarters. The black-eyed
Sita was overcome by sorrow and confusion. Ravana placed her
in the place that Maya had built through the maya of the asuras.[318]
Dashagriva told a *pishachi*[319] who was terrible in appearance. 'No
man or woman will be allowed to see Sita here. On my instructions,
give her pearls, jewels, gold, garments and ornaments—whatever she
desires. If a person loves her own life,[320] knowingly or unknowingly,
she should not speak any disagreeable words to Vaidehi.' Thus
addressed, the rakshasi agreed to what the powerful Indra among
rakshasas had said.

After emerging from the inner quarters, he thought about what
should be done next. He saw eight extremely valiant rakshasas who
survived on human flesh. Confused because of the boon he had

[318] This reference occurs again later. Maya was a demon who was skilled in the use of
maya. Using this, Maya had constructed a secret place that was hidden from view.

[319] A female pishacha.

[320] The feminine gender is used because all the guards were women.

received,[321] when he saw those extremely valiant ones, he praised their strength and valour and addressed them in these words. 'Seize many weapons and quickly go to the place named Janasthana, the spot that has been destroyed and which used to be Khara's residence earlier. Reside in Janasthana, which is now empty because the rakshasas have been slain. Cast your fear far away and resort to your manliness and strength. Khara and Dushana, extremely brave, used to reside in Janasthana, with many soldiers. However, in a battle, Rama slew them with his arrows. That is the reason an unprecedented anger is overcoming my patience. An extremely great enmity has been generated towards Rama. I wish to get over the enmity that has arisen against the enemy. I will not be able to sleep without killing the enemy in a battle. I will now slay Rama who has killed Khara and Dushana and obtain peace. He is like a poor person who has obtained some riches. While you reside in Janasthana, apparently under Rama's protection, convey to me the truth about his inclinations and about what he does. O ones who roam around in the night! Without any distractions, go. Your task is to always make attempts for Raghava to be killed. From many fields of battle, I know about your strength. That is the reason I have engaged you for Janasthana.' The eight rakshasas heard those agreeable words, deep in import, from Ravana and greeted him. Together, they left Lanka and left for Janasthana, in a form so that they could not be seen. Ravana was extremely delighted at having obtained Sita. Having abducted Maithilee, the confused rakshasa rejoiced and prepared for a great enmity with Rama.

Chapter 3(53)

Ravana commanded the eight terrible and extremely strong rakshasas. Because of the confusion in his intelligence, he thought that he had accomplished what needed to be done. Struck

---

[321] Ravana had received a boon from Brahma.

by the arrows of Kama, he thought about Vaidehi. To see Sita, he quickly entered the beautiful house. Ravana, the lord of the rakshasas, entered that residence. Amidst the grieving rakshasis, he saw the grieving Sita. Her face was overflowing with tears. She was distressed and overwhelmed by a burden of sorrow. She was like a boat that was sinking in the ocean, struck by the force of the wind. She was like a doe that had been separated from a herd of deer and was surrounded by dogs.[322] She was miserable and her face was downcast. The roamer in the night approached her. She was immersed in grief. She was miserable and helpless.

The lord of the rakshasas forcibly wished to show her his residence, which was like a residence of the gods.[323] There were mansions, palaces and ramparts, filled with thousands of women. There were large numbers of diverse birds. There were many kinds of jewels. There were beautiful pillars pleasant to behold, colourful with diamonds and lapis lazuli and inlaid with work of ivory, gold, crystal and silver. The gates were made out of molten gold and there were the sounds of divine drums. With her, he ascended the wonderful golden steps. There were handsome windows, inlaid with work in ivory and silver. In the palace there, there were rows of seats, covered with nets made out of gold. Everywhere, parts of the floor were covered with wonderful white marble. Dashagriva showed Maithilee his own residence. Sita was overcome with sorrow and Ravana showed her waterfalls and pools filled with many kinds of flowers. He showed Vaidehi all those excellent residences. The evil-souled Ravana then addressed Janaka's daughter in these words. 'There are ten crore of rakshasas and another twenty-two.[324] This is apart from the roamers in the night who are diseased, old and young. O Sita! I am the lord of all those, terrible in their deeds. To accomplish a single one of my tasks, one thousand of them will come forward. Everything that I rule over in this kingdom and my life are established in you. O large-eyed one! You are greater than my own life. O Sita! I have married many thousand women.

---

[322] Wild dogs.

[323] Therefore, from Maya's chamber, she must have been taken to Ravana's palace.

[324] That is, thirty-two crores of rakshasas. A crore is ten million.

O beloved one! Become my wife and you will be their mistress. These words of mine should appeal to your intelligence. What can be better than this? I am tormented. You should serve me and show me your favours. This Lanka extends for one hundred yojanas and is protected by the ocean. With all the gods and the asuras, even Indra is incapable of assailing it. Among the gods, the yakshas, the gandharvas and the rishis in the worlds, I do not see anyone whose valour is equal to mine. Rama is a human who is limited in energy. He is distressed and has been dislodged from his kingdom. He is an ascetic. His life is over. What will he do? O Sita! Serve me. I am a husband who is your equal. O timid one! Youth is transient. Therefore, find pleasure here with me. O one with the beautiful face! Do not vainly think about seeing Raghava. O Sita! Even if someone wishes to, how will he possess the capability to come here? In the sky, it is impossible to bind the swift-moving wind in a noose. Nor can one grasp the blazing and sparkling flame of a fire. O beautiful one! While my arms protect you, I do not see anyone in the three worlds who is valiant enough to take you away from here. Rule over this extremely large kingdom of Lanka. Wet your hair with the water of consecration and, content, give me pleasure. Earlier, you performed an extremely difficult task of residing in the forest. But that is over now. Reap the fruits of all the good acts of dharma you have performed. O Maithilee! All these garlands possess divine fragrances. These are the best of ornaments. With me, enjoy them. O one with the excellent hips! My brother, Vaishravana, had a vimana named Pushpaka. It is like the sun. Because of my spirit, I worsted him in a battle and conquered it. That vimana is large and beautiful, possessing the speed of thought. O Sita! As you please, sport in it with me. Your sparkling face is like a lotus. You are beautiful to behold. O beautiful one! O one with the beautiful face! When you are afflicted by grief, you do not look radiant. O Vaidehi! Enough of this shame. If you do this, there will be no violation of dharma. O queen! What you are going to do is entirely compatible with noble conduct. Let your gentle feet be kneaded by my heads. Quickly show me your favours. I am your servant and am under your control. I am desolate and have spoken these words because

I have been completely dried up. Otherwise, Ravana never bows
his head down before any woman.' Ravana said this to Maithilee,
Janaka's daughter. Since he was under the subjugation of Destiny,
he thought that she had become his.

Chapter 3(54)

Vaidehi, afflicted by grief, was addressed in this way. But she
was not frightened. She placed a blade of grass between her
and Ravana and replied.[325] 'King Dasharatha was a bridge of
dharma and never wavered. He was known for being devoted to
the truth. Raghava is his son. His name is Rama. He has dharma
in his soul and he is famous in the three worlds. He is long-armed
and large-eyed. That divinity is my husband. He has been born in
the Ikshvaku lineage. He possesses the shoulders of a lion and he is
immensely radiant. With his brother, Lakshmana, he will rob you of
your life. Had you forcibly oppressed me in his presence, like Khara
in Janasthana, you would have been slain in battle and would have
been lying down. You have spoken about these extremely strong
rakshasas who are terrible in form. Raghava will take away all their
poison, like Suparna from the serpents. Arrows decorated with gold
will be shot from his bowstring and will pierce your body, like waves
against the banks of the Ganga. O Ravana! Even if you cannot be
slain by the asuras and the gods, you have caused a great enmity and
you will not escape from this with your life. The powerful Raghava
will bring an end to what is left of your life. You are like an animal
that has been tied to a sacrificial stake and therefore, getting life
back will be extremely difficult. O rakshasa! If Rama looks at you
with eyes blazing with rage, he will burn you down today and you
will be instantly vanquished. From the sky, he can make the moon
fall down on earth and destroy it. He can dry up the ocean. He is

---

[325] There has been speculation about this blade of grass existing in a palace. There is
also a story about a curse on Ravana. According to this curse, his head would shatter into a
thousand fragments if he forced himself on to a woman, without her consent.

the one who will free Sita. Your lifespan is over. Your prosperity is over. Your spirit is over. Your senses are over. Because of what you have done, Lanka will become a widow. No happiness will result from the wicked deed you have perpetrated. You have brought me here from the forest and have separated me from my husband's side. My immensely radiant husband is tinged with divinity. He resorts to valour and is fearless. He dwells alone in Dandaka. In an encounter, he will shower down arrows on your body and thus take away your insolence, strength, valour and rashness. When they are goaded by destiny, the destruction of creatures is seen. When they come under the subjugation of destiny, men are confused in their deeds. O worst among rakshasas! By oppressing me, you have brought that destiny and destruction on to your own self, the rakshasas and those in the inner quarters. There may be a sacrificial altar in the midst of a sacrifice, decorated with ladles and vessels and sanctified by the mantras of brahmanas. A *chandala* cannot step on it.[326] You can bind or oppress my senseless body. O rakshasa! I may not be able to protect this body or my life. However, as long as I am on this earth, I am incapable of tolerating any dishonour.' Angry, Vaidehi spoke these harsh words. After that, Maithilee did not say anything more to Ravana.

He heard Sita's harsh words, which made the body hair stand up. He replied to Sita in words meant to generate fear. 'O Maithilee! O beautiful one! Listen to my words. O one with the beautiful smiles! If you do not accept me within a period of twelve months, then the cooks will slice you into tiny pieces and make breakfast.'[327] Ravana, who made his enemies scream, uttered these harsh words. Angry, he addressed the rakshasis in these words. 'O rakshasis! O ones who

[326] Chandala has different nuances and a chandala is not necessarily a shudra. A chandala is also of mixed parentage, with a shudra father and a brahmana mother. More generally, chandalas are outcastes, while shudras are within the caste fold. Sita is being compared to the sacrificial altar.

[327] There is a reason for this period of twelve months. A king may defeat another king. The vanquished king may have wives who have also now been conquered by the victor. According to the prevailing norms, the vanquished was given one year to fight back. If he didn't succeed during that period, his wives belonged to the victor. The wives were inviolate for twelve months.

are malformed and terrible to behold! O ones who subsist on flesh and blood! You must quickly destroy this one's pride.' Hearing his words, the ones who were malformed and terrible to behold joined their hands in salutation and encircled Maithilee. They were terrible to behold. King Ravana seemed to shatter the earth with his footsteps, making it tremble. He said, 'Convey Maithilee to the grove of ashoka trees. Surround her and secretly guard her there. Use terrible imprecations against Maithilee, followed by words of reassurance. Use every means to bring her under your control, like one does to a wild she-elephant.' The rakshasis were thus commanded by Ravana. They seized Maithilee and went to the grove of ashoka trees. The trees there had many kinds of flowers and fruits. The fruits yielded every object of desire. In every season, the place was full of maddened birds. Maithilee's limbs were overcome by grief. Janaka's daughter was under the subjugation of those rakshasis, like a doe with tigresses. Maithilee did not find any peace there. She was severely intimidated by those with malformed eyes. She remembered her beloved husband and her brother-in-law. She was overcome by fear and sorrow and lost her senses.

Chapter 3(55)

The rakshasa Maricha could assume any form at will and was wandering around in the form of a deer. After having killed him, Rama started to quickly return along the path. He hurried because he wished to see Maithilee. However, behind him, he heard a jackal howl in a hideous voice.[328] He heard that harsh and terrible howl, which made the body hair stand up. He was concerned and worried at the ominous tone of the jackal. 'I think that this howling of the jackal is inauspicious. I hope that Vaidehi is well and that the rakshasas have not eaten her up. Maricha, in the form of the deer, knew what my voice was like and mimicked me. Lakshmana may

---

[328] An inauspicious sign.

have heard it. If Soumitri has heard it, or if Maithilee has heard it and urged him, he may abandon her and swiftly rush here for my sake. The rakshasas are certainly collectively aspiring to bring about Sita's death. He assumed the form of a golden deer and removed me from the hermitage. When I was taken far away, the rakshasa Maricha was killed by the arrow. However, he spoke the words, "Alas, Lakshmana! I have been slain." Without me, I hope the two of them are safe in the forest. Because of what happened in Janasthana, I have generated an enmity amidst the rakshasas. Many kinds of terrible portents can be seen now.' Having heard the howling of the jackal, Rama thought in this way. He had been led away by the rakshasa in the form of a deer. Worrying, Raghava returned to Janasthana.[329] His mind was distressed and the animals and birds were also distressed. Screaming in terrible voices, they circled the great-souled one on the left. Raghava saw those extremely terrible portents.

He then saw Lakshmana approaching, devoid of his usual radiance. While they were still some distance away, Lakshmana met Rama. A distressed person met another distressed person. A miserable person met another miserable person. He saw Lakshmana arrive, leaving Sita in a desolate forest frequented by rakshasas. The elder brother reprimanded him. The descendant of the Raghu lineage grasped Lakshmana's left hand in his hand. He addressed him in words that were both sweet and harsh, like one who was afflicted.[330] 'Alas, Lakshmana! You have committed a reprehensible deed by abandoning Sita. O amiable one! I hope that she is safe. O brave one! There are rakshasas who wander around in the forest. I have no doubt that she has been killed or devoured by them. Many kinds of inauspicious portents are manifesting themselves before me. O Lakshmana! I hope we get Sita back, hale. This rakshasa assumed the form of a deer, tempting me, and I followed it a long distance away. I killed him with a great deal of effort. However, while dying, he assumed the form of a rakshasa. My mind is

---

[329] The hermitage in Janasthana.

[330] Harsh because Lakshmana had left Sita alone. Sweet because it was not Lakshmana's fault alone, he having been urged by Sita.

distressed and without joy. My left eye is twitching. O Lakshmana!
I am worried that Sita may have been abducted, killed or led astray
along the wrong path.'

Chapter 3(56)

Dasharatha's son saw Lakshmana in that desolate spot and
was distressed. The one with dharma in his soul asked him
why he had come without Vaidehi. 'When I left for Dandakaranya,
she followed me. O Lakshmana! Where is that Vaidehi? You have
forsaken her and have come here. I was distressed, dislodged from
the kingdom, wandering around in Dandaka. She is a companion
in my sorrows. Where is that slender-waisted Vaidehi? O brave
one! Without her, I am not interested in remaining alive even for
an instant. Where is Sita, a companion in my breath of life and the
equal of a daughter of the gods? O Lakshmana! Without the gold-
complexioned daughter of Janaka, I do not desire lordship over the
immortals or on earth. I love Vaidehi more than my own life. Is
she alive? O amiable one! I hope this exile of mine is not rendered
fruitless. O Soumitri! When Sita is dead and so am I, will Kaikeyee
accomplish her desires and be happy? Kaikeyee will be successful
with her son, having obtained the kingdom and prosperity. O
amiable one! With her son dead, will the ascetic Kousalya have to
serve her? We will again return to the hermitage only if Vaidehi is
alive. She is excellent in her conduct. O Lakshmana! With her gone,
I will give up my life. O Lakshmana! When I go to the hermitage,
if Vaidehi does not address me, if Sita does not laugh again, I will
destroy myself. O Lakshmana! Tell me whether Vaidehi is alive
or not. You have been distracted from the task of guarding her
and perhaps the ascetic one has been devoured. She is delicate and
young and has never had to face unhappiness. Separated from
me, it is evident that Vaidehi will be distressed in her mind and
will grieve. That extremely evil-souled and deceitful rakshasa
said "Lakshmana!" Because of that, every kind of fear has been

generated in me. I suspect that Vaidehi may have heard a voice that resembled mine. She must have been frightened and sent you, and you have quickly come here to see me. By abandoning Sita in the forest, you have caused her a hardship in every way. You have given an opportunity to the cruel rakshasas to act against us. The rakshasas, who survive on flesh, are miserable at Khara having been killed. There is no doubt that those terrible ones have killed Sita. O destroyer of enemies! Alas! In every way, I am submerged in a catastrophe. Having faced this state of uncertainty, what will I do now?' In this way, Raghava thought about the beautiful Sita. With Lakshmana, he quickly hurried towards Janasthana. Afflicted, he reprimanded his younger brother. His face was distressed. He sighed and with hunger, exhaustion and thirst, his mouth dried up. He returned and found that everything was empty. The brave one entered his own hermitage and went to the places where they used to sport and where they used to dwell. He was distressed and his body hair stood up.

Chapter 3(57)

R ama, the descendant of the Raghu lineage, was afflicted by grief and again asked Soumitri, who had moved away from the centre of the hermitage.[331] 'I trusted you and left her in the forest, without me. Why did you abandon Maithilee and come here? O Lakshmana! My mind was truly distressed and I suspected a great evil. That has been reinforced at the sight of you coming here, after abandoning Maithilee. O Lakshmana! My left arm and eye and my heart are twitching ever since I saw you from a distance, on this path and without Sita.'

Soumitri, Lakshmana, with the auspicious signs, was thus addressed and was filled with sorrow. He miserably told Rama, 'I

[331] These shlokas are not juxtaposed properly. Towards the end of the earlier chapter, they have already reached the hermitage. In the course of the conversation in this chapter, Rama and Lakshmana are still on their way towards the hermitage.

did not abandon her and come here because of my own wishes. She was anxious and I had come to you, urged by her. She heard the words, as if they were spoken by your noble self. "Alas, Sita! Alas, Lakshmana! Save me." Maithilee heard these words. Maithilee heard those miserable words. Driven by her affection for you, she was senseless because of her fear. She wept and told me, "Go. Go." In many ways, she urged me to leave. Because of my confidence, I replied to Maithilee in these words. "I do not see any rakshasa who can cause him any fear. There is someone else who is mimicking him. Be reassured. O Sita! He is noble and saves the gods. How can he utter these reprehensible and inferior words, 'Save me'? For some reason, someone is mimicking my brother's voice. That is the reason such distorted words have been uttered, 'Lakshmana, save me.' You should not be distressed, like an ordinary and inferior woman. Enough of this lassitude. Regain your composure and be confident. There is no man in this world who can face Raghava in a battle. No one has been born or will be born, who can defeat him in an encounter." Though I said this, Vaidehi's senses were confused. She shed tears and addressed me in these terrible words. "You are driven by this extremely wicked sentiment that your brother should be destroyed. However, you will not be able to obtain me. You have followed Rama because of a deal with Bharata. Therefore, despite his screaming in this extremely terrible way, you are not going there. You are an enemy in disguise and have followed him because of me. You have desired to find a weakness in Raghava and that is the reason you are not rushing to him." When Vaidehi said this, I became angry. My lips quivering in rage and with reddened eyes, I left the hermitage.'

Rama was confused and tormented. When Soumitri said this, Rama said, 'O amiable one! Nevertheless, you have committed an undesirable act by coming here without her. You know that I am capable of countering the rakshasas. Because of some angry words that Maithilee spoke, you have come away. I am not satisfied that you abandoned Maithilee in this way. Hearing the harsh words of an angry woman, you have come here. Having fallen prey to anger, you did not act in accordance with my instructions in any way. You came away, just because you had been urged by Sita. This rakshasa is lying down, having been slain by my arrows. He is the one who assumed the form of a deer and drew me away from the hermitage. I stretched the bow and playfully affixed an arrow. My arrow struck him. He cast aside that deer's body and became a rakshasa with armlets, lamenting piteously. Struck by the arrow, he uttered words of affliction. He mimicked my voice and it could be heard a long distance away. He uttered those extremely terrible words that led you to abandon Maithilee and come here.'

Chapter 3(58)

Rama's lower left eyelid fluttered and twitched severely. He stumbled and was overcome by lassitude. He repeatedly witnessed inauspicious portents. He kept saying, 'I hope Sita is safe.' Desiring to see Sita, he hurried. On seeing that the residence was deserted, his mind became anxious. Quickly, the descendant of the Raghu lineage rushed around, here and there. He explored every part of the cottage. But he saw that Sita wasn't there in that cottage made of leaves. It was bereft of all beauty, like a lake full of lotuses, devastated during the winter. The trees seemed to weep. The flowers, the animals and the birds were jaded. Everything was devastated and robbed of beauty. The divinities of the forest seemed to have left. The deerskin and kusha grass were strewn around. The seats, made of tender grass, were unkempt. On seeing that the cottage was empty, he lamented repeatedly. 'She may have been abducted, killed, destroyed or devoured. Perhaps the timid one has sought refuge in the forest and has hidden herself. Or she may have gone to gather flowers and fruits and lost her senses. Perhaps she went to a lake or river for water.'

He carefully searched everywhere in the forest for his beloved. The prosperous one's eyes were red with grief and he seemed to be mad. He rushed from tree to tree, amidst the mountains and male and female rivers. Rama lamented and he was submerged in a grief that was like an ocean full of mud. 'O kadamba tree! Have you seen my beloved, the one who loved you? She is the one with the beautiful face. O kadamba! If you know about Sita, tell me. O bilva tree! She is attired in ochre silken garments and she is as gentle as your leaves. Her breasts are like bilva fruit. Tell me if you have seen her. O *arjuna* tree! My beloved loved the arjuna tree. Tell me if you know whether Janaka's slender daughter is alive or dead. O *kakubha* tree! This tree has creepers and foliage and is full of flowers. Her thighs are like the kakubha. It is evident that it knows about Maithilee. O tilaka tree! You are the best among trees, and bees sing around you. She loved you. It is evident that the tilaka knows about her. O ashoka tree! You are the one who dispels sorrow and my senses are overcome by sorrow.[332] Quickly show me my beloved and make your name come true. O tala tree! Her breasts are like ripe palm fruit. If you have any compassion towards me, tell me about the beautiful one. O *jambu* tree! Her complexion is like molten gold.[333] If you have seen my beloved Sita, do not hesitate. Tell me. O deer! Maithilee's eyes are like those of a fawn. Do you know about her? The beautiful one's glances are like those of a deer. Is she with the female deer? O elephant! O supreme among elephants! Her thighs are like an elephant's nose.[334] I think you know about her. Tell me. O tiger! Her face is like the full moon. Do not be frightened. You have nothing to fear. If you have seen my beloved Maithilee, tell me. O beloved! O lotus-eyed one! Why are you running away and not showing yourself? Why are you hiding yourself behind the trees and not answering me? Stay. O beautiful one! Stay. Why aren't you showing me your compassion? Your good conduct is excellent. Why are you ignoring me? O one who is beautiful in complexion! Even if you run away from me, you will be known through your ochre silken garments. Stay. Because of affection towards me, stay. O one with the beautiful smiles! I am in the middle of a great hardship. If she is cruel and continues to ignore me, she will not be like her true self. Therefore, it is evident

---

[332] There is a pun. *Shoka* means sorrow and *a-shoka* means without sorrow.

[333] There is another pun. Molten gold is *jambunada*.

[334] That is, trunk.

that the child has been devoured by rakshasas who subsist on flesh. My beloved was separated from me and they have divided up her limbs. Her teeth and lips are excellent. Her nose is excellent. She wears sparkling earrings. Her face is like the full moon and when she was devoured, must have lost its radiance. Her complexion is like the champaka flower. Her neck is adorned with ornaments meant for the neck. She is delicate. As the auspicious and beautiful one was being devoured, she must have lamented. Her arms are as gentle as leaves and the hands have bracelets and ornaments. As she was being devoured, they must have trembled and she must have flung them around. Separated from me, the child could have been devoured by rakshasas. Despite possessing many relatives, she was like an abandoned caravan and must have been devoured. Alas, Lakshmana! O mighty-armed one! Have you seen my beloved? Alas, beloved! O fortunate one! Alas, Sita! Where have you gone?' He lamented repeatedly.

Lamenting in this way, Rama rushed from forest to forest. He was engaged in searching for his beloved. Sometimes, he seemed to be mad. Sometimes, he was confused and rushed around. Sometimes, he used his powers to control himself. He was restless and quickly rushed around—amidst the forests, rivers, mountains, waterfalls and groves. He wandered around that great forest and looked around for Maithilee all around it. Concentrating his hopes, he repeatedly made great efforts to find his beloved in all the different paths.

Chapter 3(59)

Rama, Dasharatha's son, saw that the hermitage was deserted. She was not there in that cottage made of leaves and the seats were scattered around. He looked everywhere and could not see Vaidehi. Rama grasped his[335] beautiful arms and said, 'O

---

[335] Lakshmana's.

Lakshmana! Where is Vaidehi? Where could she have gone from
here? O Soumitri! Who could have abducted her? Who could have
devoured my beloved? O Sita! If you have hidden yourself amidst
the trees for the sake of laughing at me, enough of this sport. I am
extremely miserable. It is time to come to me. O Sita! You used
to play with the fawns that trusted you. O amiable one! Without
you, they are brooding now, their eyes full of tears. Because of
Sita's abduction and because of this great grief, I will die. The great
king, my father, will certainly see me in the world hereafter. It is
evident that in the world hereafter, my father will tell me, "What
happened to the pledge that I engaged you in? The period is not
yet over, but you have come to me. Like an ignoble person, you
have acted according to your own wishes. You uttered a falsehood
to me. Shame on you." I am tormented by grief and helpless. I am
distressed. All my wishes have been shattered. Save me from this
piteous state, which is like the deeds of a man who is not upright.
O beautiful one! O slender-waisted one! Abandoning me, where
have you gone? Separated from you, I will give up my life.' Desiring
to see Sita, Rama lamented in this way. Unable to see Janaka's
daughter, Raghava was extremely miserable and afflicted. Unable
to get Sita, Dasharatha's son was suffering, like an elephant sinking
into a great pool of mud.

Desiring Rama's supreme welfare, Lakshmana spoke to him. 'O
immensely intelligent one! Do not grieve. Make efforts with me. O
brave one! This excellent mountain is adorned with many caverns.
Maithilee is careless and loves to wander around in the groves and
forests. She may have entered the forest, or gone to a lake filled
with blooming lotuses. Or she may have gone to a river or pond
filled with a large number of fish. Perhaps she wished to scare us
and has hidden herself in some grove. O bull among men! Vaidehi
may have wished to test you and me. O prosperous one! We should
make efforts to search for her. O Kakutstha! If you so think, let us
search everywhere in the forest for Janaka's daughter. Turn your
mind away from this futile grief.' Full of affection, Lakshmana said
this. Rama controlled himself and, with Soumitri, started to search.
Dasharatha's two sons searched everywhere for Sita, in the forests,

mountains, rivers, lakes, the summit of that mountain, caves and peaks. They searched everywhere, but did not find her. Having searched everywhere on the mountain, Rama told Lakshmana, 'O Soumitri! I do not see Vaidehi here, on this auspicious mountain.' His brother, blazing in his energy, was wandering around Dandakaranya. Tormented by grief, Lakshmana addressed him in these words. 'O immensely wise one! You will get back Maithilee, Janaka's daughter, just as the mighty-armed Vishnu bound up Bali and regained this earth.' Raghava was thus addressed by the brave Lakshmana. His senses were afflicted by grief. Distressed, he replied in these words. 'We have searched everywhere in this forest and in the lakes, with blossoming lotuses, and in this mountain, with its many caverns and waterfalls. O immensely wise one! I do not see Vaidehi, whom I love more than my own life.'[336] Afflicted by Sita's abduction, Rama lamented in this way. Overcome by distress and grief, for a while, he lost his senses. All his limbs faltered. He lost his intelligence and his senses. Afflicted and distressed, he sank down. He sighed for a long time, as if during summer. The lotus-eyed Rama sighed many times. With tears choking his voice, he repeatedly exclaimed, 'Alas, beloved!' Lakshmana, his beloved relative and knowledgeable about dharma, joined his hands in salutation and subserviently, consoled him in many kinds of ways. He paid no heed to the words that emerged from Lakshmana's lips. Unable to see his beloved Sita, he repeatedly lamented.

Chapter 3(60)

Distressed, he addressed Lakshmana in these miserable words. 'O Lakshmana! Let us quickly go to the river Godavari and find out. Perhaps Sita has gone to the Godavari to fetch lotuses.' Addressed by Rama in this fashion, Lakshmana, swift in his valour, again went to the beautiful river Godavari. Having searched the

[336] The text actually says lives, in the plural.

place that was full of tirthas, Lakshmana told Rama, 'I have not
been able to find her in the tirthas, nor have I heard her voice.
Vaidehi is the one who dispels difficulties. Where can she be? O
Rama! I do not know where that slender-waisted one is.' Hearing
Lakshmana's words, he was miserable and became confused because
of his torment. Rama himself directly went to the river Godavari.
Having reached, Rama exclaimed, 'O Sita! Where are you? Just
as the creatures had not told Rama about her abduction by the
Indra among rakshasas, who deserved to be killed, neither did the
river Godavari. All the creatures urged her[337] to tell him about his
beloved. However, though she was asked by the grieving Rama, she
did not tell him about Sita. She was terrified of the kind of deeds the
evil-souled Ravana had perpetrated. Thinking about this, the river
did not tell him about Vaidehi. His hope of being able to see Sita
near the river was destroyed. Rama, devastated at not being able
to see Sita, spoke to Soumitri. 'O Lakshmana! What disagreeable
words will I use when I meet Janaka, or Vaidehi's mother, without
Vaidehi with me? I was in the forest, deprived of the kingdom,
surviving on forest fare. Vaidehi dispelled all those sorrows. Where
has she gone now? I am without my kin and my allies. I cannot
see the princess. I think that the nights will be long and I will have
to remain awake. I will search everywhere in the Mandakinee,[338]
Janasthana and Mount Prasravana, in case Sita is found.'

While those two brothers were conversing with each other in
this way, they saw a path along which the earth was strewn with
flowers. Rama saw that a shower of flowers had fallen down on
the ground. Miserable, the brave one addressed Lakshmana in
these grieving words. 'O Lakshmana! I recognize the flowers that
are here. These are the ones I gave Vaidehi in the grove and she
fastened them.'[339] The mighty-armed one said this to Lakshmana,
bull among men. He was angry and spoke to the mountain, like
a lion addressing inferior animals. 'O mountain! Her complexion
is golden. Her limbs are golden. Show me Sita. Otherwise, I will

---

[337] The Godavari river.
[338] In this context, Mandakinee means Godavari.
[339] In her hair.

destroy all your summits. The fire of my arrows will consume and reduce you to ashes. Without trees and foliage, no one will ever frequent you again. O Lakshmana! If this river does not tell me about Sita, whose face is like that of the moon, now, I will dry it up.' The enraged Rama seemed to burn everything down with his eyes.

Then, on the ground, he saw the giant footprints of the rakshasa, left when he departed. He saw Sita's footprints, overtaken by those of the rakshasa. Terrified in his heart, Rama spoke to his beloved brother. 'O Lakshmana! O Soumitri! Look at the bits of gold strewn around from Vaidehi's ornaments and the many kinds of garlands. O Soumitri! Behold. Everywhere, the surface of the ground is covered with colourful drops of blood from wounds, like beads of molten gold. O Lakshmana! I think rakshasas, who can assume any form at will, have divided her up, shared her and eaten her up. O Soumitri! Two terrible rakshasas may have had a dispute and a fight here over Vaidehi. O amiable one! This giant bow has been shattered and is lying down on the ground. It is adorned with pearls and jewels and is decorated with molten gold. Whom does it belong to? Whose golden armour has been shattered and is lying down on the ground? It resembles the rising sun and is decorated with beads of lapis lazuli. This umbrella has one hundred spokes and is decorated with divine garlands. Its shaft has been fragmented and is lying down on the ground. O amiable one! Whom does it belong to? These mules have faces like pishachas and are covered with golden breastplates. They are terrible in battle and are gigantic in size. Who has slain them in a battle? This standard blazed in battle and is like a radiant fire. It has been shattered and fragmented. Whom does this chariot, used for fighting, belong to? These arrows are decorated with molten gold and are as long as a chariot's wheel. They are strewn around. Who was killed with these arrows and which performer of terrible deeds used them? O amiable one! This is the work of rakshasas who can assume any form at will and are extremely terrible in their hearts. Behold. My enmity has increased a hundredfold and I will bring an end to their lives. The ascetic Sita has been abducted, killed or devoured. When Sita was abducted in the great forest, dharma

could not save her. O Lakshmana! Vaidehi has been devoured or
abducted. O amiable one! Where are my gods? In this world, who
is capable of doing something agreeable for me? O Lakshmana!
The brave creator of the worlds, who knew about this piteous
account, did not know about this and will be disrespected by all the
creatures. I am gentle and am engaged in the welfare of the worlds.
I am controlled, though I know about this piteous account. I think
it is certain that the lords of the thirty gods take me to be devoid of
valour. O Lakshmana! See how the qualities I have obtained have
been enveloped in taints.[340] From today, all the creatures and the
rakshasas will be destroyed. I will restrain the gentle beams of the
moon and the great sun will arise. O Lakshmana! The yakshas, the
gandharvas, the pishachas, the rakshasas, the kinnaras and men will
not be able to find happiness. O Lakshmana! Behold. My weapons
and arrows will envelop the sky. Today, I will render the three
worlds such that they will be impossible to travel in. I will block all
the planets and obstruct the path of the moon. The radiance of the
fire, the Maruts and the sun will be destroyed and withdrawn. The
summits of the mountains will be shattered. The waterbodies will
be dried up. The trees, creepers and shrubs will be devastated. The
ocean will be destroyed. O Soumitri! Until my gods return Sita safely
to me, this very instant, they will witness my valour. O Lakshmana!
An incessant net of arrows will be released from the string of my
bow and the creatures will not be able to rise up into the sky. The
animals and birds will be mangled, devastated and confused by my
iron arrows. O Lakshmana! Today, the universe will be in turmoil
and all the boundaries will be crossed. I will draw my bow back to
my ears and release unstoppable arrows in the world of the living.
For Maithilee's sake, I will not leave any pishachas or rakshasas.
In my intolerance and rage, I will shoot arrows that will travel a
long distance. Let the gods witness my strength now. When the
three worlds are destroyed by my rage, there will not be any gods,
daityas, pishachas or rakshasas left. The torrents of my arrows will

---

[340] The sense seems to be the following. Rama, being gentle, should not kill the
rakshasas unnecessarily. But that has become a fault.

reduce the gods, the danavas, the yakshas and the rakshasas in the worlds into many fragments and they will fall down. Today, my arrows will destroy all the agreements in the worlds. O Lakshmana! All beings can never counter old age, death, time and destiny. In that way, when I am enraged, there is no doubt that I cannot be repulsed. If you do not show me the beautiful and unblemished one, Sita Maithilee, as used to be the case earlier, I will make the world and the mountains whirl, together with the gods, the gandharvas, men and serpents.'

Chapter 3(61)

Rama was afflicted because of Sita's abduction and was about to scorch the worlds, like the fire of final destruction. He glanced at his strung bow and sighed repeatedly. He desired to kill the animals, like the enraged Rudra at the time of Daksha's sacrifice. This sight of Rama being enraged was not something that Lakshmana had ever seen earlier. With his mouth dry, he joined his hands in salutation and spoke these words. 'Earlier, you were gentle and controlled, engaged in the welfare of all beings. You should not fall prey to rage. You should resume your natural self. The prosperity of the moon, the radiance of the sun, the speed of the wind, the forgiveness of the earth—all these always exist in you and you also possess supreme fame. I do not know whom this shattered chariot, used for fighting, belongs to. I do not know whom the weapon and equipment belong to, nor who shattered them and for what reason. This place has been struck by hooves and an axle. It is sprinkled with drops of blood. O son of a king! This is a spot where a terrible clash has taken place. O supreme among eloquent ones! A single person has been killed here, not both. Nor are there signs of the footprints and conduct of a large army. You should not destroy the worlds because of what a single person has done. Calm kings use the rod of chastisement mildly. You have always been the supreme refuge for all creatures. O Raghava! If you destroy them because of your wife, who will think that you are virtuous? The rivers, oceans, mountains, gods, gandharvas and danavas have behaved like virtuous ones who have consecrated themselves for a sacrifice and have not done anything disagreeable towards you. O king! You should search for the one who has abducted Sita. With a bow in my hand, I will be your second, and the supreme rishis will be our aides. We will search the oceans, the mountains, the forests, the many dreadful caverns and all the lakes in the mountains. We will control ourselves and search the worlds of the gods and the gandharvas, until we have found the person who has abducted your wife. O Indra of Kosala! If the lords of the thirty gods do not peacefully return your wife to you, it is only after that, at the right time, that you should do what you have to. O Indra among men! If you do not get Sita back through good conduct, conciliation, humility and good policy, it is only then that you should use torrents of gold-tufted arrows that are like the great Indra's vajra.'

Chapter 3(62)

He[341] was tormented by grief and lamented like one who was without a protector. A great confusion pervaded him and he lost his senses. After a while, Soumitri Lakshmana comforted him. He kneaded Rama's feet and addressed him. 'O Rama! Like the immortals obtained amrita, King Dasharatha obtained you after great austerities and great deeds. He was attached to your qualities. We have heard from Bharata that it was because of separation from you that the king, the lord of the earth, obtained divinity. O Kakutstha! If you are unable to bear the misery that you are facing now, how will one who is inferior, an ordinary one with limited spirits, withstand it? O tiger among men! If in your misery, you wish your energy to destroy the worlds, to whom will afflicted subjects go, searching for refuge? This is the way of the world.

[341] Rama.

Yayati, Nahusha's son, went to Shakra's world and became like him. However, he was touched by bad policy.[342] There is maharshi Vasishtha, our father's priest. In a single day, he had one hundred sons. But they were slain again.[343] This goddess, the mother of the world,[344] is worshipped by the worlds. O one who resorts to the truth! However, even the earth can be seen to quake. These two extremely strong ones, the sun and the moon, are the eyes of the world and everything is established in them. However, even they are invaded by eclipses. O bull among men! The greatest among creatures, the gods and all creatures who bear bodies cannot free themselves from destiny. O tiger among men! It has been heard that the present gods,[345] Shakra and the others, also face the good and the bad. You should not be distressed at this.[346] O unblemished one! O brave one! Even if Vaidehi has been destroyed, even if she has been abducted, unlike an ordinary person, you should not grieve. O Rama! Those who are like you and always see the truth, those who are detached in their wisdom, do not sorrow, even when they face a great hardship. O best among men! You should use your intelligence to think about the truth. When they use their intelligence, immensely wise ones know what is right and what is wrong. The results of deeds are not certain, their good and bad aspects have not been seen.[347] If a deed is in the heart, but has not been performed, its cherished fruits will not materialize. O brave one! Earlier, you have yourself told me about this several times. You are like Brihaspati himself. Who can instruct you? O immensely wise one! Even the gods cannot comprehend your intelligence. Because of your sorrow, your knowledge is asleep and I am trying to wake it. O bull of the Ikshvaku lineage! Your own valour is both divine and human. Even if you cast your eye on an enemy, he will be killed. O bull among

---

[342] Yayati's story is given in the Mahabharata. He went to the world of the gods and became Indra. However, because of various transgressions, he was dislodged from heaven.

[343] Vishvamitra killed them.

[344] The earth.

[345] Gods change from one *manvantara* (era) to another.

[346] Some of the shlokas in this chapter bear a striking resemblance to the Bhagavadgita.

[347] Because they may occur later, perhaps in the next life.

men! Why should you try to destroy everything? You should find
out who the wicked enemy is and uproot him.'

Chapter 3(63)

No sooner had Lakshmana told his elder brother a little bit of
those excellent words, Raghava, who could grasp the essence,
understood the great gist and accepted it. The mighty-armed one
controlled his increasing rage. Holding on to his colourful bow,
Rama told Lakshmana, 'O child! What will we do? O Lakshmana!
Where will we go? You should now think about what means we will
use to find Sita.' Rama was afflicted by torment and Lakshmana
spoke to him. 'You should search in Janasthana. It is covered by
trees and creepers and populated by many kinds of rakshasas. There
are mountains that are difficult to traverse and glades and valleys.
There are many kinds of terrible caves, populated by many kinds
of animals. There are the abodes of kinnaras and the residences of
gandharvas. With me, you should search all these. O bull among
men! That is what an intelligent and great-souled person like
you should do. They do not tremble because of a calamity, like
mountains against the force of the wind.' Thus addressed, with
Lakshmana, he roamed around everywhere in the forest. The angry
Rama affixed a sharp and terrible arrow to his bow.

He saw the greatly fortunate Jatayu, supreme among birds,
lying down, with the complexion of a mountain top, and the ground
was wet with the blood from his wounds. His complexion was like
the summit of a mountain. On seeing him, Rama told Lakshmana,
'There is no doubt that this is the one who has devoured Sita
Vaidehi. It is evident that this rakshasa has been roaming around in
the forest in the form of an eagle. Having eaten the large-eyed Sita,
he is now resting happily. I will slay him with straight-flying and
terrible arrows that blaze at the tips.' Having said this, he affixed
the sharp arrow to his bow and advanced towards the eagle. The
angry Rama made the earth, right up to the frontiers of the ocean,
tremble. Vomiting froth and blood, the miserable bird addressed

Rama, Dasharatha's son, in grieving words. 'O one with a long life! You are searching for a herb in this great forest. But Ravana has abducted both that queen and my life. O Raghava! The queen was without you and Lakshmana. While I looked on, the stronger Ravana abducted her. I tried to rescue Sita and in the encounter, destroyed his chariot and umbrella and also brought Ravana down on the ground here. This is his shattered bow and this is his armour. O Rama! In the encounter, I shattered the chariot that he used to fight. I was exhausted and Ravana severed my wings with his sword. He seized Vaidehi and leapt up into the sky. The rakshasa has already killed me. You should not slay me.' From him, Rama got to know the account about his beloved Sita. He embraced the king of the eagles and, with Lakshmana, wept.

He[348] was taking a single breath with difficulty and sighed repeatedly. On seeing him, the miserable Rama spoke to Soumitri. 'I have been dislodged from the kingdom. I am residing in the forest. Sita has been lost. The bird is dead. Like a fire, this kind of adversity is burning me. The great ocean is full. However, such is the nature of my adversity, that were I to enter it, the lord of the rivers would dry up. In the world, with all its mobile and immobile objects, there is no one as unfortunate as I am. Why have I faced this devastating calamity? This aged king of the eagles is my father's friend. Because of my misfortune, he has been slain and is lying down on the ground.' With Lakshmana, Raghava said this and many other things. As a sign of affection towards his father, he touched Jatayu's body. His wings had been severed and he was wet with blood. Rama embraced the king of the eagles. 'Where is Maithilee, who is like my own life?' Shedding tears, he fell down on the ground.

Chapter 3(64)

Rama looked at the eagle, who had been brought down on the ground in that terrible way. Soumitri was filled with friendship

[348] Jatayu.

for him and he addressed him in these words. 'This bird certainly tried for my sake. The rakshasa killed him in the encounter. He has given up his life, which is extremely difficult to give up. O Lakshmana! His body has been mangled, but a little bit of life still remains. It seems that he is filled with lassitude and has lost his voice. O Jatayu! If you can, please speak again. O fortunate one! Speak about Sita. Speak about how you were killed. Why did Ravana abduct Sita? What have I done against him? Since Ravana abducted my beloved, what crime did he see? O supreme among birds! At that time, how was that beautiful face, which is like the moon? What did Sita say? How was the rakshasa's valour? What was his form? What were his deeds? Where is his residence? O father![349] I am asking you. Tell me.' Distressed in his soul, he glanced towards him and lamented thereafter.

With a quivering voice, Jatayu addressed Rama in these words. 'She was abducted by Ravana, Indra among the rakshasas, through the sky. He resorted to maya and created a great storm, as if it was a bad day. O son![350] I was exhausted and the roamer in the night severed my wings. Seizing Sita Vaidehi, he left in a southern direction. O Raghava! My breath of life is obstructed and my sight is whirling. I can see trees made of gold, with grass on their tops.[351] O Kakutstha! The muhurta when Ravana seized Sita is the muhurta known as Vinda, but he did not realize this.[352] At this time, the owner of riches quickly loses them.[353] He will be swiftly destroyed, like a fish that has swallowed a baited hook. You should not sorrow on account of Janaka's daughter. You will soon sport with Vaidehi, after having killed the rakshasa in a battle.' With some senses still left, the eagle replied to Rama. As he was about to die, blood and

---

[349] The word used is tata.

[350] The word used is tata.

[351] A portent signifying death.

[352] A muhurta is a period of forty-eight minutes and in a twenty-four-hour period, there are thirty muhurtas. Some are regarded as good or auspicious muhurtas, others as bad and inauspicious. In a standard list of muhurta names used today, Vinda does not figure. Vinda used to be the name of the eleventh muhurta, regarded as bad. These days, it will often be referred to as Vijaya.

[353] If an act is undertaken at that time.

141

bits of flesh oozed out of his mouth. 'He is the son of Vishrava and the brother of Vaishravana[354] himself.' Having said this, the lord of the birds gave up his life, which is so very difficult to obtain. Rama joined his hands in salutation and said, 'Tell me. Please tell me.' But the eagle's breath of life gave up his body and rose up into the sky. The head fell down on the ground and the legs were outstretched. His body trembled and he fell down on the ground. The eagle's eyes were coppery red. He had lost his life and was like a mountain.

Afflicted by many kinds of grief, the distressed Rama spoke to Soumitri. 'This bird happily lived in Dandakaranya for many years, amidst the rakshasas. He has now been destroyed. After many years, Destiny has taken him upwards. He has been killed and is lying down now. It is impossible to cross destiny. O Lakshmana! Behold. This eagle tried to help me and has been killed. He tried to rescue Sita, but Ravana was stronger. He has given up the great kingdom of the eagles that belonged to his fathers and grandfathers. This lord of birds has released his breath of life for my sake. Virtuous ones, those who follow dharma, are indeed seen everywhere. O Soumitri! Brave ones are born even among inferior species. O amiable one! O scorcher of enemies! My grief at Sita's abduction is not as much as that caused by the eagle being destroyed for my sake. The prosperous and famous King Dasharatha should be worshipped by me, but this lord of the birds should also be revered. O Soumitri! Fetch wood. I will kindle a fire. I will cremate the king of the eagles, who has been killed because of me. I will place the lord of the world of the birds on a pyre. O Soumitri! I will cremate the one who has been killed by a terrible rakshasa. There are destinations for those who perform sacrifices. There are destinations for those who light sacrificial fires. There are destinations for those who do not return[355] and for those who donate land. O great-spirited king of the eagles! With the rites of purification performed by me, take my leave and go to those supreme worlds.' Saying this, he placed the lord of the birds on that blazing pyre. Rama, with dharma in his soul, sadly cremated his

[354] Kubera.
[355] Are not born again.

friend. With Soumitri, the valiant Rama then went to the forest. He killed a large gazelle,[356] laid it out on sacred grass and offered it to the bird. The immensely illustrious Rama took out pieces of meat from the flesh of the gazelle, laid it out on green grass and offered it to the bird. When a mortal person goes to the world hereafter, brahmanas chant hymns for his journey to heaven. Quickly, Rama recited these. The two, best among men, then went to the river Godavari. Both of them offered water to the king of the eagles. The king of the eagles had performed an illustrious deed. Having performed an extremely difficult deed, he had been brought down in the battle. With his rites of purification performed by one who was the equal of a maharshi,[357] he went to the auspicious and sacred worlds that were meant for him.

Chapter 3(65)

Having performed the water rites for him, the two Raghavas left. Heading in the western direction, they searched the forest for Sita. With bows, arrows and swords in their hands, they then left for the southern direction. Those two from the Ikshvaku lineage then came upon a path that was not often used. It was shrouded in many lantanas, trees and creepers. It was covered everywhere and was impenetrable, dense and terrible to behold. Having chosen the southern direction, the two immensely strong ones quickly crossed over and traversed this terrible part of the great forest. The two Raghavas went three *kroshas*[358] beyond Janasthana. Those two immensely energetic ones entered the dense Krouncha forest. There were many dense black clouds there and everything seemed to be happy. There were auspicious flowers of many hues. There were large numbers of animals and birds. They looked around that forest, searching for Vaidehi. Afflicted because of Sita's abduction,

[356] *Maharohi.*
[357] Rama.
[358] One krosha is two miles. However, the definition of krosha was not standardized.

they searched here and there. The spirited and immensely energetic
Lakshmana was auspicious and good in conduct. He joined his
hands in salutation and addressed his brother, blazing in his energy,
in these words. 'My left arm is twitching and my mind is anxious.
When something like this is felt, it is usually a bad omen. O noble
one! Therefore, act in accordance with my beneficial words and
be ready. These portents seem to be telling me that some danger
is nearby. This bird known as *vanjulaka*[359] is extremely terrible.
It is shrieking, as if signifying our victory in a battle.' Those two
energetic ones searched everywhere in the forest.

They then heard a tumultuous sound that seemed to shatter
the forest. It was as if an extremely strong storm had struck the
desolate forest. The sound filled everything up and rose up into the
sky. Desiring to know what was causing the sound, Rama and his
younger brother seized their swords. They saw an extremely gigantic
and broad-chested rakshasa. The two of them approached the
rakshasa who was standing in front of them. This was Kabandha.[360]
He was large and was without a head or a neck. His mouth was
placed in his stomach. His body hair was thick and sharp. He rose
up like a giant mountain. He was as terrible as a dark blue cloud.
His roar was like that of thunder. There was only a single sharp-
sighted and terrible eye on his chest. This was large in size and had
tawny eyelashes. He licked his giant mouth, which possessed large
teeth. He ate extremely terrible bears, lions, animals and elephants.
He stretched out his horrible arms and each of them was one
yojana long. With these arms, he seized many kinds of bears, large
numbers of birds and animals. He pulled towards him, and hurled
away, many herds of animals. When the two brothers turned up
there, he stood there, obstructing their path. When they saw him,
they had only travelled for one krosha.[361] Kabandha was gigantic,
terrible and horrible and he stretched out his arms. He seized the
two Raghavas in his two hands,[362] brought his hands together and

[359] Kind of bird.
[360] *Kabandha* means a headless torso.
[361] After entering the Krouncha forest.
[362] One in each hand.

crushed them with force. They wielded swords and firm bows. They were mighty-armed and fierce in their energy. However, when they were dragged in this way, those two immensely strong brothers could do nothing. The mighty-armed Kabandha, supreme among danavas, spoke to them. 'Who are you? You have shoulders like bulls. You wield gigantic swords and bows. You have reached this terrible place and are like food brought to me. Tell me the reason why you have come here. You have come to the place where I was lying in wait, suffering from hunger. You possess arrows, bows and swords, like two bulls with sharp horns. Now that you have come before me, it is impossible for you to remain alive.'

Lakshmana's mouth dried up at the words of the evil-souled Kabandha. But Rama told him, 'O one with truth as his valour! We face this terrible situation and have moved from one catastrophe to a greater catastrophe. Earlier, I couldn't obtain my beloved and we now face a calamity that will bring an end to our lives. O Lakshmana! Among all beings, the valour of destiny is extremely great. O tiger among men! Behold. We are confused because of this hardship. O Lakshmana! Among all creatures, divinity's burden is extremely great.[363] There may be brave and powerful ones who are accomplished in the use of weapons in the field of battle. However, when they are overcome by destiny, they are destroyed, like a dam made out of sand.' The immensely illustrious and powerful Dasharatha's son, who was firm and truthful in his valour, said this. He looked at Soumitri, who was fierce in his valour. He[364] then acted so as to compose his own intelligence.

Chapter 3(66)

Kabandha saw that those two brothers, Rama and Lakshmana, had composed themselves, though they were still writhing

---

[363] The text actually says, the burden isn't great. Since this can't be right, we have corrected the typo and followed non-Critical versions, which say that the burden is great.
[364] Rama.

around, within the bondage of his hands. He addressed them in
these words. 'O bulls among kshatriyas! You can see that I am
afflicted by hunger. How can you be so composed? Destiny has
instructed that you should be here as my food. You should lose
your senses.' Lakshmana was suffering. However, hearing this, he
decided that it was time to exhibit valour and spoke these beneficial
words that were appropriate for the occasion.[365] 'O senior! Before
this worst among rakshasas can quickly devour us, we should
swiftly use swords to severe his arms.' The two Raghavas knew
about the time and the place. Extremely cheerful, they used their
swords to sever his arms at the shoulders. On the right, Rama used
force and his unsheathed sword to slice off the right arm and the
brave Lakshmana did this with the left. With his arms severed,
the mighty-armed one fell down. Roaring like a thunder cloud, he
emitted a loud scream that echoed in the sky, the earth and the
directions. The arms were severed and he was covered with torrents
of blood. On seeing this, the danava was distressed and asked, 'O
brave ones! Who are you?'

Hearing what he said, the immensely strong Lakshmana, the
possessor of auspicious signs, told Kabandha about Kakutstha.
'This is the descendant of the Ikshvaku lineage. Among people, he is
known by the name of Rama. Know me to be his younger brother,
Lakshmana. Though he possesses the power of a god, he is residing
in this desolate forest. A rakshasa has abducted his wife. We wished
to find her and came here. But who are you? Why are you in the
forest, in the form of a headless torso? Your legs have been shattered
and cannot move. You possess a blazing mouth in the middle of
your stomach.' Thus addressed, Kabandha was extremely delighted,
because he remembered Indra's words. He replied to Lakshmana in
these words. 'O tigers among men! Welcome. It is good fortune that
I have seen you. It is good fortune that you have severed the bonds of
my arms. My form turned to this malformed state because of my lack
of humility. O tiger among men![366] I will tell you. Listen to the truth.'

[365] He spoke to Rama.
[366] In the singular.

Chapter 3(67)

'O Rama! O mighty-armed one! O one who is great in strength and valour! Earlier, I possessed an unthinkable form that was famous in the three worlds, like that of Soma, Shakra, Surya or Vayu. In that form, I caused great fright in the worlds. O Rama! I went to the forest and here and there, terrified the rishis. A maharshi named Sthulashira was enraged with me. Thinking of many kinds of wild forms,[367] I used one of those to oppress him. On seeing me, he inflicted this terrible curse on me. "This is a terrible and contemptible form and you will remain in this." When the angry one cursed me in this way, I sought from him a means to end the curse. He addressed me in these words. "Rama will sever your arms and cremate you in the desolate forest. When that happens, you will regain your own large and auspicious form." O Lakshmana! Know me to be Danu's son, blazing in his beauty. Because of Indra's anger, I obtained this form in the field of battle. I performed fierce austerities and satisfied the grandfather.[368] He granted me a long life and I became confused. Now that I have obtained a long life, what can Shakra do to me? Resorting to this kind of intelligence, I oppressed Shakra in a battle. Using his arm, he released the vajra that has one hundred edges. That made my thighs and head penetrate my body. Though I beseeched him, he did not convey me to Yama's abode. He told me, "Let the grandfather's words come true." However, with my thighs, head and mouth shattered, how could I satisfy my hunger? Struck by the vajra, I would have to remain alive for an extremely long period of time. Thus addressed, Shakra thought of arms that were one yojana long for me. He gave me a mouth with sharp teeth in my stomach. I have been roaming around in this forest. Using these long arms, from every direction, I have dragged lions, elephants, animals and tigers and eaten them. Indra told me, "In an encounter, when Rama and Lakshmana sever your arms, you will go to heaven." You are that fortunate Rama. O

[367] He could assume any form at will.
[368] Brahma.

Raghava! In truth, no one else is capable of slaying me. This is what
the maharshi had said. O bull among men! O friend! I will use my
intelligence to advise and instruct you about what should be done.
The two of you must cremate me in a fire.'

Thus addressed, while Lakshmana heard, Raghava, with
dharma in his soul, spoke these words to Danu's son. 'My illustrious
wife has been abducted by Ravana. With my brother, I have
therefore left Janasthana and am wandering around. I only know
the rakshasa's name and not his form. We do not know his age, his
powers, or where he lives. We are like ones without a protector,
roaming around, afflicted by grief. If you show us your compassion,
we will also do an equivalent deed for you.[369] We will bring wood
that has been shattered by elephants at different times. O brave
one! We will construct a huge trench and burn you in it. If you
know the truth, do this extremely good deed for us. Tell us about
the person who has abducted Sita and where he has taken her.'
Danu's son was addressed by Rama in these excellent words. Both
he and Raghava were skilled in the use of words and he replied. 'I
do not possess divine knowledge. Nor do I know about Maithilee.
However, when you cremate me, I will assume my own form and
will tell you what I know.[370] O lord! Until I am cremated, I do not
possess the capacity to know about the extremely valiant rakshasa
who has abducted Sita. O Raghava! As a consequence of the curse,
my extensive knowledge has been destroyed. Because of my own
deeds, I obtained this present form, condemned by the worlds. I
am like the setting sun, when its mounts are exhausted. O Rama!
Fling me into the trench, follow the prescribed rites, and cremate
me. O descendant of the Raghu lineage! Fling me into the trench
and properly cremate me. O brave one! I will then tell you about
the person who knows about that rakshasa. O Raghava! You must
follow an appropriate course of conduct and strike a friendship with
me. Dextrous in his valour, he will be delighted and will think of a
means to help you. O Raghava! There is nothing in the three worlds

[369] If you tell us about Ravana, we will cremate you.
[370] The knowledge will return in his own form.

that is unknown to him. Earlier, because of a different reason, he circled all the worlds.'[371]

Chapter 3(68)

Those two brave ones, lords among men, were thus addressed by Kabandha. They went to a crevice in the mountain and prepared to light a fire there. In every direction, Lakshmana lit blazing and giant torches. He also lit the pyre, which blazed everywhere. Kabandha's body was like a large vessel filled with ghee. The fire gently cooked the fat. Soon, a form that was like a fire without smoke emerged from the smoking pyre. The immensely strong one was adorned in divine garlands and sparkling garments and dazzled. In dazzling and sparkling garments and ornaments adorning every limb, he swiftly leapt up from the pyre, delighted. He was astride a resplendent vimana that brings fame to those who are in it, yoked to swans. In his radiance, the extremely energetic one illuminated the ten directions.

Having ascended into the sky, Kabandha addressed Rama in these words. 'O Raghava! Hear the truth about how you will get Sita back. O Rama! In this world, everyone mentions six kinds of policy.[372] Someone who has been touched by an unfortunate situation will have to ally with another who is suffering from misfortune. O Rama! With Lakshmana, you are suffering and are in an unfortunate situation. There is a person who has oppressed your wife and has created this hardship for you. O one who is best among friends! You must certainly find a friend who is in a similar situation. On reflection, I think that without doing this, you will not

---

[371] A reference to Sugriva, who has still not been named.

[372] These are six kinds of policy (really foreign policy) recommended for a king in different situations, enumerated extensively in Kautilya's *Arthashastra*. They are alliances, hostility, waging war, waiting it out, creating divisions in the enemy and seeking shelter with an equal.

be successful. O Rama! Listen. I will tell you about the ape[373] named
Sugriva. His brother, Shakra's son, Vali, angrily restrained him.
The excellent mountain of Rishyamuka is on the beautiful shores
of the Pampa. Controlling himself, the brave one resides there, with
four other apes. O Raghava! Quickly go there now and strike up a
friendship with him. Approach him and before a blazing fire, make
an alliance of non-violence towards each other. You should not
disrespect Sugriva, lord of the apes. The valiant one can assume any
form at will. He will be grateful and will find ways to help you. The
two of you will be able to perform the task he desires of you now.
Whether his wishes are fulfilled or unfulfilled, you must do what
needs to be done. He is the son of Riksharaja, born from the sun
god.[374] However, Vali acted sinfully towards him and scared, he is
roaming around the Pampa. The ape roams around in the forest
and has found an abode in Rishyamuka. O Raghava! Quickly take
your weapons and make a pledge of friendship with him.[375] That
elephant among apes is accomplished and knows about all the places
in this world frequented by those who survive on human flesh.[376] O
Raghava! O scorcher of enemies! As long as Surya, the one with the
thousand rays, radiates heat, there is nothing in the world that is
unknown to him. With the apes, he will search the rivers, the large
mountains and impenetrable summits and caverns until your wife
is found. O Raghava! You are grieving because of separation from
Sita. He will dispatch extremely large-sized apes in all the directions
to search for her. Whether that unblemished one has been taken to
the summit of Mount Meru, or has been taken to the nether regions

---

[373] We have translated *vanara* as ape, for want of a better word. This is not a happy
translation, since vanara means a special kind of *nara* (man).

[374] Vali and Sugriva's father was Riksharaja. But it was customary to have *kshetraja*
sons, born through the father's field (the mother), but through a different biological father.
Riksharaja was temporarily transformed into a woman. In that feminine form, Vali was
born through Indra and Sugriva through Surya.

[375] Other than the obvious meaning of taking the weapons, the language is such that
other meanings are also possible—in addition to the fire, swear on your weapons; since
this is an act of friendship, cast aside your weapons.

[376] The rakshasas.

and has found a refuge there, that supreme among apes[377] will find your beloved. He will ensure that the rakshasas are killed and she is returned to you.'

Chapter 3(69)

Kabandha knew about the purport of words. He instructed Rama about the way he would get Sita back. He then again addressed him in words that were full of meaning. 'O Rama! Resort to the western direction, along this auspicious path along which beautiful and blossoming trees can be seen—jambu, priyala, panasa, plaksha, nyagrodha, tinduka, ashvattha, karnikara, chuta[378] and others. Either climb the trees, or use force to make the fruit fall down on the ground. They are like amrita. Having eaten, proceed. Pass over excellent regions, from mountain to mountain and from forest to forest. O brave ones! In this way, go to Lake Pampa. O Rama! It is decorated with sandbanks. The banks are even on all sides, so that one can descend into the water. It is not slippery. There is no moss, nor any pebbles. It is adorned with lotuses and water lilies. O Raghava! There are swans, cranes, curlews and kingfishers. They frequent the waters of the Pampa and call out in gentle tones. Those auspicious birds do not know how to avoid men who seek to hunt them, because they have never seen them. However, you can eat those birds. They are plump, like vessels full of ghee. O Raghava! There are rohitas,[379] vakratundas[380] and nalaminas.[381] O Rama! The best of fish from the Pampa can be killed with arrows. Without any difficulty, Lakshmana will remove their scales, fins and bones, grill them and give them to you to eat. After you have

---

[377] The word used for ape is plavanga, meaning one who moves by jumping.
[378] Mango.
[379] Red fish, the carp Rohu.
[380] With a curved snout, dolphins.
[381] Kind of fish.

eaten the fish, he will use vessels made of leaves[382] to offer you
the auspicious waters of the Pampa, fragrant with the scent of
lotuses. It is pleasant, cool and not polluted. Lakshmana will then
collect the clean water that sparkles like crystal in a lotus leaf and
drink it. The apes who roam in the forest lie down in a large and
excellent mountain cavern. O supreme among men! Roaring like
bulls, they will come to the Pampa, in search of water, and you will
see them in that form. O Rama! Adorned in garlands of flowers
collected from the trees, they will come there in the evening. On
seeing the auspicious waters of the Pampa, your sorrow will vanish.
O Raghava! Your mind will delight there in the many tilakas,
naktamalakas[383] and blooming blue and red lotuses. O Raghava!
No man has ever made garlands out of those flowers, which do
not decay or fade. O Kakutstha! Having gone there, you will see a
mendicant lady named Shabaree, wandering around. She has lived
for a long time. She is always devoted to dharma and is worshipped
by all creatures. O Rama! You are like a god and having seen you,
she will go to the world of heaven. O Rama! After that, stick to the
western bank of the Pampa. O Kakutstha! You will see a hermitage
that is hidden extremely well. The elephants are incapable of entering
that hermitage. That is because the rishi Matanga has laid out
the grove in that fashion. That forest is like a forest of the gods,
like Nandana. O Rama! It is full of many birds and you will find
delight there. Rishyamuka, with many blossoming trees, is right
in front of the Pampa. It is protected by baby elephants and it is
extremely difficult to climb it. In earlier times, the generous Brahma
had constructed it. O Rama! If a man reaches the summit of that
mountain and lies down there, when he wakes up, he obtains all
the riches he dreamt of in his sleep. However, if a person who is
wicked in deeds and inappropriate in conduct climbs it, rakshasas
seize him while he is asleep and strike him. O Rama! The great noise
of baby elephants trumpeting and playing can be heard around
the Pampa and by the residents of Matanga's hermitage. Supreme

[382] From lotus flowers.
[383] The Indian beech tree.

elephants clash against each other and become wet with flows of blood. They are spirited, with the complexions of clouds. They clash, roam around separately and clash again. Having drunk the sparkling, clean and undecaying waters, the residents of the forest withdraw and collectively enter the forest again. O Rama! There is a large and radiant cave in that mountain. O Kakutstha! A large boulder prevents entry and it is extremely difficult to enter it. Right in front of the eastern entry to the cave, there is a large lake with cool waters. It is beautiful and there are many trees, laden with roots and fruits, there. With four other apes, Sugriva resides there. He can sometimes also be found on the summit of the mountain.'

After this, adorned in a radiant garland with the complexion of the sun, the valiant Kabandha, stationed in the sky, took his leave from the two of them, Rama and Lakshmana. The immensely fortunate Kabandha was stationed in the sky near them and they gave him permission to leave. He told them, 'Leave, so that you may be successful in your objective.' Delighted, Kabandha took their permission and departed. Kabandha obtained his own form, surrounded in prosperity and radiant in all his limbs. Moving further away in the sky, he glanced towards Rama and said, 'Strike that friendship.'

Chapter 3(70)

In the forest, the two of them followed the path to the Pampa that had been indicated by Kabandha. Those two best of princes resorted to the western direction.[384] In the mountain, they saw many small trees that were laden with fruit. Having seen those, Rama and Lakshmana proceeded, so as to see Sugriva. The two descendants of the Raghu lineage found an abode on the slopes of the mountain. The two Raghavas then approached the Pampa's western bank. They reached the western bank of Lake Pampa and saw Shabaree's beautiful

---

[384] They first headed west and then turned towards the east.

hermitage there. They reached that hermitage, shrouded by many trees. Having seen that beautiful place, they approached Shabaree. On seeing them, the successful one arose and joined her hands in salutation. She touched Rama's feet and that of the intelligent Lakshmana. The mendicant was firm in her vows and Rama addressed her. 'Have you been able to conquer all the impediments? Are your austerities prospering? O one rich in austerities! Have you been able to control your anger and your food? Are you observing the rituals? Is there happiness in your mind? O one who is beautiful in speech! Has your service to your seniors become successful?'

The successful and ascetic lady, who had observed the norms laid down for virtuous ones, was thus asked by Rama. The aged one replied to Rama. 'There were those I served. When you arrived in Chitrakuta, those ones, unmatched in radiance, left for heaven, astride vimanas. Those immensely fortunate maharshis are knowledgeable about dharma. They told me, "Rama will come to this sacred hermitage. With Soumitri, you should receive him as a guest. Once you have seen him, you will go to the supreme and undecaying worlds." O bull among men! O tiger among men! I have collected many kinds of forest fare for you from the banks of the Pampa.' The one with dharma in his soul was thus addressed by Shabaree, who was never deprived from access to knowledge.[385] Raghava told Shabaree, 'I have heard about your powers from Danu's great-souled son.[386] If you so think, I desire to directly see what I have heard about.'[387] These are the words that emerged from Rama's mouth. Hearing these, Shabaree showed the two of them the great forest. 'Behold. It is full of animals and birds and is like a dense cloud. O descendant of the Raghu lineage! This is famous as Matanga's forest. My immensely radiant preceptors, cleansed in their souls, were here. They knew about mantras. In this tirtha, they offered oblations, worshipping with the use of mantras. There is a sacrificial altar to the west and I have kept it clean. With

---

[385] This implies that Shabaree belonged to a class that did not usually have access to knowledge.

[386] Kabandha.

[387] The hermitage.

trembling hands,[388] they made efforts to render offerings of flowers. O supreme among the Raghu lineage! Behold. The power of their austerities exists even now. The altars are unmatched in their radiance and are illuminating the directions with their resplendence. Because of fasting, they could not make the exertions required to leave this place.[389] Behold! As soon as they thought of it, the seven seas assembled here. After they had their baths, they placed their garments made of bark on these trees. O descendant of the Raghu lineage! Even today, they have not yet dried. You have seen this entire forest. You have heard everything that deserves to be heard. I wish to obtain your permission to cast aside this body. I desire to go near the ones with cleansed souls, the sages whom I have served in this hermitage.'

Raghava, with Lakshmana, heard the words of the one who was devoted to dharma. With delight on his face, he granted her permission to depart. Having obtained Rama's permission, she offered herself as an oblation into the fire. Dazzling like a flaming fire, she went to heaven. Maharshis who perform good deeds find pleasure in a place. Immersing herself in meditation, Shabaree went to that sacred spot.

Chapter 3(71)

Because of her own deeds, Shabaree went to heaven. With his brother Lakshmana, Raghava started to think. The one with dharma in his soul thought about the powers of those great-souled ones. Raghava spoke to Lakshmana, who was single-mindedly devoted to ensuring his welfare. 'O amiable one! I have seen this hermitage and the many wonders performed by those self-controlled ones. It is full of many animals, tigers and birds that are trusting. O Lakshmana! We must properly touch the water of this tirtha,

---

[388] Because they were old.
[389] To go and bathe in the ocean. The seven seas came to the Pampa.

which has the seven seas in it, and satisfy the ancestors through water rites. This will destroy all that is inauspicious in us and good fortune will present itself. O Lakshmana! My mind will be delighted if we do this now. O tiger among men! My heart is full of auspicious sentiments. Come. Therefore, let us go to the Pampa, which is pleasant to behold. Not very far from there, Mount Rishyamuka can be seen. Sugriva, with dharma in his soul and the son of the one with the rays, resides there with four apes, always terrified because of fear from Vali. I wish to hurry and see Sugriva, bull among apes. O amiable one! The task of finding out where Sita has gone devolves on him.' Thus addressed, Soumitri told Rama, 'Let us quickly go there. My mind is also urging us to hurry.'

The lord of the earth emerged from the hermitage. With the lord Lakshmana, he went to the Pampa. Everywhere, he saw large trees that were laden with flowers. There were plover birds, peacocks, aquatic birds and parrots. Many other birds called out in that great forest. Rama saw many other trees and diverse kinds of lakes. Tormented by desire, he saw that supreme lake.[390] From a distance, Rama approached it, full of water. He bathed in a lake, a lake that was named after Matanga. Rama, Dasharatha's son, was overcome by sorrow. He entered the area of the lake, one that was covered with lotuses. There were tilakas, ashokas, punnagas, *bakulas*,[391] *uddalas*[392] and reeds. They were like obstructions to that beautiful grove and the water, where lotuses brushed against each other. The water was like crystal and the sand was always soft. There were large numbers of fish and turtles and the banks were adorned with trees. The creepers clung to each other, like friends. It was frequented by kinnaras, serpents, yakshas and rakshasas. It was enveloped by many trees and creepers. The store of water was auspicious and cool. There were clumps of fragrant lotuses and lilies, red and white. There were clumps of blue lotuses and with many other colours, it looked like a many-hued painting. There were pink and black lotuses, full of fragrance. It was surrounded

[390] This is not the Pampa. This is a different lake, named after Matanga.
[391] Tree with fragrant flowers.
[392] The Assyrian plum.

by flowering mango trees, and peacocks called. With Soumitri, Rama saw the Pampa. Filled with desire, Dasharatha's spirited son lamented. There were tilakas, citrus trees, banyan trees, white trees, blossoming *karaviras*,[393] flowering punnagas, *malatis*,[394] *kundas*,[395] creepers, *bhandiras*,[396] *nichulas*,[397] ashokas, *saptaparnas*,[398] ketakas and *atimuktakas*.[399] There were many other trees and it[400] looked like an ornamented woman.

The mountain, full of minerals, spoken about earlier, was near its banks. With blossoming and colourful groves, it was famous as the Rishyamuka. Riksharaja's son was the great-souled ape. That immensely valorous one ruled over the place and was famous as Sugriva. He[401] then addressed Lakshmana, with truth as his valour, in these words. 'O bull among men! Go to Sugriva, Indra among apes. We must go a long distance to accomplish the great task.' Looking at the forest, they progressively proceeded and saw the auspicious Pampa and saw those groves. There were flocks of many kinds of birds there.

This ends Aranya Kanda.

---

[393] Oleander.
[394] Jasmine.
[395] Another variety of jasmine.
[396] The amaranth or flea tree.
[397] The rattan plant.
[398] The Indian devil tree (*Alstonia scholaris*).
[399] The *harimantha* tree.
[400] The lake.
[401] Rama.

CHAPTER FOUR

Kishkindha Kanda

Chapter 4(1)

Rama went to the lake, full of lotuses, lilies and fish. His senses were overcome and with Soumitri, he started to lament. On seeing it, his senses were filled with delight and he started to tremble. Overcome by desire, he addressed Soumitri. 'O Soumitri! Behold. Pampa's[1] grove is auspicious to behold. The trees, with tops like mountains, are radiant. Grief is tormenting me and my senses are suffering because of Bharata's misery and Vaidehi's abduction. The blue-and-yellow grass seems to be even more radiant and it is strewn with flowers from many trees, like a carpet. O Soumitri! The breeze is pleasant and this is the time when Manmatha wanders around. This month is filled with fragrant scents and there are flowers and fruits on the trees. O Soumitri! The forests are laden with flowers. Behold their forms. A shower of flowers has been created, like rain during the monsoon season. There are many groves and trees on the beautiful plains. The force of the wind is making them wave and the flowers are showering down on the ground. The wind that blows is pleasant to the touch, like cool sandalwood. Bees are humming in the fragrant forests. There are lovely flowers on the beautiful slopes of the mountain. Large and radiant trees cling on to the summit of the mountain. In every direction, look at the karnikara trees, with flowers on their tops. They look like men attired in yellow

---

[1] Pampa has been identified as the area around Hampi (in Karnataka). This is at the confluence of the rivers Tunga and Bhadra (combining to form Tungabhadra) and there is also a lake there. Hence, Pampa is sometimes described as a lake and sometimes as a river.

garments, decorated with ornaments made out of molten gold. O
Soumitri! This is the spring, when many kinds of birds call. The
separation from Sita is igniting a sorrow in me. I am overcome
by sorrow and Manmatha is tormenting me more. The cuckoo is
calling happily and seems to be summoning me. O Lakshmana! This
datyuha[2] is calling out to me from this beautiful mountain waterfall.
O Lakshmana! I am already overcome by Manmatha and its call is
drying me up further. The male birds are freely moving around in
their unblemished flocks. O Soumitri! Delighted, the *bhringaraja*[3]
is calling out in a melodious tone. O Soumitri! Sorrow and worry
over that fawn-eyed one[4] are tormenting me, like a cruel forest
conflagration in the month of Chaitra.[5] Suffused by desire, on the
slopes of the mountains, peacocks are surrounded by peahens and
this is increasing my desire. O Lakshmana! Behold. On the slopes
of the mountains, afflicted by desire, peahens are dancing around
their husbands, the peacocks. It is evident that in the forest, no
rakshasa has abducted the peacock's beloved. Without her, living in
this month of flowers is extremely difficult for me. O Lakshmana!
Behold. At the end of the winter, the forests are rich with a burden
of flowers. However, these flowers are futile for me. Delighted,
the birds are calling out amidst their flocks. They are summoning
each other and this is making me mad with desire. It is certain that
Sita, under someone else's subjugation, will be grieving like me. My
beloved is young,[6] with eyes like the petals of lotuses and is gentle
in speech. The breeze bears the fragrance of flowers. Though it is as
cold as snow, it is pleasant to the touch. However, thinking of that
beautiful one, it seems to me to be like a fire. At that time,[7] this crow
perched on a tree and called happily. Though she is not here, the bird
is still cawing.[8] There, a bird[9] told us about Vaidehi's abductor. This

[2] The gallinule.
[3] Shrike or thrush.
[4] Sita.
[5] March–April.
[6] The text uses the word *shyama*. The natural meaning of this is dark. However,
shyama also means a woman who hasn't been married (or is a virgin).
[7] When she was with me.
[8] Signifying her return.
[9] Jatayu.

bird will lead us to the large-eyed one. O Lakshmana! Behold. In the forest, the birds are calling from the tops of the trees full of flowers, and this enhances desire. O Soumitri! Look at the colourful forests around the Pampa. Like rising suns, there are dazzling lotuses in the water. The sparkling waters have lotuses and blue water lilies. The Pampa, with red lotuses, is full of swans and ducks. At the end of the colourful forest, there are always chakravaka birds there. Herds of elephants and animals come there, desiring the radiant water. O Lakshmana! When I see the petals of lotus buds, I think that they are like Sita's eyes. The pleasant breeze, emanating from amidst the trees, carries pollen from the lotuses. But when it blows, it is like Sita's breath. O Soumitri! Look at the mountain peaks to the south of the Pampa. Full of flowers, the trunks of the karnikara trees are extremely beautiful. There is one that is like a king of mountains over the others. It is decorated with minerals. Driven by the force of the wind, a wonderful dust has been generated there. O Soumitri! Everywhere, the slope of that mountain is full of flowers. The beautiful kimshuka trees are making it blaze and the leaves are hidden behind flowers. There are fragrant flowers along the banks of the Pampa—malati, *mallika*, *shanda* and blossoming karaviras.[10] In the spring, there are blooming *ketaki*s and *sindhuvara*s.[11] Everywhere, there are *madhavi*s and kunda creepers, full of fragrances.[12] There are *chiribilva*s, madhukas, *vanjula*s, bakulas, champakas, tilakas and flowering *nagavriksha*s.[13] There are neepas, *varana*s, flowering *kharjura*s, *ankola*s, *kuranta*s, *churnaka*s and *paribhadraka*s.[14] There are chutas, patalas and flowering *kovidara*s.[15] *Muchukunda*s

[10] Malati is jasmine, mallika is another variety of jasmine, shanda is a group of plants and karavira is the oleander.

[11] Ketaki is the fragrant crew pine, sindhuvara is the five-leaved chaste tree.

[12] Madhavi is a spring flower, kunda is a kind of jasmine.

[13] Chiribilva is a bilva sapling, madhuka is the honey tree, vanjula is a tree that is similar to the ashoka, bakula is a tree with fragrant flowers, champaka is a tree with yellow and fragrant flowers, tilaka is a tree with beautiful flowers and nagavriksha is a flowering tree.

[14] Nipa is another name for the kadamba tree, varana is the garlic pear tree, kharjura is date, ankola cannot be identified, kuranta is the yellow amaranth, churnaka should probably be *purnaka* (a kind of tree) and paribhadraka is the flame tree.

[15] Chuta is mango, patala is the *Bignonia suaveolens* and kovidara is a kind of orchid.

and arjunas can be seen on the slope of the mountain.[16] There
are ketakas, *uddalaka*s, *shirisha*s, *shimshapa*s, dhavas, shalmalis,
kimshukas, *rakta*s, *kurubaka*s, tinishas, *naktamala*s, *chandana*s
and syandanas.[17] O Soumitri! Many diverse kinds of flowers are
spread out on the slopes of the mountain and they have made
the rocks yellow and red in complexion. O Soumitri! Behold.
At the end of the winter, the trees are blooming with flowers.
This is the month of flowers and the blossoming flowers seem to
be competing against each other. O Soumitri! Behold these cool
waters, filled with lotuses. Chakravakas are roaming around and
karandavas frequent the place.[18] Is if full of *plava*s and *krouncha*s
and the place is frequented by boars and deer.[19] Because of the
calling of the birds, the Pampa is even more beautiful. These many
kinds of delighted birds are igniting desire in me. I remember
the young one,[20] with a face like the moon and eyes like lotuses.
Behold. On the slope, there are female spotted deer with male
deer. And then, I have been separated from Vaidehi, the one with
eyes like a fawn.'

With senses afflicted by grief, he lamented there, on seeing the
sacred and beautiful Pampa, the bearer of auspicious waters. The
great-souled one quickly looked around all the forests, waterfalls
and caves. With Lakshmana, anxious in his mind and afflicted by
grief, he kept thinking and proceeded. Together, they advanced
towards Rishyamuka, inhabited by the ape Sugriva. On seeing
the two immensely energetic ones, Raghava and Lakshmana,
approaching, the apes were frightened.

[16] Muchukunda is the cork-leaved bayur tree and arjuna is a tall tree.

[17] Ketaka is a flowering plant (but this may be *kaitaka*, the fragrant crew pine),
uddalaka is probably any tree from which honey is gathered, shirisha is a variety of acacia
or mimosa, shimshapa is a tree usually associated with cremation grounds, dhava is axle-
wood, shalmali is the silk-cotton tree, kimshuka is a tree with red blossoms, rakta is either
the Indian globe thistle or the Indian madder, kurubaka is a kind of amaranth tree, tinisha
is the Indian rosewood, naktamala or (naktamalaka) is a tree that flowers in the night,
chandana is sandalwood and syandana is the *sandana* tree (chariots were made from this).

[18] Chakravaka is the ruddy goose or Brahmany duck and karandava is a type of duck.

[19] Plava is a diving aquatic bird, krouncha is a curlew.

[20] Shyama.

Chapter 4(2)

The two brave and great-souled brothers, Rama and Lakshmana, wielded the best of weapons. On seeing them, Sugriva was uncertain. Anxious in his heart, he looked at all the directions. The bull among apes was incapable of remaining in one fixed place. As he looked at those two extremely strong ones, he was incapable of steadying his mind. The ape was extremely frightened and his mind suffered. The one with dharma in his soul reflected and weighed his strengths and weaknesses. With all his companions, Sugriva was greatly anxious. Extremely anxious when he saw Rama and Lakshmana, Sugriva, the lord of the apes, spoke to his advisers. 'They have certainly been sent to this impenetrable forest by Vali. They are roaming around and coming here, disguising themselves in garments made of bark.' Having seen those two supreme archers, Sugriva, with his advisers, moved away from the summit of the mountain to another excellent peak. As the others in the herd swiftly left, the apes who were the leaders of the herds came and surrounded the best among the apes.[21] Leaping from one mountain to another mountain, they followed different paths and the force made the summits of the mountain tremble. All those extremely strong apes leapt around. In the process, they shattered the flowering trees in that impenetrable mountain. Everywhere on that giant mountain, the supreme apes jumped around. Deer, wildcats and tigers were frightened and fled. Then, all of Sugriva's advisers, best among apes, composed themselves. On that Indra among mountains, all of them joined their hands in salutation and surrounded him.

Sugriva was terrified and afraid, suspecting that Vali was going to cause injury. However, Hanumat, eloquent in the use of words, addressed him in these words. 'O bull among apes! You ran away, your senses anxious because of the cruel Vali. However, I do not see the cruel-looking one here. O amiable one! You are frightened of your evil-acting elder brother. However, the evil-souled

[21] Sugriva.

Vali isn't here and I do not perceive any fear. Alas! O ape! It is evident that you have acted like an ape. You have shown yourself to be fickle and are unable to control your thoughts. You possess intelligence and knowledge. Always act in accordance with the signs. A king who falls prey to lack to intelligence cannot command all the creatures.' Sugriva heard all the auspicious words that Hanumat had spoken. He replied to Hanumat in words that were even more auspicious. 'They are long-armed and large-eyed. They wield bows, arrows and swords. These two are like the sons of gods. On seeing them, who will not be frightened? I suspect that these two supreme men have been engaged by Vali. Kings have many friends.[22] In this case, trust cannot be pardoned. Men should be known as enemies, they are deceitful in conduct. They should not be trusted. Finding a weakness in those who trust, they strike. The intelligent Vali has undertaken many deeds and kings are extensive in their foresight. Even ordinary men know that they are the ones who slay the enemy. O ape! Go there, assuming an ordinary form.[23] Ascertain through their conduct, forms and speech whether our suspicions are true. If they are cheerful in their minds, find out their sentiments through signs. Repeatedly praise them and gain their trust. O bull among apes! When you ask them, stand with your face towards me.[24] Ask those two archers the reason why they have entered the forest. O ape! You will get to know if they are pure in soul, or whether they intend evil policies, from their forms and the conversation.' Marut's son[25] was thus instructed by the king of the apes. He made up his mind to go where Rama and Lakshmana were. He honoured the words of the unassailable, but extremely terrified, ape.[26] The greatly fortunate and immensely strong Hanumat went to where Rama and Lakshmana were.

[22] Meaning Vali.

[23] So that they do not recognize Hanumat.

[24] So that Sugriva can find out what is going on, from Hanumat's facial signs, despite Hanumat being a fair distance away.

[25] Hanumat. Hanumat was the son of Marut (the wind god).

[26] Sugriva.

Chapter 4(3)

Hanumat understood the words of the great-souled Sugriva.
From Mount Rishyamuka, he leapt to where the two
Raghavas were. Having gone there, the powerful Hanumat, for
whom truth was his valour, supreme among apes and eloquent in
the use of words, prepared to speak mildly. The ape abandoned
his own form and adopted that of a mendicant. He addressed
those two brave ones and praised them appropriately. 'You are
like royal sages, equal to the gods. You are ascetics, firm in your
vows. You are handsome in appearance. Why have you come
to this spot? You have frightened large numbers of animals and
others who roam around in the forest. You are looking at the
trees that grow everywhere, on the banks of the Pampa. O spirited
ones! You are making the auspicious waters of this river radiant.
You are patient and golden in complexion, but you are attired in
bark. Who are you? O brave ones! Your glances are like those
of lions. Your valour is more than that of lions. In your large
arms, you are wielding bows that are like those of Shakra. Your
forms are prosperous and handsome. Your valour is like that
of excellent bulls. O bulls among men! Your arms are like the
trunks of elephants. You are dazzling. This radiant Indra among
mountains has become resplendent because of you. You deserve
kingdoms meant for the best among gods. Why have you come
to this region? Your eyes are like lotus petals. You are brave.
However, you sport masses of matted hair. O brave ones! You are
like each other in appearance. Have you come here from the world
of the gods? O brave ones! Your chests are broad. You are gods
in the form of humans. As you wish, you have come to earth, like
the sun and the moon. Your shoulders are like those of lions. You
are great in spirit. You are like sacred bulls. Your arms are long
and well rounded, they are like clubs. They deserve to be adorned
in all kinds of ornaments. Why are you not ornamented? I think
that the two of you are capable of protecting the entire earth,
with all its oceans and forests and decorated with the Vindhya
and the Meru. These colourful and smooth bows are marked with

wonderful signs. They are decorated with diamonds and gold and
are as radiant as Indra's bow. These quivers, auspicious to see,
are filled with sharp arrows that are terrible and are as flaming
as serpents, bringing an end to lives. These radiant swords are
like snakes released from their skins. They are gigantic in size
and are decorated with molten gold. I have spoken to you in this
way. Why are you not replying? There is someone named Sugriva
and he is the leader of a band of apes. He possesses dharma in
his soul. The brave one has been banished by his brother and is
miserably roaming around in the world. Sent by the great-souled
Sugriva, the king of the best among apes, I have come here. I am
an ape named Hanumat. Sugriva, with dharma in his soul, wishes
to strike a friendship with the two of you. I should be known
as his adviser, the ape who is the son of the wind god. I can go
wherever I want and can assume any form I desire. To do what
brings pleasure to Sugriva, I have disguised myself as a mendicant
and have come here from Rishyamuka.' Hanumat told the brave
Rama and Lakshmana this. Accomplished in speech and skilled in
the use of words, he did not say anything after this.

Having heard his words, with a cheerful face, the handsome
Rama spoke to his brother Lakshmana, who was standing by his
side. 'This is an aide of the great-souled Sugriva, Indra among apes.
He is the one I desired to meet and this one has come here to me.
O Soumitri! You speak to the ape who is Sugriva's ambassador.[27]
O scorcher of enemies! You are eloquent in the use of words. Use
gentle words that are full of affection.'

Chapter 4(4)

When these words were uttered, Hanumat was delighted.
Having heard the sweet words, he thought that Sugriva's
intentions would become successful. 'It is possible that the great-

---

[27] Generally, kings did not speak to ambassadors directly.

souled Sugriva will get his kingdom back. That must be the reason why these two have come here, to do what needs to be done.'[28] Extremely delighted, Hanumat, supreme among apes and eloquent in the use of words, replied to Rama in these words. 'Why have you come to this terrible forest, with groves around the Pampa? With your younger brother, why you have come to this impenetrable region, full of many predatory beasts and animals?'

On hearing these words, Rama urged Lakshmana and he[29] told him about the great-souled Rama, Dasharatha's son. 'The king named Dasharatha was radiant and devoted to dharma. This is his eldest son, known among people by the name of Rama. He is the refuge of all creatures and is devoted to the instructions of his father. Among Dasharatha's sons, he is the eldest and supreme in qualities. He was dislodged from the kingdom and resides in the forest with me. I have come here with him. The immensely fortunate one's wife, Sita, is devoted to him and followed him. The immensely radiant one is like the sun, with a resplendence like that at the end of the day. I am his younger brother and my qualities are such that I am like a servant to this grateful and learned one. I am known by the name of Lakshmana. He deserves happiness and great prosperity. His mind is devoted to the welfare of all beings. However, deprived of his prosperity, he has now resorted to residing in the forest. He is separated from his wife, who has been abducted by a rakshasa who can assume any form at will. We do not know the rakshasa who has abducted his wife. Shri's son, named Danu, was cursed that he would become a rakshasa.[30] He told us that Sugriva, lord of the apes, would be capable of telling us this. "The immensely valiant one will know who abducted

---

[28] These are Hanumat's thoughts. There is a break in continuity. Lakshmana was supposed to speak to Hanumat. Those sections exist in non-Critical versions, but have been excised in the Critical Edition.

[29] Lakshmana.

[30] This means Kabandha. Kabandha was Diti's son, Danu and Diti being sisters. Both Danu and Diti were married to the sage Kashyapa. Diti's offspring were daityas and Danu's offspring were danavas. The interchange between Danu and Diti is understandable. But Kabandha/Danu cannot be Shri's son. Shri also means prosperity. What may originally have been meant is that Kabandha was cursed, thereby being deprived of prosperity.

your wife." Saying this, in a radiant form, Danu happily went
to heaven. I have truthfully told you everything that you asked
me about. Rama and I are therefore seeking refuge with Sugriva.
Earlier, he[31] donated riches and obtained unmatched fame. He
used to be the protector of the worlds, but desires that Sugriva
should be his protector. Rama is overcome by grief. Afflicted by
sorrow, he seeks a refuge. With all the other leaders of the herds,
Sugriva should show him his favours.' Shedding piteous tears,
Soumitri said this.

Hanumat, accomplished in the use of words, spoke these
words in reply. 'You are full of intelligence. You have conquered
anger. You have conquered your senses. It is good fortune that
you have come here to see the Indra among apes. He has also
been dislodged from his kingdom, because of Vali's enmity.
Severely deprived by his brother, and with his wife abducted, he
is in this forest, terrified. The son of the sun will help you. With
Sugriva, we will also help in finding out where Sita has gone.' In
gentle and sweet words, Hanumat said this and told Raghava,
'Let us go to Sugriva.' When Hanumat said this, Lakshmana,
with dharma in his soul, honoured him in the proper way and
told Raghava, 'This ape, the son of the wind god, has spoken
to us in a cheerful way. He has come here because something
needs to be done. Let us do that and also become successful.
The complexion of his face is happy and it is evident that he
is speaking cheerfully. The brave Hanumat, Marut's son, is not
uttering a falsehood.'

The extremely wise Hanumat, Marut's son, then grasped the
two brave Raghavas and took them to the king of the apes.[32] The
extremely famous and supreme ape was delighted that he had
accomplished his task. Great in his valour and auspicious in his
intelligence, he went to that supreme mountain with Rama and
Lakshmana.

---

[31] Rama.

[32] The Critical Edition has excised a shloka where Hanumat abandoned the form of
a mendicant, assumed the form of an ape and placed Rama and Lakshmana on his back.

Chapter 4(5)

From Rishyamuka, Hanumat went to Mount Malaya and told the king of the apes about the two brave Raghavas.[33] 'Rama, immensely wise and firm in his valour, has arrived, with his brother Lakshmana. For Rama, truth is his valour. Rama is Dasharatha's son and has been born in the lineage of the Ikshvakus. He is devoted to dharma and therefore acts in accordance with his father's instructions. That is the reason the great-souled one controls himself and resides in the forest. A rakshasa has abducted his wife and he has come here, seeking refuge with you. There was one[34] who performed royal and horse sacrifices and offered oblations into the fire, donating hundreds and thousands of cows as *dakshina*.[35] He performed austerities and was truthful in speech, ruling the world. Rama is his son. Because of a woman,[36] he now solicits refuge with you. The two brothers, Rama and Lakshmana, desire your friendship. You should receive them and honour them, because they deserve to be worshipped.'

Hearing Hanumat's words, Sugriva was delighted in his mind. He lost his anxiety and gave up his terrible fear of Raghava. Sugriva, the lord of the apes, adopted a human form. Assuming a form that could be seen, he cheerfully spoke to Raghava. 'You follow dharma and are humble. You are brave and are kind to everyone. Vayu's son has told me the truth about your qualities. O lord! It is a great gain for me that you desire to strike a friendship with an ape like me. You have shown me honour. If you desire my friendship, I am stretching out my hand. Accept my hand in your hand and let your bond of friendship be firm.' Hearing the excellent words spoken by Sugriva, he[37] was cheerful in his mind and accepted his hand in his

---

[33] Clearly, Rishyamuka and Malaya were two adjacent mountains. Hanumat seems to have left Rama and Lakshmana on Rishyamuka and gone to Malaya, where Sugriva was. In that event, Hanumat must have returned to Rishyamuka and taken Rama and Lakshmana to Malaya.

[34] Dasharatha.

[35] Sacrificial fee. These were donated symbolically.

[36] Kaikeyee.

[37] Rama.

own hand. Delighted at the friendship, he grasped him and embraced him. At this, Hanumat, the destroyer of enemies, abandoned his form of a mendicant. In his own form, he used wood to kindle a fire. When the fire was blazing properly, he worshipped it with flowers. Extremely happy and controlling himself, he placed it between the two of them.[38] The two of them circumambulated the blazing fire. Sugriva and Raghava thus had a pact of friendship. Both the ape and Raghava were extremely delighted in their minds. Though they kept glancing at each other, they were not content. Rama, Dasharatha's son, knew about everything. The energetic Sugriva addressed him in these words, telling him what was in his mind.

Chapter 4(6)

'O Rama! Hanumat, my adviser and supreme among ministers, has told me about the reason why you have come to this desolate forest, about why you are residing in this forest with your brother Lakshmana and about Maithilee, Janaka's daughter, being abducted by a rakshasa. Separated from you and the intelligent Lakshmana, she was weeping. Looking for an opportunity, he[39] slew the eagle Jatayu. Without waiting for a long period of time, you will be freed from the misery that has occurred on account of you being separated from your wife. I will bring her here, like the sacred texts of the Vedas when they were lost.[40] O scorcher of enemies! Whether your wife is in the nether regions or in a world in the firmament, I will fetch her and hand her over to you. O Raghava! Know that these words of mine are true. O mighty-armed one! Abandon your grief. I will bring your beloved back. I imagine I know about Maithilee. There is no doubt. I saw her when she was being abducted by the rakshasa of the cruel deeds. O Rama!

---

[38] Rama and Sugriva, the pledge of friendship was taken with the fire as a witness.

[39] Ravana. Sugriva is saying that Hanumat has told him all this.

[40] This is a reference to the Vedas having been stolen by the demons Madhu and Kaitabha and Vishnu saving them in his fish (*matsya*) incarnation.

She piteously shrieked, "Alas, Rama! Alas, Lakshmana!" She was writhing along Ravana's flank, like the wife of an Indra among serpents. While I was the fifth person stationed on the slope of the mountain, she saw me and cast aside her upper garment and her auspicious ornaments.[41] O Raghava! We collected them and kept them. I will bring them. You should try to identify them.'

Sugriva spoke these pleasant words and Rama told him, 'O friend! Bring them. Why are you delaying?' Thus addressed, wishing to do what would bring Raghava pleasure, Sugriva quickly entered that deep cave. The ape took the upper garment and the ornaments, showed them to Rama and said, 'Look at these.' When he accepted the garment and the auspicious ornaments, tears arose, like the moon being filled with mist. The tears were tainted[42] because of his affection for Sita. He wept, 'Alas, beloved!' Abandoning all patience, he fell down on the ground. Several times, he pressed those supreme ornaments against his breast. He sighed gravely, like an angry snake in its hole. A continuous torrent of tears was released and standing by his side, Soumitri looked on distressed. Like Rama, he too lamented. 'O Lakshmana! Behold. When Vaidehi was being abducted, she cast aside this upper garment and these ornaments from her body on to the ground. When Sita was being abducted, she must certainly have flung them on some grass on the ground. The forms of the ornaments can be seen to be exactly as they were. O Sugriva! Tell me. What did you notice? In which direction did the rakshasa, terrible in form, abduct the beloved whom I love more than my own life? Where does the rakshasa who caused this great hardship to me reside, as a result of whom I will destroy all the rakshasas? He has abducted Maithilee and has certainly generated a great rage in me. He has brought an end to his own life and has opened up the doors to death. My beloved was abducted from the forest by a roamer in the night who oppressed her. O lord of the apes! Who is the enemy whom I have to convey to Yama's presence today?'

[41] More explicitly, though there were four other apes there, Sugriva is the only one Sita saw.

[42] They weren't tears of joy.

Chapter 4(7)

Rama was afflicted. Thus addressed, the ape Sugriva joined his hands in salutation. With his face full of tears, and tears choking his voice, he said, 'I do not know the residence or anything else about that wicked rakshasa—his capacity, valour and the wickedness of his lineage. However, I tell you truthfully that I will find out. O scorcher of enemies! Cast aside your grief. I will make every effort so that you get Maithilee back. You will slay Ravana and his followers and satisfy your own manliness. I will act so that this happens quickly and you become happy. Enough of this despairing. Remember your own patience and resort to it. It is not appropriate for someone like you to have this fickleness in intelligence. Because my wife was abducted, I too face a great calamity. I did not sorrow in this way. Nor do I abandon patience. Though I am an ordinary ape, I did not grieve. A great-souled and learned person like you should resort to his great perseverance. You should use your patience to control the tears you are shedding. That is the pledge of those who are spirited and you should not abandon perseverance. A persevering person does not forget his own intelligence and does not despair in the midst of hardship, loss of fortune, fear or an end to life. A man who always resorts to lassitude is foolish. He is helplessly submerged in grief, like a burdened boat in the water. In affection, I am joining my hands in salutation and seeking your favours. Resort to your manliness. You should not be consumed by this internal grief. Those who are immersed in sorrow do not obtain happiness. Their energy diminishes. You should not grieve. I am saying this because I have your welfare in mind. I am not instructing you. Considering my friendship, you should not grieve.'

Raghava was comforted by Sugriva in this gentle way. His face was overflowing with tears and he wiped it with the end of his garment. Having regained his normal state, the lord Kakutstha addressed Sugriva in these words. 'This is what a friend should do, gently and with one's welfare in mind. O Sugriva! You have done what is appropriate. O friend! Entreated by you, I have regained my normal state. Such a friend is extremely rare, especially at a time like this. You must make efforts to find out where that terrible and evil-souled rakshasa, Ravana, has taken Maithilee. It is proper that I believe you will succeed in this, like seeds sown in a well-prepared field during the monsoon. I have not spoken these words out of excessive confidence. O tiger among apes! They should be taken as my belief in your being able to do this. I have never uttered a falsehood earlier, nor will I ever do it. I know this to be the truth and I am taking a pledge on it.' At this, Sugriva, with the apes who were his advisers, was delighted, especially on having heard Raghava's words and his pledge. The lord of the apes and the immensely fortunate and intelligent lord of men heard each other's words. The foremost among the brave apes thought that his objective would be accomplished.

Chapter 4(8)

The ape Sugriva was satisfied at these words. He spoke these words to Rama, Lakshmana's elder brother. 'You possess all the qualities and you have become my friend. Therefore, there is no doubt that the gods have also shown me their favours in every possible way. O Rama! O unblemished one! O lord! With your help, I am capable of obtaining the kingdom of the gods, not to speak of regaining my own kingdom. With the fire as a witness, I have obtained a friend from the lineage of Raghava! O Raghava! You have become my revered friend and well-wisher. You will slowly get to know that I am a deserving friend. I am incapable of telling you about my own qualities. O supreme among those who have controlled their souls! The affection and patience of great-souled ones like you are steadfast, particularly when they have taken a pledge. When virtuous people meet other virtuous ones, gold, silver and sparkling ornaments do not have to be shared between them. Whether one is rich or poor, happy or unhappy, guilty or innocent, a friend is the supreme recourse. Even if riches have to be given up, even if happiness has to be discarded, even if life has to be given up,

friendship born out of affection is seen to continue in the same way.'
Sugriva was pleasant in appearance. The prosperous Lakshmana, as
intelligent as Vasava, was in front. Rama agreed that it was indeed
this way.

Sugriva saw that Rama was stationed there, with the immensely
strong Lakshmana. He quickly cast his glance around everywhere
in the forest. Not very far away, the lord of the apes saw a sala tree.
It was covered with many flowers and leaves and ornamented with
bees. Sugriva broke down a branch of that sala tree, filled with
many flowers and leaves, and spread it out. He and Raghava seated
themselves on it. On seeing that they were seated, Hanumat also
broke a branch from the sala tree and Lakshmana humbly seated
himself on it. Sugriva was delighted. In soft and auspicious words
that were filled with affection, in syllables that were filled with joy,
he addressed Rama in these words. 'I have been banished by my
brother and am roaming around here, on Rishyamuka, best among
mountains, afflicted by fear. I am extremely miserable, because my
wife has been seized. I am terrified and shattered by fear. Bereft of
my senses, I reside in this forest. O Raghava! Because of enmity, my
brother Vali has exiled me in this way. O one who grants all the
worlds freedom from fear! Because of Vali, I am afflicted by fear.
You should show your favours to someone like me, who is without
a protector.'

Kakutstha was energetic and knowledgeable about dharma. He
was devoted to dharma. Thus addressed, he seemed to laugh when he
replied. 'Doing a good deed is the sign of a friend. Doing a bad deed
is the sign of an enemy. I will slay the one who abducted your wife
today. These extremely forceful arrows are fierce in their energy.
They have been crafted with reeds from Kartikeya's forest and are
embellished with gold.[43] The shafts have feathers from herons and
they are like the great Indra's vajra. The joints are well constructed
and they are extremely sharp. They are like angry serpents. Behold.
Any enemy like your brother, named Vali, who has sinned, will be
slain by these arrows and shattered like a mountain.'

[43] Kartikeya was born in a clump of reeds.

Sugriva was the leader of armies. Hearing Raghava's words, he was extremely happy and uttered words of praise. 'O Rama! I am overwhelmed by grief. For those who are afflicted, you are the refuge. Since we have a pact of friendship, I will tell you about my lamentations. With the fire as a witness, you have extended your hand and have become my friend. I have taken a pledge of truth and you are more dear to me than my own life.[44] Since you are my friend, I can trust you and tell you about the misery that constantly consumes the inner recesses of my heart.' As he spoke these words, his eyes were full of tears. His voice choked with tears and he was incapable of saying anything. The flood of tears was like the turbulent force of a river. In Rama's presence, Sugriva resorted to his patience and controlled himself. He controlled his tears and wiped his auspicious eyes. The energetic one sighed and again addressed Raghava. 'O Rama! On an earlier occasion, Vali forcibly evicted me from my own kingdom. He was stronger and made me listen to harsh words when he exiled me. He abducted my wife, who was dearer to me than my own life.[45] Those who were my well-wishers were tied up in bondage. O Raghava! The extremely evil-souled one made efforts to destroy me. I have slain many apes who were thus engaged by him. O Raghava! I suspected this when I saw you too. Since I was scared, I did not come near you. A frightened person sees fear everywhere. My only recourse is foremost aides like Hanumat. Despite confronting a hardship, I am sustaining my life because of them. These gentle apes protect me from every direction. They go everywhere with me. They stay where I stay. O Rama! I have briefly told you this. What is the need to narrate it in detail? My elder brother is my enemy and Vali is famous for his manliness. My misery will end when he is destroyed. After his death and destruction, I will live happily for whatever is left of my life. O Rama! Afflicted by grief, I have told you how my misery can come to an end. Whether in happiness or in misery, a friend is always a friend's refuge.'

[44] The text has life in the plural, lives.
[45] Lives again.

Hearing what Sugriva had said, Rama addressed him in these words. 'I wish to hear the truth about what caused this enmity. O ape! On knowing about the reason for the enmity, I will be able to weigh the strengths and the weaknesses and easily ascertain how the necessary course of action can be undertaken. On hearing that you have been shown disrespect, my intolerance has become stronger. The trembling of my heart has increased, like the force of water during the rainy season. Be happy and trust me when I say that before I have strung my arrow, before I have released my arrow, your enemy has been restrained.' Sugriva was thus addressed by the great-souled Kakutstha. With the four other apes, he obtained unmatched joy. With a cheerful face, Sugriva started to tell Lakshmana's elder brother the truth about the reason for the enmity.

Chapter 4(9)

'O slayer of enemies! My elder brother, named Vali, was always greatly loved by our father, and initially, I loved him too. After our father died, the ministers showed a great deal of respect to the eldest and instated him in the kingdom, as the lord of the apes. He ruled over the great kingdom of our fathers and grandfathers and all the time, I stationed myself and bowed before him, like a servant. There was a spirited one named Mayavi and he was Dundubhi's elder brother and son.[46] On an earlier occasion, due to a woman, there was a great enmity between him and Vali.[47] When people were sleeping in the night, he appeared at the gates of Kishkindha. He roared loudly and challenged Vali to a duel. My brother was asleep. However, when he heard that terrible roar, he could not tolerate it. He quickly emerged. I and the women prostrated ourselves and

[46] He couldn't have been both, but this is what the text says. Mayavi was Maya's son and Maya and Rambha had sons named Mayavi, Dundubhi and Mahisha. Mandodari was their sister.

[47] The reason for this enmity is not clear and is not mentioned in any other text either.

tried to restrain him. However, because of his rage, he emerged to kill that supreme asura. The immensely strong one ignored all of us and emerged. Because I wished him well, I also emerged with Vali. From a distance, on seeing me and my brother stationed there, fear was generated in the asura and he quickly ran away. When he fled in fear, we also swiftly followed him, along a path that was lit up by the beams of the rising moon. The asura quickly entered a great and impenetrable hole in the ground, covered by grass. We reached and stood there. On seeing that the enemy had entered the hole, with his senses agitated and overcome by rage, Vali addressed me in these words. "O Sugriva! Steady yourself and stay here now, at the entrance to the hole, until I enter and slay the enemy in an encounter." O scorcher of enemies! In those words, he sought this from me. He made me take a pledge on his feet and entered the hole. After he had entered that hole, more than a year passed. During all that time, I stood at the entrance. I did not see my brother and was worried that something evil might have befallen him. Because of my affection, I was concerned that he might have been killed. After a long period of time, I saw red blood mixed with foam emerge from the hole and was extremely miserable. The sound of the roaring asura entered my ears. However, there were no sounds of my senior shouting as he engaged in the encounter. From the signs, I came to the conclusion that my brother had been killed. I covered the entrance to the hole with a boulder that was as large as a mountain. O friend! In distress, I performed the water rites and returned to Kishkindha. Though I tried to hide the truth, the ministers made efforts and learnt what had occurred. I was summoned by the assembly and consecrated. O Raghava! While I duly ruled over the kingdom, Vali returned, having slain that supreme asura. On seeing that I had been consecrated, his eyes turned red with rage. He bound up all my ministers and spoke harsh words. O Raghava! Though I was capable of restraining that wicked one, I did not feel inclined to do that, on account of respect towards my brother. I honoured the great-souled one and greeted him, as was proper. However, his inner thoughts were not satisfied and he did not pronounce benedictions.'

Chapter 4(10)

'He was suffused with anger and intolerance. Desiring his pleasure, I approached him and sought to placate him. "It is good fortune that you are well and that you have slain your enemy and have returned. O one who delights those who don't have a protector! I am without a protector and you alone are my protector. This umbrella has many ribs and is like a moon that has arisen. It also has whisks made out of hair. Let me hold this above your head. You are the king and deserve honours. I will remain as I used to be earlier. This kingdom was with me in trust and am returning it to you. O amiable one! O slayer of enemies! Do not be angry with me. O king! With my head bowed and my hands joined in salutation, I am beseeching you. Desiring to ensure that the kingdom wasn't empty, the ministers and the residents of the city assembled together and forcibly thrust the task of being a king on me." Though I spoke gently, the ape censured me. He repeatedly told me, "Shame! Shame!" He summoned the respected ministers and ordinary people and in their midst, abused me and my well-wishers in words full of great condemnation. "You know that earlier, in the night, the great asura, Mayavi, wished to fight. The cruel and extremely evil-minded one challenged me. Hearing his words, I emerged from the royal residence. This extremely terrible brother of mine quickly followed me. On seeing a second extremely strong one next to me, he fled in fear. Seeing that we were following, he speedily ran away and entered a great hole. Knowing that he had entered that extremely terrible and extremely large hole, I told this cruel-looking brother of mine, 'Without killing him, I am incapable of leaving this place and returning to the city. Until I have slain him, wait for me at the entrance to the hole.' Thinking that he would be stationed there, I entered that extremely impenetrable place.. While I searched for him,[48] a year passed. Eventually, I found that fearful enemy and without any effort, killed the asura and all his relatives. As he lay down on the ground and shrieked, torrents of blood completely filled

---

[48] Mayavi.

the hole and it was impossible to pass. After having slain the valiant
enemy, Dundubhi's son, I could not find a way of emerging from the
hole, since the mouth was covered. I repeatedly shouted, 'Sugriva!
Sugriva!' However, there was no reply and I was extremely sad. With
several kicks from my feet, I shattered it.[49] Emerging, I have returned
again. This cruel Sugriva forgot all affection for his brother. Seeking
a way to obtain the kingdom for himself, he confined me there."
Having said this, the ape Vali, forgetting all virtue, banished me in
a single garment. O Raghava! Having cast me away, he seized my
wife. Out of fear for him, I am roaming around this entire earth,
with its forests and oceans. Miserable because my wife has been
abducted, I have entered Rishyamuka, supreme among mountains.
Because of a different reason, Vali cannot penetrate it.[50] I have told
you everything about the great reason for the enmity. O Raghava!
Behold the hardship I face, despite being innocent. O one who dispels
the fear of all the worlds! O brave one! You should show me your
favours and save me from fear of Vali, by restraining him.'

The energetic one, knowledgeable about dharma and full of
dharma, was thus addressed. As if laughing, he started to address
Sugriva in these words. 'These arrows of mine are sharp. They are
invincible and are like the sun. Imbibed with my rage, they will
bring down Vali, the one who is wicked in conduct. The evil-souled
Vali, wicked in conduct and the abductor of your wife, remains
alive only until I cast my eyes on him. I can myself see the ocean
of grief you are immersed in. I will save you and you will obtain
everything that you desire.'

Chapter 4(11)

Rama's words were designed to increase delight and manliness.
Hearing them, Sugriva praised Raghava and worshipped him.

---

[49] The boulder.
[50] The reason will be told later.

'There is no doubt that when you are angry, your sharp, blazing and straight-flying arrows can consume the worlds, like the sun at the end of a yuga. Single-mindedly, hear from me about Vali's manliness, valour and perseverance, so that you can decide on what should be done next. When the sun rises, without any effort, Vali strides from the western ocean to the eastern and from the southern to the northern to offer oblations of water.[51] He climbs the summits of mountains and the greatest of peaks. The valiant one uproots them, tosses them up and catches them again.[52] To demonstrate his strength, Vali quickly shatters many sturdy trees in diverse forests. There was a buffalo named Dundubhi and his complexion was like the summit of Kailasa.[53] The valiant one bore the strength of one thousand elephants. The evil-souled one was excited because of his valour and confused because he had obtained a boon. The extremely gigantic one went to the ocean, the lord of the rivers. He sighted the ocean, full of waves and the store of jewels. He told the great ocean, "Fight with me." With dharma in his soul, the extremely strong ocean arose. O king! He addressed the asura, who had been goaded by his destiny, in these words. "O one who is accomplished in fighting! I am not capable of fighting with you. But listen. I will tell you about the one who can fight with you. In the great forest, there is a king of the mountains and he is the supreme refuge for ascetics. He is Shankara's father-in-law[54] and he is famous by the name Himalayas. He is decorated with many caves and waterfalls. There are caverns and streams. He is capable of granting you unmatched delight in a battle." The supreme among asuras realized that the ocean was frightened. Like an arrow released from a bow, he went to the forests around the Himalayas. On the white mountain there, there were large boulders that were like gigantic elephants. Dundubhi hurled many of these on the ground

---

[51] The average person offers oblations to the rising sun at the nearest waterbody.

[52] Like playing with a ball.

[53] Dundubhi assumed the form of a buffalo. *Mahisha* means buffalo. This can also be interpreted as Dundubhi having assumed the form of the demon Mahisha. But we have already explained that Mahisha and Dundubhi were brothers and therefore, distinct.

[54] Parvati was the daughter of the Himalayas.

and roared loudly. Himalayas had the form of a white cloud and was pleasant and agreeable in appearance. Stationed on his summit, he spoke these words. "O Dundubhi! O one devoted to dharma! You should not cause a difficulty for me. I am unskilled in the task of fighting. I am a refuge for ascetics." On hearing the words of the intelligent king of the mountains, Dundubhi's eyes turned red with rage and he spoke these words. "Whether you are unskilled in fighting or whether you are disinterested because of your fear of me, tell me about the person who can grant me a good fight in an encounter." Himalayas, accomplished in the use of words, heard this. With dharma in his soul, he had never uttered words of rage. However, he now did this and told the supreme among asuras, "There is an immensely wise one named Vali and he is like Shakra in his valour. The prosperous ape is in Kishkindha, matchless and infinite in splendour. He is immensely wise and skilled in fighting. He is capable of granting you a duel, like Namuchi did to Vasava.[55] If you desire an encounter, quickly go to him. He is always brave in all deeds in an encounter and cannot be assailed." Hearing what the Himalayas said, Dundubhi was filled with anger. He went to Vali, in the city of Kishkindha. He assumed the fearful form of a buffalo with sharp horns. He was like a giant cloud in the sky, filled with water during the rainy season. The immensely strong one arrived at Kishkindha's gate and roared like a war drum, making the earth tremble.[56] He uprooted trees that were nearby and shattered the ground with his hooves. Like an elephant, he insolently used his horns to gouge the gate. Vali had gone to his inner quarters. Hearing the sound, he became intolerant. He emerged with the women, like the moon with the stars. Vali was the lord of the apes and all those who roam around in the forest. He briefly spoke to Dundubhi, with limited syllables and sentences.[57] "Why are you roaring in this way in front of a city gate that has been barred? O Dundubhi! O immensely strong one! I know of you. Therefore, save your life."

[55] Indra killed a demon named Namuchi.

[56] There is a pun, *dundubhi* means war drum.

[57] Loosely, *akshara* is syllable and *pada* is sentence. He used these sparingly and therefore, spoke briefly.

Hearing the words of the intelligent Indra among apes, Dundubhi's eyes turned red with rage and he spoke these words. "O brave one! Since you are in the presence of women, you should not speak words like these. Grant me a battle today, so that I can get to know your strength. Or let me restrain my rage until this night is over. O ape! Accept the time till dawn to indulge in gratifying your desires with sensual objects. If one kills a person who is mad, intoxicated, sleeping, without weapons or suffering, in this world, one becomes guilty of foeticide. You are now intoxicated and confused in that way." Only slightly angered, he[58] laughed and let all the women, Tara[59] and the others, go. He told the supreme among asuras, "If you are not scared of a clash, do not take me to be intoxicated. Take this intoxication to be an indication of my capacity to drink like a hero before a skirmish." Having said this, he angrily cast aside the golden garland, given to him by his father, the great Indra. He readied himself for battle. Dundubhi was like a mountain and he seized him by the horns. Vali roared loudly as he whirled him around and flung him down. Dundubhi was crushed in a battle that robbed him of his life. When he fell down, blood began to ooze out of his ears. Having lost his life, the one who was gigantic in form fell down on the ground. He was unconscious and lost his life. Using his arms, Vali raised up the dead body and powerfully hurled it one yojana away.[60] Hurled with force, some drops of blood oozed out from the mouth and, borne by the wind, descended on Matanga's hermitage. On seeing the drops of blood fall down, the sage inflicted a great curse on Vali, the one who had done the hurling. "If he enters this place, he will die as soon as he enters." He[61] approached the maharshi, joined his hands in salutation and beseeched him. O lord of men! Scared and terrified of the curse, the ape does not wish to enter the giant mountain of Rishyamuka, or even look at it. O Rama! Knowing that he was incapable of entering

---

[58] Vali.

[59] Tara was Vali's wife.

[60] There are interpretations that a yojana in this context means the length of one hundred bows, that is, 600 feet.

[61] Vali.

this great forest, I gave up my distress and roam around here, with my advisers. A giant mass of bones can be seen, like the radiant summit of a mountain. These belong to Dundubhi, hurled by the valiant one.[62] These are seven large sala trees, laden with branches. Using his energy, one by one, Vali is capable of rendering them leafless.[63] O Rama! I have thus recounted to you his valour. O king! How will you be able to slay Vali in a battle? O mighty-armed one! If you can pierce these sala trees with a single arrow, I will know that you are capable of slaying Vali.'

Hearing the words of the great-souled Sugriva, Raghava playfully raised Dundubhi's skeleton with his big toe. Raising it, the mighty-armed one flung it ten yojanas away. Seeing that the skeleton had been flung away, with Lakshmana standing in front, Sugriva again spoke words that were full of import. 'O friend! When he had hurled the body away earlier, it was wet,[64] full of flesh and fresh. O Raghava! Without flesh, it is light now, in a state like that of grass. I am not yet capable of knowing whether your strength is superior to his.'

Chapter 4(12)

Hearing the words spoken by Sugriva, to instil confidence in him, the immensely energetic Rama picked up his bow. The one who bestows honours seized his bow and a terrible arrow. He shot it in the direction of the sala trees and the twang of the bowstring made the directions reverberate. The arrow, polished with gold, was released powerfully. It penetrated the seven sala trees, the slope of the mountain and then entered the ground. In an instant, the extremely swift arrow penetrated the nether regions, quickly emerged again and returned to its own quiver. On seeing that it had pierced through the seven sala trees, the bull among

---

[62] Vali.

[63] He shook the trees and rendered them leafless.

[64] With blood.

apes was supremely astounded at the force of Rama's arrow. With his ornaments dangling, he lowered his head down on the ground. Sugriva was extremely delighted and joined his hands in salutation before Raghava. Rejoicing, he spoke these words to Rama, who knew about dharma, was learned in all the weapons and was the best among brave ones, standing right in front of him. 'O bull among men! O lord! Using your arrows, in a battle, you are capable of slaying all the gods, with Indra, not to speak of Vali. O Kakutstha! You are the one who has shattered the seven giant sala trees, the mountain and the earth with a single arrow. Who is capable of standing before you in a battle? My sorrow has been dispelled now and I am filled with great joy. I have gained a well-wisher who is the great Indra and Varuna's equal. O Kakutstha! I am joining my hands in supplication. I have an enemy in the form of a brother. To bring pleasure to me today, please kill Vali.'

At this, Rama embraced Sugriva, who was pleasant in appearance. The immensely wise one replied in words that had Lakshmana's approval. 'With you in front, let us quickly go to Kishkindha. O Sugriva! Having gone there, challenge Vali, who is a brother only in name.' All of them swiftly went to Kishkindha, Vali's city. They remained in the dense forest and hid themselves behind the trees. Sugriva girded his loins and roared terribly, challenging Vali. The force of his roar seemed to shatter the sky. Hearing his brother's roar, the immensely strong Vali was enraged. He angrily emerged, like a sun that was about to set.[65]

There was a tumultuous clash between Vali and Sugriva. It was like an encounter in the sky between two terrible planets, Mercury and Mars. Senseless with anger, the two brothers struck each other in the encounter, using palms and fists that were like the vajra. With a bow in his hand, Rama looked at both of them. Both the brave ones were like the gods, the two Ashvins, and were exactly like each other in appearance.[66] Until Raghava could distinguish Sugriva from Vali, he could not make up his mind to release an arrow that would

---

[65] Alternatively, like a sun emerging from behind clouds.
[66] The Ashvins are twins.

bring an end to life. Meanwhile, Sugriva could not see his protector, Raghava. He was crushed by Vali and fled to Rishyamuka. He was exhausted. His limbs were smeared with blood. He was suffering from the force of the blows. Chased by an angry Vali, he entered the great forest. Vali was terrified of the curse. Therefore, on seeing him enter the forest, the immensely strong one retreated, saying, 'You have been saved.'

Raghava and his brother, with Hanumat, went to the forest, where the ape Sugriva was. On seeing Rama arrive, with Lakshmana, Sugriva was ashamed and distressed. He looked towards the ground and said, 'You showed me your valour and asked me to challenge him. What is it that you have done? I have been devastated by the enemy. O Raghava! At that time, you should have told me the truth, that you would not kill Vali. In that case, I wouldn't have come here.' This is what the great-souled Sugriva said, distressed and in a pitiable state. Raghava again addressed him in these words. 'O Sugriva! O son![67] Listen. Do not yield to anger. There is a reason why I could not release this arrow. O Sugriva! You and Vali were identical to each other in ornaments, garments, size and movements. O ape! I could not find any evident difference in voice, radiance, sight, valour or words. O supreme among apes! I was confused at the similarity of your appearances and could not release this immensely forceful arrow that slays enemies. As soon as I am able to identify Vali in an encounter, I will restrain him with a single arrow and he will writhe on the ground. O lord of the apes! Think of a sign to identify yourself, so that I can recognize you when you are fighting in the duel. O Lakshmana! Uproot this blossoming *gajapushpi* creeper. O Lakshmana! Hang it around the great-souled Sugriva's neck. O Lakshmana! The gajapushpi creeper has flowers and is growing on the slope of the mountain. Uproot it and hang it around his neck.' With that beautiful creeper around his neck, he was radiant. He looked like a rain cloud, garlanded with cranes. His form was resplendent. Assured by Rama's words, he again went to Kishkindha, ruled by Vali, with Rama.

[67] The word used is tata.

Chapter 4(13)

With Sugriva, Lakshmana's elder brother, with dharma in his soul, went to Kishkindha, ruled valiantly by Vali. Rama wielded a giant bow decorated with gold. He grasped arrows that were like the sun, which ensured success in a battle. Ahead of the great-souled Raghava, there were the firm-necked Sugriva and immensely strong Lakshmana. Behind them were the brave Hanumat, Nala, the valiant Nila and the immensely energetic Tara[68]—the leaders of herds of apes. They glanced at the trees that were bending down because of the burden of flowers and at rivers full of sparkling water, heading towards the ocean. There were caverns, waterfalls and caves in the mountains, the best of summits and valleys that were pleasant to see. There was water that sparkled like lapis lazuli, filled with lotuses, with leaves, buds and stamens. Along the road, they saw beautiful lakes. There were karandavas, herons, swans, vanjulakas, waterfowl, chakravakas and other kinds of birds that were calling. Without any fear from those who roamed around in the forest, they fed on the soft grass and sprouts. Everywhere, they saw deer grazing or standing on the ground. There were terrible wild elephants roaming around alone.[69] Decorated with white tusks, they were the enemies of the lakes, because they destroyed the banks. There were many others wandering around in the forest and birds flying in the sky. As they looked at these, they swiftly advanced, following Sugriva's lead.

While they were quickly proceeding, the descendant of the Raghu lineage saw a grove with a clump of trees. Rama told Sugriva, 'This clump of trees looks like a cloud in the sky. Indeed, it is like a large mass of clouds in the sky and is circled by plantain trees on the outside. O friend! What is this? My curiosity is great and I wish to know about this. I wish that you should act so as to satisfy my curiosity.' As they advanced, Sugriva heard the great-

---

[68] Not to be confused with Taaraa, Vali's wife. This is Taara, one of the four apes who were with Sugriva.

[69] Solitary male tuskers.

souled Raghava's words. Sugriva told him about the great forest.
'O Raghava! This extensive hermitage removes all exhaustion.
There are gardens and groves, filled with succulent roots and
fruits and tasty water. There were sages named *saptajana*s and
they were rigid in their vows. There were seven of them.[70] They
controlled themselves, with their heads downwards, or lay down
in the water. Residing in the forest, they survived only on air,
having that only once in seven nights. After one hundred years had
passed, those seven went to heaven in their own physical bodies.
It is because of their powers that there is a wall of trees all around
this place. This hermitage cannot be assailed, even by Indra, the
gods and the asuras. The birds avoid this place and so do the
others who roam around in the forest. In their confusion, if they
enter, they do not return again. The sounds of ornaments can be
heard from there, with rhythm and syllables. O Raghava! There
are the sounds of singing and the playing of musical instruments.
There is a divine fragrance too. The three fires are lit there and
the smoke can be seen.[71] It circles up around the tops of the trees,
thick and red, like the body of a pigeon. O Raghava! Bow down
towards them, with dharma in their souls. With your brother,
Lakshmana, control yourself and join your hands in salutation.
O Rama! If people bow down to the rishis who had cleansed their
souls, nothing inauspicious is ever seen to occur in their bodies.'
At this, with his brother, Lakshmana, Rama joined his hands in
salutation in the direction of the great-souled rishis and honoured
them. With dharma in his soul, having honoured them, with
his brother Lakshmana, Rama proceeded with the ape Sugriva,
cheerful in his mind. They proceeded a long distance from the
hermitage of the saptajanas and saw the unassailable Kishkindha,
ruled over by Vali.

[70] Saptajana means seven (*sapta*) people (*jana*). They are also known as *punyajanas*
and were originally rakshasas.

[71] The three sacrificial fires are *ahavaniya*, *garhapatya* and *dakshinatya* (the fire that
burns in a southern direction). Garhapatya is the fire that burns in households. Ahavaniya
has various meanings, the simplest being the monthly sacrificial rites offered to the
ancestors on the day of the new moon.

Chapter 4(14)

All of them quickly hurried and reached Kishkindha, ruled over by Vali. They remained in the dense forest, hiding themselves behind the trees. The large-necked Sugriva loved forests. He cast his glance around everywhere in the forest and was filled with great rage. He roared loudly, issuing a challenge for a duel. Surrounded by his friends, he roared like a cloud. He was like a rising sun and his proud stride was like that of a lion. On seeing Rama, who was accomplished in his tasks, Sugriva addressed him in these words. 'We have reached Kishkindha, Vali's city. The gates are made out of molten gold and the firm flags are rising up. This extensive place is inhabited by many apes. O brave one! Fulfil the pledge you made earlier about killing Vali. Quickly make it successful, like a creeper whose time has come.'[72]

Raghava, with dharma in his soul, was thus addressed by Sugriva. The slayer of enemies replied to Sugriva in these words. 'This gajapushpi is now a sign that you can be identified with. The sun in the sky and the garland of nakshatras are seen to traverse in a contrary direction.[73] O ape! Do not be scared. Vali and the enmity will be uprooted today. I will free you with a single arrow that is released in the course of the encounter. O Sugriva! Show me the enemy who is in the form of a brother. Vali will be slain and will writhe around in the dust of the forest. If he returns with his life even after he has come into my line of vision, I will be guilty of a crime and you can then censure me. You have seen how I shattered seven sala trees with an arrow. Know that with that strength, Vali will be killed by me today. O brave one! Even though I have faced hardship, I have never uttered a falsehood earlier. Nor will I ever utter it. I am tied down by my love for dharma. Conquer your fear.

---

[72] The image of a creeper requires explanation. A growing creeper needs a tree for support. Sugriva is being compared to a creeper and Rama to a tree that offers support.

[73] This has been subjected to many interpretations, the obvious one being an evil portent for Vali. Alternatively, Sugriva is being compared to the sun. But the sun is not surrounded by nakshatras during the day. Thus, this means no more than an extraordinary combination of events.

I will make the pledge come true, the way Shatakratu uses showers for budding seedlings in a field. Therefore, summon Vali, the wearer of the golden garland. O Sugriva! Make a sound so that the ape emerges. He desires victory. He prides himself on his victories. He has never suffered at your hands. Since he loves fighting, Vali will emerge alone. When he hears brave enemies challenge him to an encounter, he cannot tolerate it, especially in the presence of women. He knows about his own valour.'

Sugriva was golden and tawny in complexion. Hearing Rama's words, he roared loudly and cruelly, as if he was shattering the sky. The cows were frightened at this sound and lost their radiance. The noble ladies were anxious, as if they were suffering from the sins of a king. Like horses routed in a war, the deer quickly fled. The birds fell down on the ground, like planets that had exhausted their merits. Surya's son[74] thus enhanced his valour and his energy, roaring like the thunder of a mass of clouds. He quickly emitted the roar he was known for. He was like the lord of the rivers, when a wind makes the waves turbulent.

Chapter 4(15)

The intolerant Vali was in his inner quarters and heard the roar of his brother, the great-souled Sugriva. He heard the roar that made all the creatures tremble. On hearing this, in an instant, his intoxication was disturbed, because a great rage intruded on it. With rage all over his limbs, Vali assumed the hue of the evening, when the sun has just lost its radiance and is tinged with red. Vali gnashed his teeth and because of his rage, his complexion assumed that of the fire. He looked like a lake where red lotuses had been uprooted, together with their stalks. Hearing that intolerable sound, the ape leapt up and the force of his steps seemed to shatter the earth.

[74] Sugriva.

Tara, the well-wisher, showed her affection by embracing him.
Terrified and scared, she uttered words that were for his benefit. 'O
brave one! At a time when you have just woken up, it is best to cast
aside this anger, like a garland that has been enjoyed. It has arrived
like a flood in a river. I do not like this idea of your emerging
suddenly. You should hear the reason why I am asking you to
restrain yourself. Earlier, he descended in rage and challenged you
to a duel. Though he descended, he was contained and crushed,
and fled in various directions. He was contained and especially
crushed by you. Since he has come here and is challenging you
again, a suspicion has been generated in my mind. There cannot
be a minor reason behind his insolence, conduct, this kind of
roaring and the rage in the roaring. I do not think that Sugriva
has come to you without any help. There must be a foundation of
help and he is roaring on the basis of that. That ape is naturally
skilled and intelligent. He does not enter into a friendship without
testing the other person's valour. O brave one! I have earlier heard
the account spoken about by Prince Angada. I will tell you about
those beneficial words. Rama is one who crushes the armies of
others and he has arisen, like the fire of destruction at the end of a
yuga. The famous one is harsh in fighting and he has become your
brother's aide. He is the supreme refuge for the distressed and is
like a tree virtuous ones seek out for a residence under. He is the
refuge for the afflicted and is the only abode for fame. He possesses
knowledge and learning and is engaged in following his father's
commands. He is the great store of all qualities, and like an Indra
among mountains possessing minerals. There should be peace, not
dissension, with that great-souled one. In deeds connected with
war, he is immeasurable and is impossible to vanquish. O brave
one! I am telling you a little bit about this, because I do not wish
you to be malicious. I have told you what is beneficial. You should
act in accordance with what you have heard. It is best to quickly
instate Sugriva as the heir apparent. O brave one! O king! Why
should one unnecessarily have a conflict with a younger brother?
I think that peace and fraternal relations with Rama and great
affection for Sugriva, casting this enmity a long distance away, are

best. The ape who is your younger brother should be nurtured. Whether he is there or close at hand here, he always remains your relative. If you wish to do something that brings pleasure to me, if you wish to ensure my welfare, I am lovingly beseeching you to act in accordance with my virtuous words.'

Chapter 4(16)

With a face like that of the lord of the stars, Tara said this.[75] However, Vali reprimanded her and addressed her in these words. 'This extremely angry brother of mine is roaring and he is also an enemy. O one with the beautiful face! What is the reason for me to tolerate him? O timid one! To brave ones who cannot be assailed and do not retreat from a battle, the tolerance of a challenge is said to be worse than death. I cannot tolerate this and I am capable of fighting against those who desire a clash. Sugriva is angry, but it is the roar of a *hinagriva*.[76] You should not be distressed at the prospect of Raghava doing anything against me. He knows about dharma. He is grateful. Why should he commit a wicked act like that? Return with all the women. Why are you following me again? You have shown me your affection. You have acted faithfully towards me. Conquer your fear. I will go and fight against Sugriva. I will destroy his insolence, but I will let him escape with his life. For the sake of victory, I am taking an oath on my lives for you to return. In the encounter against my brother, I will easily be victorious and will return.' At this, Tara, agreeable in speech, embraced Vali. Weeping gently, she circumambulated him, keeping him to her right.[77] Desiring victory, she pronounced mantras of

[75] The word *tara* means star, so there is a play on words.

[76] Sugriva means someone with an excellent neck. Hinagriva means someone with an inferior neck.

[77] *Pradakshina* means to circumambulate clockwise, keeping what is being circumambulated to the right (dakshina). This is auspicious. An anticlockwise circumambulation is inauspicious.

benediction. Confused and miserable, she entered the inner quarters
with the women. With the women, Tara entered her own residence.

He emerged from the city, sighing like an enraged and large
snake. Filled with supreme rage, the immensely powerful Vali
sighed. Wishing to see the enemy, he glanced around on all sides. He
then saw the handsome Sugriva, golden and tawny in complexion.
With his loins girded, he was ready, blazing like a fire. The mighty-
armed one saw Sugriva stationed there. Filled with supreme rage,
Vali also tied up his girdle firmly. The valiant Vali firmly girded
his loins and raised his fists. Having ascertained the right time to
attack, he rushed in Sugriva's direction. Vali was adorned in a
golden garland and was advancing in rage. Sugriva also raised his
clenched fists in his direction. Sugriva, accomplished in fighting,
descended with great force. With eyes coppery red in rage, Vali
addressed him in these words. 'This fist of mine is tightly clenched
and the fingers are tucked away inside. I will strike you with force,
so that I can take away your life.' Thus addressed, Sugriva angrily
told Vali, 'My fists will descend on your head and rob you of your
life.' He[78] approached him and struck him with great rage and force.
Thereby, blood began to flow from the blows and he[79] looked like
a mountain. Though alone, Sugriva used his energy to uproot a sala
tree. He struck Vali on the body, like a bolt of thunder descending
on a large mountain. Struck by the uprooted sala tree and confused,
Vali trembled. He was like a boat with helmsmen, but suffering on
the ocean because of its heavy burden. Both of them were valiant
and terrible in strength. Their speed was like that of Suparna.[80]
The fearfulness of their forms was enhanced, like the moon and
the sun in the sky. However, Sugriva was milder in valour and his
insolence was shattered by Vali. Exhibiting his dexterity, he sought
to avoid Vali.

Raghava affixed a large arrow that was like a virulent serpent
and struck Vali in the chest with this. Struck with force, Vali
fell down on the ground. He was wet with streams of blood and

[78] Vali.
[79] Sugriva. He was like a mountain, exuding minerals.
[80] Garuda.

sweat. He was like a blossoming ashoka tree, uprooted by the wind. Vasava's son became unconscious in the encounter. He was like Indra's standard, when it is shattered and falls down on the ground.[81]

Chapter 4(17)

Vali was harsh in battle, but he was struck by Rama's arrow. He suddenly fell down, like a tree that has been severed. His limbs, decorated in ornaments made out of molten gold, sprawled out on the ground. He fell down, like the standard of the king of the gods when it has been freed from the ropes. The lord of large numbers of apes and bears fell down on the ground. He was like the moon, when it has been dislodged from the sky and no longer illuminates the earth. The great-souled one's body fell down on the ground. However, his prosperity, his life, his energy and his valour hadn't yet disappeared. Shakra had given him an excellent golden garland, decorated with jewels. The foremost among ape's life, energy and prosperity were sustained by this. The brave leader of the apes was wearing that garland and he looked like a rain cloud, tinged at the extremities with the hue of the evening. Though he had fallen down because his inner organs had been struck, the garland, his body and the arrow dazzled, as if Lakshmi had been divided into three. That weapon had the power to convey the brave one along the road to heaven. Released from Rama's bow, it would convey him to his supreme destination. Fallen down in the battle, he was like a fire without its rays. It was as if Yayati had been dislodged from the world of the gods after his store of merit was over. Though he was as unassailable as the great Indra, though he was impossible to withstand, like the great Indra, he was like the sun fallen down on the ground, when the time arrives for the end of a yuga. Vali, the

---

[81] At the time of a festival dedicated to Indra, Indra's standard is raised on a pole. However, when the festival is over, it is neglected and falls down on the ground.

great Indra's son, wearing that golden garland, was brought down.
The mighty-armed one's chest was like that of a lion. With tawny
eyes, his mouth blazed. He saw Rama approach him, followed by
Lakshmana.

On seeing Raghava and the immensely strong Lakshmana,
Vali politely uttered harsh words that were full of dharma. 'What
qualities have you achieved by slaying someone who was not facing
you? I was engaged in fighting and have met my death because of
you. You have been born in a noble lineage. You possess spirit. You
are energetic and observe vows. "Rama knows about compassion
and is engaged in the welfare of subjects. He is kind and great
in endeavour. He knows about time and is firm in following his
vows." In this way, all the creatures speak about your fame on
earth. Considering those qualities and knowing about your great
lineage, despite being restrained by Tara, I faced Sugriva. When I
did not see you, I arrived at the conclusion, "He should not hurt
me when I am distracted and am fighting against someone else." I
did not know that you have destroyed your soul and that you have
raised the banner of dharma, but follow adharma. I now know that
you are wicked in conduct, like a well hidden in grass. You are
wicked, in the disguise of a virtuous person, like a hidden fire. I did
not know that you were deceitfully enveloped in dharma. In my
kingdom, or in my city, I have not committed a wicked act towards
you. I do not know of any violent deed that I have done towards
you. I am innocent. An ape always roams around in the forest
and subsists on fruits and roots. You acted against me when I was
engaged with someone else. You are the son of a lord of men. It is
evident that you are pleasant to see. O king! All the signs show that
you are full of dharma. Which learned person, who does not have
any doubts[82] and has been born in a noble lineage, will hide himself
in the signs of dharma and perpetrate such a cruel deed? You have
been born in a royal lineage and are renowned as someone who
follows dharma. While donning the garb of morality, why are you
running after what is immoral? O king! Conciliation, donations,

[82] About right and wrong.

forgiveness, dharma, perseverance, valour and punishing those who cause injury—these are the qualities of kings. O Rama! We are animals who roam around in the forest, surviving on roots and fruits. O lord of men! This is our nature and you are a man.[83] Land, gold and silver—these are the reasons for acting against a person. What has tempted you into this forest? Which of my fruits are you after? Good policy, humility, punishing and showing favours—these represent the broad conduct of kings. Kings do not act according to their own caprices. For you, desire has been the most important. You are unsteady and prone to anger. Since you are devoted to a bow, your conduct as a king has been narrow.[84] You are not devoted to dharma. Your intelligence is not based on artha. O lord of men! You are dragged along by your senses and a conduct based on caprice. O Kakutstha! I am innocent and you have slain me with an arrow. Having performed this reprehensible deed, what will you say in an assembly of the virtuous? One who kills a king, one who kills a brahmana, one who kills a cow, one who is a thief, one who is devoted to killing creatures, one who is a non-believer[85] and one who marries before the marriage of his elder brother—all these go to hell. My skin cannot be worn. The virtuous shun my body hair and bones. My flesh cannot be eaten by those like you who follow dharma. O Raghava! Brahmanas and kshatriyas can eat five kinds of animals with five nails—a porcupine, a *shvavidha*,[86] a lizard, a hare and a turtle as the fifth. O king! Learned ones do not desire my skin and bones. I possess five nails and have been killed, though my flesh cannot be eaten. O Kakutstha! If you are the protector, the earth does not have a protector. This is like a woman with good conduct possessing a cunning husband. You are deceitful, inferior, wicked and false, though your mind seems to be generous. You violate agreements. How could you have been born to the great-souled Dasharatha? You have destroyed the harness of good conduct and transgressed the dharma of the virtuous. I have been

[83] Implying that Rama has not acted like a man.
[84] Only focusing on punishing, ignoring the others.
[85] A *nastika*. A nastika is not an atheist.
[86] Also a porcupine, though literally, something that pierces dogs.

slain by an elephant named Rama, who has abandoned the goad of
dharma. O son of a king! Had you fought with me in an encounter
when I could see you, you would have been killed by me today and
would have seen the god Vaivasvata.[87] I am unassailable and was
slain by you in an encounter when I could not see you. You were
like a serpent, attacking when a man is intoxicated with liquor and
is asleep. Had you not killed me in a desire to bring Sugriva pleasure,
I would have captured Ravana alive in a battle, bound him by the
neck and delivered him to you. Whether Maithilee has been kept in
the waters of the ocean or in the nether regions, on your command, I
would have brought her, like the white mare.[88] When I have gone to
heaven, Sugriva's obtaining the kingdom is proper. However, your
following adharma and slaying me in a battle is not proper. When
a person is urged by destiny, such an addiction to desire occurs.
But pardon me. Think about virtue and give me a reply.' The great-
souled one was suffering, having been struck by the arrow. He said
this, with his mouth dry. He glanced at Rama, who was like the sun.
The son of the king of the immortals then fell silent.

Chapter 4(18)

Vali was slain by Rama and was senseless. He humbly spoke
these beneficial and harsh words, which were in conformity
with dharma and artha. He was like the sun when it has lost its
radiance. He was like a cloud that has released its water. Like a fire
that has been pacified, the best of the apes uttered these words. The
lord of the apes spoke these supreme words, full of the qualities of
dharma and artha.

After being addressed in this way, Rama spoke to Vali. 'Without
knowing about dharma, artha, kama and the contracts that people
follow, why are you now reprimanding me in this childish way?

[87] Yama.

[88] The white mare was stolen by the demons Madhu and Kaitabha and retrieved by
Vishnu in his form of Hayagriva.

O amiable one! O ape! You desire to speak to me in your folly, without having asked those who possess intelligence, those who are aged and those who are revered preceptors. This land, with its mountains, forests and groves, belongs to the Ikshvakus,[89] granting the right to punish and reward animals, birds and humans there. Bharata, truthful and upright, with dharma in his soul, rules over this. He knows the essence of dharma, kama and artha and is engaged in punishing and rewarding. He possesses both good policy and humility and truth is well established in him. He is the king and he knows about the time and the place, and his valour has been seen. All of us, the other kings, act according to his instructions, which are based on dharma. As we wish, we roam around this entire earth, establishing dharma. Bharata, tiger among kings, is devoted to dharma. While he protects this entire earth, who can act contrary to dharma? We are supremely established in our own dharma. Placing Bharata's instructions at the forefront, as is proper, we chastise those who deviate from the path. Through your reprehensible deeds, you have tainted dharma. You have not based yourself on the path meant for kings, but have made kama the most important. Those who tread along the path of dharma know that there are three fathers—the elder brother, the father[90] and the one who grants knowledge. It is because of reasons of dharma that three have been thought to be like sons—a younger brother, one's own son[91] and a disciple who possesses the qualities. O ape! The dharma followed by the virtuous is subtle and extremely difficult to understand. One can differentiate between right and wrong through the soul that exists in the heart of all creatures. Like the fickle consulting the fickle, or those who are born blind consulting those who are born blind, how will you understand if you consult apes who have not cleansed their souls? I will explain to you what I have said. However, you should not censure me only because of your rage. Behold. This is the reason why I have killed

---

[89] Unless interpreted metaphorically, this is not quite correct, since Kishkindha wasn't part of the Ikshvaku kingdom.

[90] The biological father.

[91] The biological son.

you. Abandoning eternal dharma, you had intercourse with your brother's wife. The great-souled Sugriva is still alive. Ruma[92] is like your daughter-in-law. Falling prey to desire, you have committed a wicked act by having intercourse with her. O ape! You followed kama and transgressed dharma. You have touched your brother's wife and I have accordingly punished you. O lord of the apes! If a person acts contrary to worldly conventions, I do not think an act of punishing him is contrary to dharma. It has been said in the sacred texts that if a man follows kama and engages in intercourse with his biological sister or his younger brother's wife, he should be punished with death. Bharata is the lord of the earth and we follow his commands. You have transgressed dharma. How could that have been overlooked? Following dharma, Bharata protects the wise and punishes those who are addicted to kama and transgress this major dharma. O lord of the apes! We have only acted in accordance with Bharata's commands. According to his principles, we have punished those who violate ethical agreements. I have a friendship with Sugriva and it is just like that with Lakshmana. I will give him his wife and kingdom and he will do what is best for me. In the presence of the apes, I gave him this pledge. How can someone like me ignore a pledge that I have made? You can now comprehend all the various reasons why I have followed great dharma when I have chastised you. In every way, your chastisement is seen to be in accordance with dharma. Dharma can be seen in the act of helping a friend. Kings who wield the rod of chastisement against wicked men are unblemished and go to heaven, like virtuous ones who perform good deeds. When a mendicant performed a wicked act, like the wicked act you have performed, my noble ancestor Mandhata ensured the terrible hardship that he desired for himself.[93] If kings are distracted and ignore the sins committed by others, they perform atonement by smearing themselves in the dust of those sins. O tiger among apes! Therefore, enough of this lamentation. We are

[92] Sugriva's wife.
[93] That is, Mandhata punished the mendicant. Mandhata was from the Ikshvaku lineage and was the son of Yuvanashva. There are no details of this story about Mandhata and the mendicant, not just in the Valmiki Ramayana, but in other texts too.

subject to our own norms and have thought of dharma when killing you. Hiding themselves, men are seen to capture a large number of animals with snares, nooses and various other hidden means. This is irrespective of whether they are running away, terrified, roaming around without fear, distracted, undistracted or retreating. Men who desire flesh will certainly kill them and there is no sin in this. Therefore, royal sages who know about dharma engage in hunting. O ape! Accordingly, using an arrow, I have slain you in an encounter. Whether you are fighting or you are not fighting, you are no more than an ape. O best among apes! There is no doubt that kings are the ones who grant dharma, which is extremely difficult to obtain, and auspicious lives. On earth, they are gods in the form of men and must not be harmed, condemned, slighted, or addressed through disagreeable speech. You only base yourself on anger and do not know about dharma. Know that I am based on the dharma of my fathers and grandfathers.'

Vali was grievously hurt and was addressed by Rama in this way. Joining his hands in salutation, the lord of the apes replied to Rama. 'O best among men! There is no doubt that it is exactly as you have said. I am incapable of replying to you about what is right and what is wrong. Because I did not realize this earlier, in my confusion, I have spoken disagreeable words. O Raghava! Indeed, you should not find fault with me on that account. You are engaged in the welfare of subjects and know the truth about objectives. You are skilled in determining cause and effect. Your intelligence is unblemished. I now know how I have transgressed the most important dharma. O one who knows about dharma! Your words are in conformity with dharma. Protect me.' Vali's voice choked with tears and there was deep affliction in his tone. Like an elephant stuck in mire, he glanced towards Rama and said, 'I am not sorrowing as much over myself, Tara or my relatives, as I am over Angada. He wears golden armlets[94] and possesses the best qualities. He has been reared by me since childhood and unable to see me, he will be miserable. He will be like a lake that has gone dry

[94] Angada means armlet and there is a play on words.

because all the water has been drunk. Use your excellent intelligence
and treat Sugriva and Angada in the same way. You are the chastiser
and the protector. You know about what should be done and what
should not be done. O lord of men! O king! Your conduct towards
Angada should be the same as that towards Bharata, Lakshmana
and Sugriva. You should ensure that Sugriva does not disrespect
the ascetic Tara and punish her because of the crime I committed.
When you show your favours, a person is capable of ruling over
a kingdom. Let him follow your instructions and follow your
inclinations.'

Rama, whose foresight was evident, assured Vali. 'O supreme
among apes! You need not trouble yourself about what we will do.
We will especially bear in mind dharma when we act towards you. The
punished who is brought down through punishment and the punisher
who performs the act of punishing—both of them attain the ends of
cause and effect and do not suffer. Having faced the punishment, you
have been cleansed of all sin. Following dharma, you have obtained
your true nature and are on the path indicated by dharma.' The great-
souled one's words were sweet. They were controlled and followed
the path of dharma. Rama was the one who crushed others in battle.
Having heard his appropriate words, the ape said, 'Scorched by
the arrow, I have lost my senses. O lord! I condemned you in my
ignorance. Your terrible valour is like that of the great Indra. O lord
of men! Pardon me and show me your favours.'

Chapter 4(19)

Wounded by the arrow, the great king of the apes was lying
down. When he was addressed in these beneficial words,
there was nothing he could say in reply. His limbs had been mangled
by the rocks and he had been severely hurt by the trees.[95] Struck by
Rama's arrow his life ended and he was unconscious.

[95] In the course of fighting with Sugriva.

His wife, Tara, heard that Vali, tiger among apes, had been slain through an arrow released by Rama in the course of the encounter. She heard the extremely terrible and disagreeable news that her husband had been killed. Extremely anxious, with her son, she rushed out of many caves in the mountains.[96] There were extremely strong apes who were Angada's companions. However, on seeing Rama with his bow, they fled in different directions. She saw that the terrified apes were quickly running away. They were like animals running away when the leader of the herd has been slain. All of them were terrified and miserable, as if Rama's arrow was chasing them. Though she was herself grieving, she approached them. 'O apes! O miserable ones! Your king was a lion and he is in front of you. Why are you terrified and running away, leaving him there? From a distance, Rama has struck him with arrow that can strike at a long distance. Has his terrible brother brought him down for the sake of the kingdom?'[97] The apes could assume any form at will. Having heard the words of the ape's wife, realizing that this was a chaotic time, they spoke these words to the beautiful one. 'Retreat. Your son is still alive. Protect your son Angada. The destroyer, in Rama's form, is taking away Vali, who has been killed. He flung trees and large rocks at him. However, Vali was brought down by arrows that were like the vajra, as if he was brought down by the vajra.[98] His strength is great and extensive and he has enveloped everything here with that. His radiance is like that of Shakra and he has slain the tiger among apes. We must protect the city and all the brave ones must consecrate Angada. When Vali's son has been instated, all the apes will start to serve him. O one with the beautiful face! It is not appropriate that you should remain here. Let all the apes hasten and enter an impenetrable place. There are those who roam around

[96] The many caves means that other apes also rushed out with her. Tara was in Kishkindha. Therefore, this can only mean that Kishkindha had been built around caves.

[97] Tara has still not seen Vali. She has only heard that he has been killed.

[98] There was no fight where Vali had flung trees and rocks at Rama. Nor did Rama strike him with several arrows. All this is meant to illustrate that the apes don't quite know what has happened. It is a time of chaos.

in the forest. Some have wives. Others don't have wives. Those whom we have harmed will seek to harm us and we are suffering a great fear on account of them.'

Despite hearing this, the beautiful one proceeded some distance. The one with the beautiful smile spoke words that were appropriate for her. 'When my husband, the immensely fortunate lion among apes, has been destroyed, what will I do with a son, with a kingdom, or with my own self? I will go before the feet of that great-souled one, who has been brought down by the arrow released by Rama.' Saying this, weeping and senseless with grief, she rushed forward. In misery, she slapped her head, her thighs and her arms. Having advanced, she saw her husband lying down on the ground. He never retreated from a battle and was the slayer of Indras among danavas. Like Vasava with his vajra, he could fling away the best among mountains. He was like a great storm and roared like a dense mass of large clouds. He was like Shakra in his valour. He showered down on others, like a dense cloud. He roared against those who roared at him. The brave one had been brought down by another brave one. He was like a king of deer, killed by a tiger for the sake of flesh. He was like a sacrificial altar with its banner, worshipped by all the worlds. He was like a chaitya[99] that had been uprooted by Suparna for the sake of serpents.' The auspicious one saw Rama standing there, leaning on his bow for support. Rama's younger brother was with him and so was her husband's younger brother. She passed them and approached her husband, who had been slain in the encounter. On seeing him, she was scared and distressed and fell down on the ground. When she arose, as if from sleep, she saw her husband, bound by the nooses of death. 'O noble one!' Thus lamenting, she wept. She was shrieking like a female osprey. Seeing her, and on seeing that Angada had arrived, Sugriva suffered and was miserable.

[99] The word chaitya has several meanings—sacrificial shed, temple, altar, sanctuary and a tree that grows along the road.

Chapter 4(20)

Tara, with a face like that of the lord of the stars, saw him slain and lying down on the ground, an arrow released from Rama's bow having robbed him of his life. The beautiful one approached her husband and embraced him. She saw Vali, who was like an elephant, killed by the arrow. The Indra among apes possessed a complexion that was like that of the great Indra. He was like a tree that had been uprooted. She was tormented and miserable in her mind. She sorrowed and lamented. 'O one who was terrible in battle! O supreme among brave ones! O best among apes! I am in front of you. Why are you not speaking to me now? O tiger among apes! Arise. We will serve you with the best of beds. Supreme kings do not lie down on the ground in this way. O lord of the earth! It is evident that you love the earth greatly. Even though you have lost your life, you have cast me aside and are embracing her.[100] O brave one! It is evident that you followed dharma and constructed this beautiful city of Kishkindha on the road to heaven. There are those of us who were with you in the sweet and fragrant forests at the time of finding pleasure. You have ended that. I am without joy. I am without hope. I am immersed in an ocean of grief. O leader of the leaders of herds! You are now dead.[101] When Sugriva was banished, why did you seize his wife? O lord of the apes! That is the reason you have come to this state. O Indra among apes! I desired your welfare and spoke beneficial words to you. But you reprimanded me. Overcome by great confusion, you did what was not beneficial. There is no doubt that the power of destiny has brought an end to your life. Thereby, though you could not be subjugated, you have

---

[100] The earth.

[101] The word used is *panchatva*. Reaching a stage of panchatva, when dead, can have two possible interpretations. First, one has returned to the five (*pancha*) elements. Second, there are three normal states—being awake, sleeping (with dreams) and deep sleep (without dreams and without distractions). There is a fourth stage beyond this, known as *turiya*. This transcends consciousness and one experiences union with the brahman. The fifth stage (panchatva) is beyond this too.

come under Sugriva's subjugation. I have never faced unhappiness
or misery earlier. I have not been pitied. However, I am without
a protector now and tormented by grief because I have become
a widow, am in a pitiable state. The brave and delicate Angada
has been reared such that he is used to happiness. When his uncle
becomes senseless with rage, what state will he be in? O son!
Behold your father, who was devoted to dharma, well and do
what needs to be done. O child! It will be extremely difficult to
catch sight of him in the future. Comfort your son and instruct
him about your commands. Before you leave on your journey,
inhale the fragrance of his head. Rama performed a great deed
when he brought you down. He has repaid the debt he made to
Sugriva through his pledge. O Sugriva! When you get Ruma back,
may your wishes be satisfied. Without any anxiety, enjoy the
kingdom. The brother who was your enemy has been chastised.
I am lamenting in this way. Why are you not speaking to me
lovingly? O lord of the apes! Behold all these beautiful wives of
yours.' On hearing her lamentations, all the female apes were
distressed and miserable. They embraced Angada and shrieked in
affliction. 'O one with the brave arms, wearing armlets! Leaving
Angada behind, why are you leaving on a long journey?[102] You are
leaving, abandoning us and your beloved son, who possesses the
best of qualities. O beloved! O one attired in beautiful garments!
O protector! Have I or your son done anything unpleasant? O
brave one! I am your companion. However, abandoning me, you
are going to Yama's eternal and insolent abode. O long-armed
one! O lord of the lineage of the apes! Without thinking about
it, if I have done anything unpleasant towards you, please forgive
me. O brave one! I have come before you, with my head lowered
at your feet.' Tara wept in this piteous way near her husband, with
all the female apes. The one with the unblemished complexion sat
down on the ground near Vali, resolving to commit *praya*.[103]

---

[102] This is Tara speaking again.

[103] The practice in question is *prayopavesa*. While this means voluntary fasting to
death, it is adopted by someone who has no worldly desires left.

Chapter 4(21)

Tara fell down, like a star dislodged from the sky.[104] Hanumat, the leader of the apes, gently comforted her. 'Creatures perform good and bad, inauspicious and auspicious. Because of their own good deeds and misdeeds, they reap all the fruits after death. You should be grieved over. Why are you grieving? Whom are you grieving about? You are yourself distressed. Which miserable one are you taking compassion on? Who are you? Whom do you belong to? Why are you sorrowing over a body that is just like foam?[105] Prince Angada, your son, is alive and needs to be considered. You should think about what needs to be done next and about what he is capable of doing. You know that living beings are temporary. They come and go. The learned know that this is the nature of this world and, therefore, do everything auspicious that can be done. There are thousands, millions and hundreds of millions of apes.[106] Having acted so as to satisfy their hopes, he[107] has met his destiny. He looked towards artha and followed good policy. He was engaged in conciliation, gifts and forgiveness. After following dharma and conquering the earth, he has departed. One should not grieve over this. O unblemished one! You are the protector of all these tigers among apes, your son Angada, the lords among the apes and the bears and this kingdom. O beautiful one! These two[108] are tormented by grief. Gently inspire them. When you support him, Angada will rule over the earth. There are funeral rites that an offspring must now perform for the king. Determining the right time, let all those be done. Let the funeral rites be performed for the king of the apes and let Angada be consecrated. When you see that your son has obtained the throne, you will find peace.' She was oppressed by the hardship her husband had faced and Hanumat was standing near her. On hearing his words, Tara replied, 'Though

---

[104] The word tara means star.
[105] These shlokas are very reminiscent of the Bhagavadgita.
[106] *Prayuta* is million and *arbuda* is a hundred million.
[107] Vali.
[108] Sugriva and Angada.

there can be one hundred sons like Angada, it is best for me to embrace the body of the brave one who has died.[109] I do not seek the power of the kingdom of the apes, not even for Angada. For everything that needs to be done next, his uncle, Sugriva, is here. O Hanumat! O supreme among the apes! On your thoughts about Angada,[110] a father is a son's true relative, not the mother. There is no refuge that is better for me, in this world and in the next, than the king of the apes.[111] I will serve the brave one whose face is turned away. I am only capable of lying down with him and serving him.'

Chapter 4(22)

His[112] life was gently ebbing away and he sighed gently. He glanced around in every direction. However, he first saw Sugriva standing in front of him. Vali saw Sugriva, who was now victorious and the lord of the apes. He clearly addressed him in words that were full of affection. 'O Sugriva! Do not judge me by my crimes. Because of my sins and my destiny, my intelligence was confounded by force and I was dragged into it. O son![113] I don't think both of us are destined to enjoy happiness simultaneously. Therefore, though brothers are united by fraternal affection, it has been otherwise for us. Accept this dominion over the residents of the forest. Know that I will now go to Vaivasvata's eternal abode. While I am still alive, I am quickly giving up this kingdom, this extensive prosperity and this great and untainted glory. O brave one! O king! Given my present state, you should act in accordance with my words, although it is not easy to do. This child, Angada, is sensible. He deserves happiness and has been reared in happiness.

---

[109] That is, it is best for her to kill herself.
[110] About Angada being crowned.
[111] Vali.
[112] Vali's.
[113] The word used is tata.

Look at him, fallen down on the ground, tears flowing down his face. He is my biological son and I love this son more than my lives.[114] Without me, he will be without riches. Protect him in every way. In every way, you are the one who will give to him and save him. O lord of the apes! You are the one who will grant him freedom from fear. Tara's son is handsome and is like you in valour. In slaying the rakshasas, he will be with you, at the forefront. The powerful one will perform similar deeds of valour in a battle. Tara's son, Angada, is spirited and young. This daughter of Sushena's[115] can determine the subtleties of artha and is accomplished in all the different types of omens. One should have no doubt that whatever task she talks about is virtuous. Nothing happens that is contrary to Tara's point of view. Without any doubt, you must accomplish Raghava's task. It will be adharma if you don't do this.[116] Otherwise, he will disrespect you and cause you injury. O Sugriva! There is a pendant on this divine and golden necklace. The generous Shri is established in this, but will abandon it when I am dead.[117] Accept it.' Because of fraternal affection, Vali spoke to Sugriva in this way. He[118] was initially happy, and subsequently miserable, like the lord of the stars during an eclipse. However, pacified by Vali's words, he controlled himself and accepted the golden necklace that had been indicated.

Having given the golden necklace away, Vali saw that his son was standing in front of him. Preparing himself for death, he affectionately told Angada, 'From now on, serve Sugriva and remain under his control and with him at all times, tolerating the agreeable and the disagreeable, happiness and unhappiness, always, and at all places. O mighty-armed one! I have always reared you, but it is not going to be like that.[119] Show a great deal of respect for Sugriva. O scorcher of enemies! Do not go to those who are not

---

[114] In the plural.

[115] Meaning Tara.

[116] Because there was a pledge.

[117] Because Shri will not remain in a dead body.

[118] Sugriva.

[119] Because I am your father, I tolerated your behaviour. Sugriva will not necessarily be tolerant.

his friends. Do not go to his enemies. Sugriva is your master. Be
restrained. Remain under his control and achieve his ends. Do not
show excessive affection. Nor should you show lack of affection.
There is great sin attached to either extreme and you must look
towards what is in between.' Suffering greatly from the arrow, with
his eyes rolling, this is what he said. In his open mouth, his teeth
looked terrible. He gave up his life. When the brave lord of the
apes died, the apes there could not find any peace. They were like
cows wandering out in a forest, when there is a lion in that great
forest and the lord of the cows[120] has been slain. Tara suffered in an
ocean of affliction. She glanced towards her dead husband's face.
She was like a creeper when the great tree it was clinging to has been
severed. She sank on to the ground and embraced Vali.

Chapter 4(23)

She inhaled the fragrance from the face of the lord of the apes,
her husband who was famous in the worlds. Tara addressed the
dead one in these words. 'O brave one! Not having paid attention
to my words, you are miserably lying down on this rough ground
with pebbles on it, suffering a great hardship. O Indra among the
apes! It is clear that you love the earth more than you love me. You
are lying down, embracing her, and do not give me a reply. O brave
one! Sugriva, who loves rash acts, has shown himself to be valiant.
The foremost among the bears and apes are worshipping you, Vali.
Hearing their miserable lamentations, Angada's grieving and my
words, why are not waking up? O brave one! On earlier occasions,
your enemies were killed and lay down here. Having been slain in
an encounter, is this the bed you are going to lie down on now?
O my beloved! O pure and spirited one! O one born in a noble
lineage! O one who loved to fight! O one who conferred honours!
You have left me alone, without a protector. Indeed, learned ones

[120] The bull.

should never bestow their daughters on brave ones. Behold! I was the wife of a valiant one. With him slain, I have just become a widow. My pride has been shattered. My eternal objective has been shattered. I have been immersed in a fathomless and great ocean of grief. There is no doubt that this firm heart of mine has an essence made out of stone. Despite seeing my husband slain, it has not been shattered into a hundred fragments. You were my husband and naturally affectionate. You were my beloved. You were valiant in battle and brave. You have now met your death.[121] Even if a woman has satisfied desire and obtained sons and even if she is prosperous with wealth and grain, if she is devoid of a husband, people speak of her as a widow. O brave one! You are now lying down on a circle of blood that is oozing out of your own body. Your bedspread has the complexion of an insect[122] and you have made your own bed. O bull among apes! I am unable to embrace you in my arms. Your body is covered with dust and blood everywhere.[123] In this extremely terrible enmity, Sugriva has become successful today. With a single arrow released by Rama, he has been freed from his fear. With you having obtained death,[124] I am looking at you. When I touch you, this arrow stuck to your heart acts as a barrier.'

Then Nila took out the arrow from the body, like taking out a flaming serpent that has hidden inside a mountainous cavern. When the arrow was extracted, its radiance was like the rays of the sun, when it is setting atop Asta.[125] Like copper-coloured and ochre-coloured[126] water flowing from a mountain, blood started to flow out from all the wounds. The brave one had been struck by the weapon. With tears flowing from her eyes, she[127] wiped the dust of battle from all over his body. On seeing that all the limbs of her

---

[121] Panchatva again.

[122] The *indragopa* insect, which is red in colour.

[123] This doesn't mean that she is reluctant to embrace Vali's dead body because of the dust and blood. It means that when she embraces his dead body, the dust and the blood create a barrier in between.

[124] Panchatva.

[125] The sun is believed to set behind Mount Asta.

[126] Because of minerals.

[127] Tara.

dead husband were covered with blood, the beautiful Tara spoke to the coppery-eyed Angada. 'O son! Behold the extremely terrible western state of your father.[128] He has attained this end because of his attachment to enmity and his wicked deeds. His body was like that of the young and rising sun, but he has left for Yama's abode. O son! Show your respect to the king, your father, the one who granted honours.' Thus addressed, he arose and seized his father's feet with his thick and round arms and said, 'I am Angada.' 'Angada is greeting you, as on earlier occasions.[129] Why are you not replying and saying, "O son! May you live for a long time?" I am seated near you, with my son as my aide, senseless. I am like a cow with a calf, when a lion has just killed the bull. With Rama's weapons as the water, you have performed the rituals in a sacrifice of fighting. Having accomplished it, how can you have a bath without me, your wife?[130] Satisfied with your conduct in battles, the king of the gods gave you a necklace made out of molten gold. Why can't I see it here now? O granter of honours! Even though you have lost your life, royal prosperity has not deserted you. Your radiance is like that of the sun, as it circles the king of the mountains.[131] I was not able to restrain you with my words, which were like medication. With you having been slain in the encounter, I have been killed, with my son. Prosperity is deserting not just you, but me too.'

Chapter 4(24)

Thereafter, on seeing that Vali was dead, Raghava, the scorcher of enemies, addressed Sugriva in these comforting words.

---

[128] The imagery is that of the setting sun.

[129] This is Tara speaking again.

[130] *Avabhritha* is the most important final component of a sacrifice, characterized by the taking of a bath. As the last bath of life, avabhritha also signifies death. The battle is thus being compared to a sacrifice and the text uses the word avabhritha. Any sacrifice, and the subsequent bath, has to be taken with the wife.

[131] The sun is believed to circle around Mount Meru.

'A person who is dead does not gain anything from grieving and lamentations. One should undertake whatever task needs to be done next. This shedding of tears is in conformity with whatever is done in the worlds.[132] However, after some time, there are other tasks that need to be undertaken. In the worlds, destiny is the cause. Destiny is behind all acts that are undertaken. Destiny is the cause that makes all creatures undertake action. No one is ever the doer. No one is the master in engaging someone else to act. The world acts according to its nature and is driven by destiny. Time cannot transcend destiny and destiny is never weakened. It[133] acts according to its own nature and never exceeds it. Destiny does not recognize a relative, a cause, valour, a friend, a kin, a relationship, or a reason. It is its own master. Those who are virtuous in their insight can see the consequences of destiny. Dharma, artha and kama are encompassed by the progress of destiny. The lord of the apes pursued the auspicious objectives of dharma, artha and kama. Having reaped the consequences of his deeds, Vali has attained his own nature.[134] The great-souled one was not concerned about protecting his own life. Having been engaged in his own dharma, he has obtained heaven. The destiny obtained by the lord of the apes is the best. Therefore, there has been enough of lamenting. It is time to show him respect.'

When Rama finished speaking, Lakshmana, the slayer of enemy heroes, addressed the senseless Sugriva in words of reassurance. 'O Sugriva! Now perform the funeral rites for him. With Tara and Angada, cremate Vali. Instruct that a lot of dry wood, sandalwood and other divine wood, should be collected for Vali's cremation. Comfort Angada, whose senses are suffering. Do not be childish in your view that this city belongs to you alone now. Let Angada fetch garlands, many kinds of garments, ghee, oil, fragrances and everything else that will be required next. Showing due respect, let

[132] In these shlokas, there is scope for interpretation and therefore, there is subjectivity in the translation.
[133] Destiny.
[134] Such as, his atman.

Tara[135] go and quickly bring a palanquin. It should possess all the qualities required for a special occasion like this. Let apes who are appropriate for bearing the palanquin be prepared. They should be capable and strong enough to carry Vali.' The extender of Sumitra's delight spoke to Sugriva in this way. Lakshmana, the destroyer of enemy heroes, then stood next to his brother.

On hearing Lakshmana's words, Tara, respectful in his mind, quickly entered the cave, wishing to find a palanquin. Having found an appropriate palanquin, Tara next found brave apes who were capable of bearing the palanquin. Grieving, Sugriva, with Angada, raised Vali on to the palanquin. The dead Vali was raised on to the palanquin. He was decorated with many kinds of ornaments, garlands and garments. King Sugriva, the lord of the apes, commanded, 'Let the appropriate funeral rites be observed for the noble one. Let apes proceed ahead of the palanquin now, scattering many kinds of jewels along the path. On earth, the funeral rites of kings can be seen, especially of those who are prosperous. Let the apes follow exactly identical practices.' Angada, Tara[136] and all the other apes milled around, lamenting the death of their relative. With their leader slain, Tara[137] and all the female apes followed their husband, lamenting in piteous tones. At the sound of the female apes lamenting inside the forest, all the forests and mountains also started to weep. In a deserted spot on the sandbank of a mountain stream, many apes, who roamed around in the forest, prepared the funeral pyre. The best of bearers lowered the palanquin from their shoulders and placed it there. Filled with sorrow, all of them stood to one side.

Tara saw that her husband was lying down on the floor of the palanquin. Extremely miserable, she raised his head on to her lap and began to lament. 'Why do you not see these people who are suffering from grief? O granter of honours! Though you have lost your life, your face is happy. Your complexion is like that of the setting sun, just as it was seen to be while you were alive. O ape! In

---

[135] This is not Taaraa, Vali's wife, but the male ape, Taara.
[136] The male ape.
[137] Vali's wife.

Rama's form, destiny is dragging you away. Using a single arrow in the battle, he has made all of us widows. O Indra among kings! These female apes have always been wives to you. Grasping your feet, they came along this path. Why are you not understanding that? Don't you desire these wives, whose faces are like the moon? Why are you not seeing Sugriva, now the lord of the apes? O king! These are the advisers, Tara and the others. O unblemished one! The residents of the city have surrounded you. O slayer of enemies! Take your leave of the advisers, so that all of us can sport in the forest, intoxicated with liquor.' Enveloped by sorrow on account of her husband, Tara lamented in this way. The female apes, also afflicted by grief, raised her and took her away.

Weeping, and with his senses numbed by sorrow, with Sugriva, Angada placed his father's body on the pyre.[138] As his father left on the long journey, his senses were distracted. In the proper way, he applied the fire and performed an *apasavya* circumambulation.[139] After having cremated Vali in the proper way, the bulls among apes went to an auspicious river and performed the water rites with its cool water. They kept Angada at the front and with Sugriva and Tara,[140] the apes sprinkled themselves with water. With a misery that was just as great as that of Sugriva, the immensely strong Kakutstha arranged for the funeral rites to be undertaken.

Chapter 4(25)

Sugriva was tormented by grief and his garments were wet.[141] The apes who were great advisers surrounded him. They approached the mighty-armed Rama, the performer of unsullied deeds. All of

---

[138] They raised it from the palanquin and placed it on the pyre.

[139] This is circumambulation in anticlockwise fashion, the exact opposite of pradakshina. In pradakshina, one keeps the person/object being circumambulated on the right. In apasavya, the person/object being circumambulated is kept on the left.

[140] Vali's wife.

[141] From the water rites.

them stood there, with their hands joined in salutation, like the rishis before the grandfather.[142] Hanumat's complexion was like that of the golden mountain.[143] His complexion was like that of the rising sun. Joining his hands in salutation, the son of the wind god spoke these words. 'O lord! It is because of your favours that Sugriva has obtained this great kingdom of the apes that belonged to his fathers and grandfathers. It was extremely difficult to obtain. With your permission, he will enter this auspicious city. With all his well-wishers, he will perform the appropriate tasks. Having bathed, following the proper rites, he will be anointed with many kinds of fragrances. In particular, he will worship you with garlands and gems. You should go to this beautiful cave in the mountains. O lord! Establish this alliance with the delighted apes.' Raghava, the destroyer of enemy heroes, was addressed by Hanumat in this way. The intelligent one, accomplished in the use of words, replied to Hanumat. 'O Hanumat! O amiable one! Following the instructions of my father, I cannot enter a village or a city for fourteen years. When the brave Sugriva, bull among the apes, enters this divine and extremely prosperous cave, let him swiftly be instated in the kingdom in the proper way.' Having told Hanumat this, Rama told Sugriva, 'Let the brave Angada be instated as the heir apparent. O amiable one! The four months that are known as the monsoon season have commenced.[144] The month of Shravana, which brings rain, is in front of us. This is not the time for me to make the effort.[145] However, you should enter the city. O amiable one! I will reside on this mountain with Lakshmana. A wind blows through this large and beautiful cave in the mountain.[146] O amiable one! There is plenty of water and many red and blue lotuses. When

[142] Brahma.

[143] Meru.

[144] This deviates from the six-season format. In the six-season format, the seasons (*ritu*) are Vasanta or spring (Chaitra, Vaishakha), Grishma or summer (Jyaishtha, Ashadha), Varsha or monsoon (Shravana, Bhadrapada), Sharada or autumn (Ashvina, Kartika), Hemanta or cold season (Margashirsha, Pousha) and Shishira or winter (Magha, Phalguna). Shravana is the July–August period.

[145] Enter the city.

[146] Not to be confused with Kishkindha.

it is the month of Kartika,[147] you will make efforts for Ravana's destruction. That is our agreement. Now enter your own abode. With your delighted well-wishers, be anointed in the kingdom.'

Having thus obtained Rama's permission, Sugriva, bull among the apes, entered the beautiful city of Kishkindha, which had been ruled over by Vali. When the lord of the apes entered, thousands of delighted apes greeted him and surrounded him from all sides. On seeing the lord of the apes, all the ordinary ones controlled themselves and with their heads lowered, prostrated themselves on the ground before him. The valiant Sugriva raised all the ordinary ones and spoke to them. The amiable and extremely strong one then entered his brother's inner quarters.

When Sugriva, bull among apes, emerged again, after entering there, all the well-wishers consecrated him, like the immortals do to the one with the thousand eyes. A white umbrella, embellished with gold, was brought. There were white whisks made out of hair and a golden staff that would enhance fame. There were all the jewels and every kind of seed and herb. There were trees that exuded milky white sap and blooming creepers. There were white garments and white unguents. There were fragrant garlands and lotuses that blossom on land and in water. There was sandalwood paste and many kinds of other divine fragrances. There was *akshata*,[148] molten gold, *priyangu*,[149] honey, ghee, curds and sandals made out of the hides of tigers and boars. Pastes used before bathing were brought—made from yellow arsenic and red arsenic. Sixteen supreme and cheerful maidens were brought there. The bulls among brahmanas were satisfied with gems, garments and food. At the right time, following the right rites, the best among apes was anointed. Kusha grass was spread around the fire that had been lit with kindling. Those who knew about the mantras offered oblations sanctified with mantras into the fire. A golden throne was covered with an excellent spread. It was beautiful and colourful, decorated

---

[147] October–November.

[148] This can mean grain of any kind. But it is specifically used for threshed and winnowed rice that has not been dehusked.

[149] Creeper believed to blossom at a woman's touch.

with flowers and was at the top of the palace. To the chanting of
mantras, he was made to sit on that excellent seat, with his face
facing the east. All the bulls among the apes invited the male and
female rivers and tirthas from every direction. From every direction,
they invited the oceans. This sparkling and auspicious water was
filled in golden vessels. Following the ordinances laid down by the
maharshis in the sacred texts, the water from the golden pots was
then poured into auspicious vessels that were made out of the horns
of cows.[150] Gaja, Gavaksha, Gavaya, Sharabha, Gandhamadana,
Mainda, Dvivida, Hanumat, Jambavat consecrated Sugriva with
those pleasant and fragrant waters, like the Vasus do to Vasava.
Sugriva was consecrated by all the bulls among apes. Delighted,
hundreds and thousands of the great-souled ones roared. Following
Rama's words, Sugriva, bull among apes, embraced Angada and
instated him as the heir apparent. Roaring, the apes anointed
Angada. They praised and worshipped the great-souled Sugriva.
The beautiful city of Kishkindha, inside the cave in the mountain,
was filled with joyous and healthy people and decorated with flags
and pennants. The ape,[151] the leader of the army, then informed the
great-souled Rama about the great consecration. The valiant one
obtained his wife Ruma back and like the lord of the gods, obtained
his kingdom back.

Chapter 4(26)

When the ape Sugriva had been consecrated and had entered his
cave,[152] with his brother, Rama went to Mount Prasravana.
It was full of tigers and other animals, enveloped by the terrible
roars of lions. It was dense with many kinds of shrubs and creepers.
There were many kinds of trees. Bears, apes, golangulas and wild
cats resided there. The mountain was always sacred and purifying,

[150] Using these, the water was sprinkled over his head.
[151] Sugriva.
[152] Kishkindha.

like a thick mass of clouds. There was a large and extensive cave on
the summit of the mountain. With Soumitri, Rama accepted that as
a place to dwell in. With Lakshmana, Raghava, with dharma in his
soul, resided there, on Mount Prasravana, with many caverns and
groves that were fit to be seen. That mountain had many objects
that were extremely pleasant. However, though he resided there,
Rama did not find the slightest bit of pleasure. He remembered
the abduction of his wife, whom he loved more than his own life.
This was particularly the case when he saw the moon rise. In the
night, when he lay down and had gone to sleep, he would awaken,
his senses afflicted by tears of sorrow. Thus Kakutstha grieved,
always overcome by sorrow. His brother Lakshmana, who was just
as miserable as him, entreated him in these words. 'O brave one!
There has been enough of this grieving. You should not sorrow.
It is known to you that if people sorrow, all their objectives are
destroyed. On earth, you are the one who has to perform tasks[153]
and you are devoted to the gods. O Raghava! You are a believer,[154]
devoted to dharma, and enterprising. If you give up your enterprise,
an enemy, especially a rakshasa who is valiant and deceitful in
conduct, can be capable of killing you in a battle. You must uproot
your misery and be steady in your enterprise. You will then be able
to uproot the rakshasa, with all his relatives. O Kakutstha! You are
capable of reversing the order of the earth, with its oceans, forests
and mountains, not to speak of Ravana. I am only seeking to wake
up your valour, which is sleeping. It is like a fire hidden beneath
ashes and will blaze when the time arrives to offer oblations.'

Raghava honoured those words of Lakshmana, which were
beneficial and auspicious. He addressed his well-wisher in these
gentle words. 'O Lakshmana! You have spoken beneficial words
of devotion and affection. They are indicative of the truthfulness
of your valour. This sorrow must be abandoned. It makes all tasks
suffer. I will invoke my invincible valour, energy and enterprise. I
will await the autumn season, the monsoon season has arrived. At

---

[153] The word used is *kriyapara*. This is interpreted as being devoted to rituals, but is
not necessary.

[154] The word used is *astika*, which can also be translated as theist.

that time, I will destroy the large number of rakshasas and their kingdom.' Hearing Rama's words, Lakshmana was delighted. Sumitra's descendant again addressed him in these words. 'O destroyer of enemies! These are words that are worthy of you. O Kakutstha! You have now returned to your true nature. Knowing your own valour, you must adhere to its truth. These words are worthy of a noble and learned person. O tiger among men! O Raghava! We must therefore think about restraining the enemy, while we spend these rainy nights here. Until autumn is here, you must control your rage. With me, these four months have to be spent in patience. Let us reside on this mountain, frequented by the kings of animals.[155] You are capable of slaying the enemy, even one with enhanced powers.'

Chapter 4(27)

After Vali was killed and Sugriva was consecrated, Rama resided on the slopes of Malyavat.[156] He spoke to Lakshmana. 'The season has arrived. It is time for the rain to shower down. Behold. The sky is covered with clouds that have the complexion of mountains. For nine months, the sun in the sky uses its rays to suck up the juices from the oceans and bears them in its womb. It then gives birth to juices that sustain life.[157] Using the row of stairs provided by the clouds, it is now possible to climb up into the sky and ornament the sun with garlands made out of wild jasmine and arjuna flowers. Those clouds in the sky are coloured with the coppery red hue of advancing evening and are white at the edges. It is as if the clouds are a soft bandage, tied around a wound in the sky. The sky seems to be yearning with desire. The gentle wind is like its sigh. It is tinged with the red sandalwood paste of the evening. The white clouds are like its radiant face. This earth was suffering from the summer and

---

[155] Lions.

[156] This means that Mount Malyavat and Mount Prasravana were identical.

[157] This equates the monsoon season to three months, mid-July to mid-October.

is now flowing with the new water. Like Sita, who is tormented by grief, it is shedding tears.[158] Like using a cup made out of the leaf of a white waterlily, one can cup one's hands and drink the cool and pleasant water that has been released from the stomachs of the clouds. The wind bears the fragrance of the ketaka flower. This mountain has flowering arjuna trees and is fragrant with ketaka flowers. It is as if this downpour is anointing Sugriva, when his enemy has been pacified. The clouds are like black antelope skin that these mountains have donned. The downpour is like sacrificial threads that they are wearing. The caves are filled with a wind that blows through them. The sky seems to be suffering, as it is struck by the lightning, which is like a golden whip. Therefore, in pain internally, it seems to be crying out. It seems to be that the lightning is struggling inside that blue cloud, just as the ascetic Vaidehi must have writhed in Ravana's lap. Since the directions cannot be clearly seen, those who are with their beloveds must find it to be beneficial. The planets and the moon have disappeared, marred by the clouds. O Soumitri! Look at the flowering wild jasmine on the slope of the mountain. Having held back their tears, they are now eager at the advent of the monsoon.[159] I am overcome by sorrow and they seem to be there to ignite my desire.[160]

'The dust has been pacified. The breeze is cool now. The extreme taints of the summer have been quietened. The expeditions of the kings have ceased. Men who were in other places have returned to their own countries. The chakravakas, followed by their beloveds, have now left, desiring to reside in Lake Manasa. However, on seeing that the rainwaters have disrupted the roads, vehicles are not travelling. The sky is radiant. But with clouds scattered everywhere, it can sometimes be seen and sometimes, it cannot be seen. It looks

[158] The first rain leads to vapour rising up from a heated earth.

[159] The flowers are covered with water resembling tears. But there is another image too, that of women who have held back their tears because their husbands have been away on work. The monsoon is usually the time when the husbands return to their wives.

[160] The subsequent shlokas have a beautiful description of the monsoon and there are shlokas that are reminiscent of Kalidasa's Meghadutam. However, there is also an inconsistency. The metre changes. Normally, throughout a great epic, the same metre has to be used. Therefore, speculatively, these shlokas could be a later interpolation.

like the giant ocean when it is quiet, obstructed here and there
by mountains. Descending from the mountains, the new water is
flowing faster along the streams, bearing copper and other ores
from the mountains and flowers from sala and kadamba trees,
followed by the calling of peacocks. Jambu fruit is desired and
eaten. It is full of juices and resembles a bee.[161] However, struck
by the wind, mango fruit of many colours is falling down on the
ground, even though it is not yet ripe. The clouds are thundering
in high-pitched tones. They are garlanded with cranes and the
lightning is like flags. They look like the summits of mountains and
like large and crazy elephants that are fighting. Arrays of cranes
desire the clouds and are flying all around them. It is as if a beautiful
and long garland made out of white lotuses has been raised up by
the wind and is spread across the sky. Sleep gradually approaches
Keshava.[162] Rivers swiftly approach the ocean. Delighted cranes
approach the clouds. Filled with desire, beautiful women approach
their beloveds. The extremities of the forest are full of peacocks that
are dancing beautifully. There are kadamba flowers on the branches
of kadamba trees. Bulls approach cows that are also equally filled
with desire. The earth is full of crops and the forests are lovely. The
surging rivers are bearing along water from the rains. The peacocks
are dancing beautifully. The apes are comforting themselves. Crazy
elephants are trumpeting at the extremities of the forest. Those
separated from their beloveds are thinking about them. Inhaling
the fragrant scent from the ketaka flowers, elephants are both glad
and maddened. With the crazy peacocks, they are also trumpeting.
But hearing the sound of the waterfalls in the mountains, they are
bewildered. Bees are hanging from the kadamba flowers on the
branches, but are brought down by the downpour of rain in an
instant. However, they again immerse themselves in the honey in
the flowers and are maddened. The branches of the jambu trees are

[161] Implicitly, these are falling down when they are ripe.

[162] This is interpreted as Keshava in the sense of Vishnu, it being believed that
Vishnu sleeps from Ashadha to Kartika. However, Keshava is also another name for
the month of Margashirsha (November–December). Perhaps all it means is that one is
approaching that month.

radiant with large numbers of fruits with succulent juices, making them look like heaps of coal powder, or droves of bees feasting on them. The clouds are ornamented with flags made out of lightning. They are thundering in deep and loud tones. In their dazzling forms, they look like elephants that are eager to fight. In the forest, that large and maddened elephant was proceeding along a path in the mountains. It heard the cloud thundering, and suspecting that it was another elephant desiring to fight, decided to retreat. The water is falling down, sparkling like pearls. The extremely clean water is clinging to the leaves. Though their feathers have become discoloured because of the rain, the thirsty birds are delighted and are drinking it, a gift from Indra of the gods. Resplendent blue clouds filled with new water are dashing against other blue clouds. They look like a forest consumed by a conflagration dashing against another forest consumed by a conflagration, both moored at their roots to mountains. The Indras among elephants are maddened. The Indras among bulls are delighted. The Indras among animals[163] are resting even more in the forests. The Indras among mountains are beautiful. The Indras among men[164] have withdrawn from their campaigns. The Indra among gods is playing around with the clouds. Enveloped with water, the roads have become like enemies and the soldiers cannot proceed along the roads. Therefore, kings have stopped their campaigns. For brahmanas who wish to learn about the brahman and the singing of the Sama Veda, the time for studying, the month of Proshthapada,[165] has arrived. Having completed the task of accumulating riches, Bharata, the lord of Kosala, must have started the vow for Ashadha.[166] The Sarayu must certainly be swirling with water now. It must be making a roar like the one Ayodhya used to make when it saw me return. This

---

[163] Lions.

[164] Kings.

[165] Proshthapada is a nakshatra. More accurately, it is a collective name for two nakshatras, Purva Bhadrapada and Uttara Bhadrapada. The month of Bhadrapada, or Bhadra, is the August–September period.

[166] A *chaturmasya* sacrifice is a sacrifice performed once every four (*chatur*) months (*masa*) and is performed at the beginnings of the months of Kartika, Phalguna and Ashadha. This reference is to the one that starts on the full moon day of Ashadha.

monsoon season is prosperous with many qualities and Sugriva must
be enjoying the objects of pleasure. Having conquered the enemy, he
has his wife and kingdom and has established himself on earth. But
my wife has been abducted and I have been dislodged from a great
kingdom. O Lakshmana! I am suffering and have been devastated,
like the bank of a river. Since the monsoon has made everything
extremely impassable, my grief has been enhanced. It seems to me
that the journey to Ravana, my great enemy, is impassable. The
path is extremely difficult to traverse and I can see that one can't
travel now. Sugriva is also devoted to me. However, I have not told
him anything. After all, he has suffered a great deal and has met his
wife after a long time. Given the heavy nature of my task, I do not
desire to speak to the ape now. After resting, he will himself know
when the time has arrived. There is no doubt that Sugriva will repay
the favour. O auspicious Lakshmana! I will remain here, waiting for
that time and waiting for the favours of Sugriva and the rivers.[167]
A valiant one always repays debts resulting from something having
been done for him. Those who are virtuous in their mind are not
ungrateful, forgetting what has to be done in repayment.'

Having heard what had been said, Lakshmana joined his
hands in salutation and honoured the words that had been spoken.
Displaying the auspicious aspect of his own nature, he spoke to
Rama, who was agreeable to see. 'O Indra among men! Without
any delay, the lord of the apes will do everything that you have
said and desired. You must resort to patience and wait for autumn.
When the rains have stopped, the enemy will be chastised.'

Chapter 4(28)

The sky was clear and the lightning and clouds disappeared,
as did the flock of bustling cranes. The sky was smeared with
beautiful moonlight. Though Sugriva was prosperous in artha, he

---

[167] Because the rivers have to be crossed.

was not as swift in the pursuit of accumulating dharma. There was
only a single destination in his mind and he excessively pursued only
that objective. Now that his desired task had been accomplished,
he always sought pleasure with women. Having obtained what he
wanted, it was as if all his wishes had been satisfied. He desired
his own wife and he also desired Tara. Having accomplished his
objective and devoid of anxiety, day and night, he found pleasure
with them. He was like the lord of the gods, sporting in Nandana
with a large number of apsaras. He passed on all the tasks to the
ministers and did not supervise the ministers. Basing himself on
conduct that was full of desire, he paid no heed to news about the
kingdom.

Marut's son was clear about objectives. He knew about the
essence of artha. In particular, he knew about the dharma to be
followed at different times. He was accomplished in speech and
knew about how to use words. He sought the favours of the lord of
the apes and addressed him in beautiful and sweet words that were
full of reason. They were beneficial and truthful, like medication.
They were conciliatory, but represented good policy and were full
of dharma and artha. They were filled with love and affection and it
was certain that they would be heard. Hanumat went to the lord of
the apes and addressed him in these words. 'The kingdom and fame
have been obtained. The prosperity of the lineage has also been
enhanced. However, the task of accumulating friends still remains
to be done. A person who knows when it is time to make friends
conducts himself according to virtue. His kingdom, fame and power
are also enhanced. O lord of the earth! If a person has treasure, a
rod of chastisement, friends and his own self all working together,
then he obtains a great kingdom. Therefore, with good conduct, be
established on a path that has no dangers. You should do what your
friends approached you for. If a person does not perform a task for
a friend at the right time, then he does not accomplish the friend's
objective and brings a great calamity on to himself. O scorcher
of enemies! The time for accomplishing a task for our friend has
passed. Let us search out Vaidehi and perform Raghava's task. He
knows about time. O king! Though the time has passed, the wise

one remains subservient to you and is not hastening you. Raghava is like a flag for the lineage and prosperity. He is a friend who lasts for a long time. He is immeasurable in his own powers. No one, except he himself, can match his qualities. He has already accomplished the task that was to be done for you. Therefore, do the task for him now. O lord of apes! You should command the best among the apes. Until he actually urges us, the time has not quite passed. Once he urges us, the time for accomplishing the task will be reckoned to have been over. O lord of the apes! You have undertaken tasks for those who have done nothing for you. Why are you then not paying back someone who has given you the kingdom and riches? You are strong and valiant. You are the lord of a large number of apes and bears. Do what will bring pleasure to Dasharatha's son. Why are you not issuing the command? Indeed, if he so desires, Dasharatha's son can use his arrows to subjugate the gods, the asuras and the giant serpents. However, he wants you to fulfil the pledge. Without being scared of losing his own life, he accomplished something agreeable for you. Let us search out Vaidehi, on earth, or in the sky. The gods, the gandharvas, the asuras, the large numbers of Maruts and the yakshas can cause him no fear. What can the rakshasas do? He possesses strength, and earlier, used it to do what was agreeable to you. O lord of the tawny ones! You should do everything to bring pleasure to Rama. O lord of apes! If you command us, who will be able to obstruct our passage in the nether regions, the water, or the sky? Therefore, command us about who will exert himself to go where and for what purpose. O unblemished one! There are more than one crore of invincible apes.'

These virtuous words were appropriate for the occasion. Sugriva was full of spirit. On hearing them, he took an excellent decision. He commanded Nila, who was always full of enterprise, to gather all the soldiers from all the different directions. 'Act so that all the soldiers and all the leaders of the groups assemble quickly, with the best of armies. Swiftly follow my command. Let all the apes who are fleet and enterprising be stationed as guards at the perimeters. Summon all of them swiftly. You should yourself be at the centre of the army. If any ape comes here after fifteen nights, without even thinking about it, he will be punished by taking away his life. With Angada, approach the aged apes. Tell them that I have made up my mind about these instructions.' Arranging for all this, the valiant one entered his residence.

Chapter 4(29)

When the sky was free of clouds, Sugriva entered his cave. Overcome by desire and sorrow, Rama had spent the monsoon nights there. He saw the clear sky and the sparkling lunar disc. He saw the autumn night, smeared by the moonlight. Sugriva was engaged in acts of desire, though Janaka's daughter had been lost. He saw that the time had passed. He was severely afflicted and senseless.[168] The intelligent one regained his senses in a short while. Vaidehi was in Raghava's heart and he started to think about her. He was seated on the summit of the mountain, decorated with gold and other ores. When he saw the autumn sky, in his mind, the thoughts of his beloved came to his mind. 'The beautiful one found delight in the calling of these cranes and her voice was like the calling of a crane. The child used to find delight in the hermitage. How can she find delight now? On seeing the sparkling, blossoming and golden *asana* trees, how can the child find pleasure, when she cannot see me? Earlier, the one who is beautiful in her limbs, who speaks in a melodious voice, used to wake up to the melodious sounds of geese calling. How will she wake up now? She used to hear the sounds of the chakravakas, which roam around in couples. How is the one with eyes like a white lotus now? Without the doe-eyed one, I find no pleasure in roaming around the lakes, rivers, wells, groves and forests. Because of separation from me, Kama[169] will severely and incessantly afflict the delicate and beautiful one, when the qualities

---

[168] The time for honouring the pledge had passed. The point is that Sugriva had not told Rama about his instructions to Nila and neither Nila, nor Hanumat, could directly inform Rama. That was Sugriva's call.

[169] The god of love.

of the autumn have manifested themselves.' The son of a king, best among men, lamented in this way, like a *saranga* bird[170] that craves water from the lord of the gods.

The prosperous Lakshmana had wandered around the beautiful summit of the mountain, searching for fruits. On his return, he saw his elder brother. He was immersed in these intolerable thoughts. The spirited one was alone, deprived of his senses. On witnessing his brother's grief and lamentations, he was filled with sorrow. Soumitri addressed Rama. 'O noble one! What is the point in becoming subjugated to desire? What is achieved by your own manliness being defeated and taken away? What is the point of losing control and retreating from our path? Quieten your mind and do what needs to be done. The time has come to meditate on what needs to be done. Without a distressed spirit, depending on the capability of your aides, you should perform your own task. O protector of human lineages! With you as a protector, Janakee cannot be easily obtained by anyone else. O brave one! O one who deserves to be supreme! No one can approach the crest of a blazing fire and not be burnt.' The unassailable Lakshmana, who possessed all the natural qualities, spoke these comforting words, as beneficial as medicament, filled with good policy and immersed in dharma and artha.

Rama replied, 'We must certainly look towards what needs to be done and follow the specific courses of action. O prince! Without thinking about the fruits of valour and the act, we must engage in the task, even if it is extremely difficult.' After this, he thought about Maithilee, the lotus-eyed one. With his mouth dry, Rama spoke to Lakshmana. 'The one with the thousand eyes has satisfied the earth with water. Having performed the task of making the crops sprout, he has withdrawn. O son of a king! Thundering gently and with a deep voice from the tops of mountains and trees, the clouds have released their water and are now exhausted. They are as dark as clumps of blue lotuses. Having made the ten directions dark, the force of the clouds has now been quietened, like elephants no

---

[170] Chataka.

longer intoxicated with desire. O amiable one! The rain resulted in an extremely forceful storm, that bore the fragrance of *kutaja* and arjuna flowers and was filled with water. Having rushed around, it has withdrawn now. O Lakshmana! The sound of clouds, elephants, peacocks and waterfalls has suddenly been pacified. After the great clouds showered down on them, the summits of the mountains are clear and sparkling. They seem to have been smeared with radiance from the moon's beams. In the autumn, the river is revealing its banks very slowly, like a woman is ashamed when she gently reveals her hips, after having just indulged in an act of sexual intercourse. O amiable one! Curlews are calling in the sparkling water. Filled with large numbers of chakravakas, the waterbodies are radiant. O son of a king! O amiable one! For kings who bear enmity and desire to triumph over each other, the time for endeavour has presented itself. O son of a king! This is when kings set out on their first expeditions. However, I do not see any enterprise on Sugriva's part and he is not acting accordingly. The four months of the rainy season have passed and it has been like one hundred years.[171] O amiable one! On not being able to see Sita, I am tormented by grief. Since I have been separated from my beloved, I am afflicted by misery. I have been banished and have been deprived of my kingdom. O Lakshmana! King Sugriva is not exhibiting any compassion towards me. I have lost my kingdom and am without a protector. I have been oppressed by Ravana. I am distressed and am far from home. I am suffering from desire. He knows I have sought refuge with him. O amiable one! O scorcher of enemies! Perhaps the evil-souled king of the apes thinks of these reasons and takes me to have been subjugated. He computed the time required to search Sita out. The evil-minded one does not understand that he has contracted an agreement with me. Go and enter Kishkindha. Tell Sugriva, bull among the apes, my words. He is stupid and is addicted to carnal pleasures. "When someone who has performed a good act earlier arrives in search of some objective, a person who destroys hopes and the pledge, is the

---

[171] Since four months have passed since Sugriva's coronation, this must be the end of Kartika.

worst among the men of this world. If a person adheres to good or
bad words spoken at the time of a pledge, such a supreme person
is best among men. Whether successful or unsuccessful, those who
do not act like friends, when they are dead, even predatory beasts
do not eat the flesh from their carcasses. There is no doubt that
you wish to see me stretch my bow, with a golden back, in battle.
That bow's form is like flashes of lightning. When I am enraged
in a battle, the sound of the bowstring slapping against my palm
is terrible. You again wish to hear the rumble of that thunder."[172]
O son of a king! However, he knows about my valour and must
have fallen prey to desire. O brave one! As long as I have you as
my aide, I am not worried. O vanquisher of enemy cities! The lord
of the apes thinks he has accomplished his objective and does not
remember the pledge, nor the reason why we started on this course
of action.[173] The lord of the apes took a pledge about acting after
the monsoon period was over. However, he is amusing himself
and does not understand that the four months have passed. He is
drinking liquor and sporting with his advisers and companions.
Sugriva does not show any compassion towards us, who are
miserable and distressed. O child! O immensely strong one! It is
appropriate that you should go to Sugriva and tell him about the
form my rage is taking. Also tell him these words. "The path along
which the slain Vali advanced has not withered away. O Sugriva!
Adhere to your pledge. Do not follow Vali's path. With a single of
my arrows, Vali was slain in the battle. However, if you transgress
truth, I will slay you with your relatives." O bull among men! Our
beneficial task is being obstructed. O best among men! Therefore,
without any delay, quickly speak to him accordingly. "O lord of
the apes! Look towards eternal dharma and the pledge given and
act truthfully. Otherwise, you will now be goaded by my arrows
and follow Vali towards death and Yama's eternal abode."' He[174]
saw his distressed elder brother lamenting, with his rage increasing.

---

[172] Though the text does not clearly indicate this, the part within quotes is obviously
the message to be delivered by Lakshmana to Sugriva.

[173] The slaying of Vali.

[174] Lakshmana.

Therefore, the extender of the human lineage,[175] fierce in his energy, had harsh thoughts about the lord of the apes.

Chapter 4(30)

The son of the Indra among men,[176] the son of the god among men, was miserable and distressed in his spirit, overwhelmed by desire. Enveloped by grief, his rage increased. Rama's younger brother addressed his older brother. 'The ape will not adhere to the conduct of virtuous people. He will not think of the fruits that are consequent to actions. He will not enjoy the prosperity of the kingdom of the apes. That is the reason his intelligence does not look forward. Because of his addiction to carnal pleasures, his intelligence has been destroyed. His intelligence does not turn towards repaying what he has obtained through your favours. Let him see how his elder brother, Vali, was slain and realize that kingdoms should not be given to those who are devoid of qualities. I cannot control this anger, as its force is increasing. I will slay the false Sugriva today. After that, with the best of the apes and with Vali's son, I will search out the daughter of the king.'[177] Angry and ferocious, wishing to fight, he spoke these purposeful words. He leapt up from his seat and seized his arrows. Rama, the slayer of enemy heroes, looked towards him and spoke these words of persuasion. 'A person like you should not act in this wicked way. A noble person who slays his anger is brave and supreme among men. O Lakshmana! Following the affection we bore towards him earlier and the friendly conduct, a person like you, virtuous in conduct, should not act in this ordinary way now. Abandon harsh words and speak to him in conciliatory tones. You should tell Sugriva that the stipulated time period has passed.'

Instructed by his elder brother about what would be better, the bull among men acted exactly in that way. Lakshmana, the

[175] This is a reference to Lakshmana.
[176] Rama.
[177] Sita.

brave slayer of enemy heroes, entered the city. He was auspicious
in his intelligence and wise, engaged in ensuring what would be
agreeable and beneficial for his brother. Controlling his anger,
Lakshmana went to the ape's residence. He wielded a bow that
was like Shakra's bow. When he held it up, he looked like Mount
Mandara, with one of its peaks jutting up, and like the Destroyer.
Rama's younger brother was like Brihaspati[178] in his intelligence.
Obeying what he had been told, he thought about the order in
which he should organize his words. He was enveloped in a fire
of rage, resulting from the anger and desire[179] in his brother.
Lakshmana proceeded, as turbulent as a storm. He advanced with
force, bringing down sala, tala, ashvakarna and other trees and
shattering the tops of the mountain with his speed and strength. As
he proceeded like a swift elephant, he splintered boulders with his
steps. Since he wished to advance quickly on his designated task,
there was a long distance between one stride and the next. He saw
the great city of the king of the apes, surrounded by an army. The
tiger of the Ikshvaku lineage saw the impenetrable Kishkindha,
nestling in the mountain. With lips that were quivering because of
his rage against Sugriva, Lakshmana saw terrible apes patrolling
around Kishkindha's boundary. He was like an elephant and on
seeing him, the apes in that mountain seized hundreds of mountain
peaks and large trees. Seeing that they had seized weapons,
Lakshmana's rage was doubled, like a fire into which kindling has
been fed. Seeing him arrive, like Destiny or Death at the end of a
yuga, there were hundreds of apes whose limbs became suffused
with fear. They fled in different directions. Those bulls among
apes entered Sugriva's residence and told him that Lakshmana was
arriving in rage.

However, that bull among apes was busy satisfying his desire
with Tara and did not listen to what those brave apes said. The
advisers instructed some apes, whose complexions were like
mountains, elephants or clouds, and who therefore, made the body

[178] The preceptor of the gods.
[179] For Sita.

hair stand up. All those brave ones were terrible and malformed.
With nails and teeth as weapons, they emerged from the city. All
of them were like tigers in their insolence. All of them possessed
disfigured faces. Some of them possessed the strength of ten
elephants, others strength that was ten times more. There were some
whose valour was equal to that of one thousand elephants. The
angry Lakshmana saw the unassailable Kishkindha, covered with
extremely strong apes who held trees in their hands. All those apes
emerged from inside the walls and the moats. They were suddenly
seen there, fierce in their spirit. On seeing them, the brave and
controlled one remembered Sugriva's transgression and his elder
brother's objective and was again suffused with rage. His sighs were
warm and long. His eyes turned red with rage. The tiger among men
was like a fire with smoke. Because of his energy, he was like a five-
hooded serpent filled with poison. His bow was like the serpent's
hood and the arrows were like flickering tongues. He blazed like the
fire of destruction. He was as enraged as an Indra among serpents.
When he approached, Angada was terrified and filled with great
sorrow. His eyes coppery red with rage, the immensely illustrious
one instructed Angada, 'Let Sugriva be informed about my arrival.
Tell him that Rama's younger brother, the destroyer of enemies, has
come to see him. Tormented by his brother's hardship, Lakshmana
is waiting at the gate.'

Hearing Lakshmana's words, Angada was filled with sorrow.
He went to his father[180] and said, 'Lakshmana has come here.'
On seeing Lakshmana nearby, like a gigantic storm, they roared
like lions,[181] in a tone that was like that of lightning and thunder.
Because of that great noise, the ape[182] woke up. His garlands and
ornaments were scattered around and his eyes were coppery red,
intoxicated with liquor. Hearing Angada's words, two respected
advisers who were broad in their outlook also approached the Indra
among the apes. These two, the advisers Plaksha and Prabhava, also

---

[180] Sugriva.

[181] The Critical Edition excises some shlokas and that breaks the continuity. The
apes roared, on seeing Lakshmana.

[182] Sugriva.

told him about Lakshmana's arrival, using words that were full of
dharma and artha. They placated Sugriva in words of conciliation,
while he was seated like Shakra, the lord of the Maruts. 'The two
immensely fortunate brothers, Rama and Lakshmana, have truth
as their objective. They have come to you as friends. Though they
deserved the kingdom, they bestowed the kingdom on you. One of
them, Lakshmana, is at the door, with a bow in his hand. Since they
are terrified of him and are trembling, the apes are emitting this
roar. Raghava's brother, Lakshmana, is on a chariot made out of
words. He has come here on Rama's instructions, using a chariot
that is the objective. With your son and your relatives, bow your
head down at his feet. O king! You should adhere to the truth and
the pledge that you yourself took.'

Chapter 4(31)

Hearing Angada's words and those of his ministers and learning
that Lakshmana was angry, the controlled Sugriva arose from
his seat. He was established in good advice, knew about counsels
and was accomplished in following proper policy. He told them,
'I have not shown any misconduct towards them, nor have I done
them any harm. I am wondering why Lakshmana, Raghava's
brother, should be angry with me. My ill-wishers and enemies are
always seeking out blemishes in me. They must have told Raghava's
younger brother about my sins that aren't real. That being the
case, all of you accomplished ones use your intelligence and all
your techniques to gently determine what his sentiments are. On
account of Lakshmana or Raghava, I do not suffer from any fear.
However, if a friend is unnecessarily angry, that does lead me to
worry. It is always extremely easy to make a friend, but satisfying
that friendship is very difficult. The mind is fickle and a trifle is
enough to shatter affection. That is the reason I am scared of the
great-souled Rama. I am incapable of repaying the good deed that
he has done to me.'

When Sugriva said this, in the midst of the apes who were advisers, Hanumat, bull among the apes, voiced his own arguments. 'O lord of a large number of apes! It is not at all surprising that you should never forget the auspicious and extremely gentle deed that has been done towards you. The brave Raghava flung his fear far away. To accomplish a desirable objective for you, he slew Vali, who was like Shakra in his valour. Raghava is always affectionate towards you, but there is no doubt that he is angry. That is the reason he urged his brother Lakshmana, the extender of prosperity. O one who is supreme among those who know about time! Since you were intoxicated, you did not know that time had passed. The auspicious autumn has presented itself and is pervaded by dark and blossoming seven-leaves.[183] The planets and nakshatras are in a clear sky and the clouds have been dispelled. All the directions, the rivers and the lakes are pleasant. O bull among the apes! The time for action has arrived, but you did not realize this. It is evident that you were intoxicated and that is the reason Lakshmana has come here. With his wife abducted, the great-souled Raghava is afflicted. His harsh words, sent through another person,[184] should be tolerated. You have committed a crime. I do not see a way other than that of joining your hands in salutation and seeking Lakshmana's favours and forgiveness. The appointed ministers must certainly speak words that are for the king's benefit. That is the reason I have cast aside my fear and have addressed you in these steadfast words. If Raghava is enraged, he is capable of raising his bow and bringing the entire world, with the gods, the asuras and the gandharvas, under his subjugation. If one can seek his favours, one should not anger him. In particular, you should be grateful and remember the good deed he has done towards you earlier. With your son and your well-wishers, bow your head down and prostrate yourself before him. O king! Like a wife who is obedient towards her husband, adhere to the pledge you have yourself made. O Indra among the apes! You should cast aside any thoughts you might have of not

---

[183] Plantain trees have seven leaves.
[184] Lakshmana.

sticking to Rama's and Rama's younger brother's instructions. In
your mind, you know about the human strength of Raghava, who
is like Indra of the gods in his radiance.'

Chapter 4(32)

Following Rama's instructions and invited in this way,
Lakshmana, the destroyer of enemy heroes, entered the beautiful
cave of Kishkindha.[185] There were immensely strong apes at the gate,
gigantic in size. On seeing Lakshmana, they joined their hands in
salutation and stood there. The apes saw that Dasharatha's son was
angry and was sighing. Therefore, they were terrified and did not
surround him. He saw that huge cave, divinely beautiful and filled
with jewels and flowering groves. It was handsome, strewn with
gems. There were mansions, palaces and walls, adorned with many
kinds of wares. It was ornamented with flowering trees, laden with
fruits that yielded every object of desire. The apes were the sons of
gods and gandharvas and could assume any form at will. They were
handsome and pleasant in appearance, wearing celestial garlands
and garments. There were beautiful fragrances from sandalwood,
aloe and lotuses. The large roads seemed to be intoxicated with
maireya and *madhu* trees.[186] There were multi-story palaces that
were like the mountains Vindhya and Meru. Raghava saw sparkling
mountain streams there. Along the royal road, Lakshmana saw
the expansive and handsome houses of the best among the apes—
Angada, Mainda, Dvivida, Gavaya, Gavaksha, Gaja, Sharabha,
Vidyunmali, Subahu, the great-souled Nala, Kumuda, Sushena,
Tara, Jambavat, Dadhivaktra, Nila, Supatala and Sunetra. They
looked like white clouds and were decorated with divine garlands.
They were ornamented with large quantities of riches and grain and

---

[185] Kishkindha is often referred to as a cave (*guha*). However, as this chapter makes
clearer, Kishkindha was much more than an ordinary cave.

[186] Maireya is made from molasses or grain. A maireya tree probably means sugar cane.
Madhu is the madhuka tree, used to make liquor.

with gems among women. The handsome house of the Indra among
the apes was like the great Indra's residence. It was extremely
difficult to approach and a white mountain offered protection all
around it. The white summit of the palace was like the summit
of Kailasa. There were flowering trees, with fruits that yielded all
the objects of desire. It was prosperous and had been bestowed
by the great Indra. It was like a dark blue cloud. There were trees
with divine flowers and fruits, offering cool and pleasant shade.
Powerful apes protected the entrance, with weapons in their hands.
The sparkling gates were made out of molten gold and were covered
with celestial garlands.

The immensely strong Soumitri entered Sugriva's beautiful
residence, like a sun that cannot be impeded entering a giant cloud.
The one with dharma in his soul passed through seven chambers
that were filled with vehicles and seats. He entered an extremely
protected area and saw the gigantic inner quarters. There were many
couches made out of gold and silver and with supreme seats. They
were resplendent there, covered with extremely expensive spreads.
As soon as he entered, he heard the continuous sound of sweet music.
There was the sound of singing and the quatrains and syllables of the
songs were even.[187] In Sugriva's residence, the immensely strong one
saw many women of diverse types, proud of their youth and beauty.
Those noble ladies were fashioning garlands made out of flowers.
Adorned in excellent garments, they were eagerly fashioning these
excellent garlands. They were all content and were not anxious. All
of them were attired in wonderful garments. Lakshmana noticed the
female servants who waited upon Sugriva. Sugriva was seated on a
golden and excellent throne that was covered with an extremely
expensive spread. He saw him, looking like the sun. There were
colourful and divine ornaments on his limbs and the illustrious one
had a divine form. With divine ornaments and garments, he was
as invincible as the great Indra. He was surrounded by women,
wearing divine ornaments and garlands. The brave one, with a
complexion like that of excellent gold, was seated on that excellent

[187] That is, not discordant.

throne, closely embracing Ruma. Not distressed in spirit, the large-eyed one looked at the large-eyed Soumitri.

Chapter 4(33)

Lakshmana, bull among men, angrily entered, unobstructed. On seeing him, Sugriva's senses were afflicted. He saw Dasharatha's son, tormented because of his brother's hardship, blazing in his energy and sighing angrily. The best among apes left his golden throne and leapt up, as if a large and ornamented standard of the great Indra was being raised up. When he leapt up, so did Ruma and the other women. It was as if Sugriva was the full moon in the sky, surrounded by a large number of stars. His eyes red,[188] the handsome one joined his hands in salutation and lurched forward. He stood there, like a giant *kalpavriksha*.[189] As Sugriva stood amidst the women, like the moon among stars, Ruma was the second one who stood there.

Lakshmana spoke to him. 'A king who is spirited, noble in birth, compassionate, grateful, truthful in speech and one who has conquered his senses is said to be great in this world. But who can be more cruel than a king who is established in adharma, harms his friends and takes false pledges? Falsehood is tantamount to killing one hundred horses.[190] Falsehood is tantamount to killing one thousand cows. A man who indulges in falsehood kills himself and his relatives for several generations. O lord of the apes! If a person does not repay the good deeds friends have formerly done to make him attain his objectives, he is an ingrate. Among all creatures, he is the one who deserves to be killed. On seeing an ungrateful person, Brahma, worshipped by all the worlds, was enraged and chanted a shloka. O ape! Hear it. "The virtuous have laid down means of atonement for the sins of killing a cow, drinking liquor, theft and

---

[188] Because of liquor.
[189] Tree that yields all the objects of desire.
[190] The sin of killing one hundred horses.

breaking a vow. But there is no salvation for an ingrate." O ape!
You are ignoble and ungrateful. You are also false in speech. Rama
performed a good deed for you earlier, but you are not paying him
back. O ape! Through Rama, you have indeed accomplished your
task. He desired that you should make efforts to search out Sita.
You took a false pledge and are engaged in carnal pursuits. Rama
did not recognize you as a snake, though you croak like a frog. You
are wicked and evil-souled. Driven by compassion, the immensely
fortunate and great-souled Rama conferred the kingdom of the
apes on you. You are not recognizing what Rama, unblemished in
his deeds, has done for you. You will instantly be slain with sharp
arrows and will see Vali. The slain Vali proceeded along a path
that has still not been withdrawn. O Sugriva! Stick to your pledge
and do not follow Vali's path. It is certain that you have not seen
arrows, which are like the vajra, being shot from the bow of one
who is best among those of the Ikshvaku lineage. That is the reason
your mind has not looked towards Rama's task and you are happy
in your pursuit of a pleasure that goes by the name of happiness.'

Chapter 4(34)

Blazing in his energy, Soumitri said this. Tara, whose face was like
the lord of the stars, spoke to Lakshmana.[191] 'O Lakshmana!
The lord of the apes does not deserve to hear the harsh words that
he has just heard, especially from the lips of someone like you.
Sugriva is not ungrateful, deceitful or terrible. O brave one! The
lord of the apes has not indulged in duplicity, or uttered a falsehood.
O brave one! The ape has not forgotten the good deed that was
done to him. O brave one! In an encounter, Rama did for Sugriva
what anyone else would find extremely difficult to accomplish.
O scorcher of enemies! It is because of Rama's favours and deeds
that the ape Sugriva has obtained this eternal kingdom, Ruma and

[191] The moon is the lord of the stars (tara) and there is a play on the word Tara.

me. He used to lie down in extreme hardship earlier and has now obtained this supreme delight. Like the sage Vishvamitra, he did not realize that the appointed time had arrived. O Lakshmana! Attached to Ghritachee,[192] Vishvamitra, the great sage, with dharma in his soul, spent ten years and thought that only a single day had elapsed. The immensely energetic Vishvamitra is supreme among those who know about time. But even he did not realize that the appointed time had arrived, not to speak of ordinary people. O Lakshmana! Satisfying the dharma of the body, he was exhausted. His desire was not satiated. Rama should pardon him. O father![193] O Lakshmana! You should not suddenly succumb to anger, like an ordinary person, without ascertaining and knowing the details. O bull among men! Spirited men like you do not rashly and suddenly succumb to rage. O one who knows about dharma! For Sugriva's sake, I am controlling myself and seeking your favours. Cast aside this intolerance and great rage that has arisen. To bring pleasure to Rama, Sugriva will fling away Ruma and me, and this kingdom of the apes with its wealth, grain and riches. That is my view. Having slain Ravana in a battle, Sugriva will bring Sita and unite her with Raghava, like the moon god with Rohini.[194] Indeed, there are one trillion, three hundred and sixty thousand, one hundred thousand and one thousand rakshasas in Lanka.[195] Without slaying those invincible rakshasas, who can assume any form at will, one will not be capable of killing Ravana, Maithilee's abductor. Ravana is cruel in his deeds. O Lakshmana! Without an aide, someone like Sugriva will not be able to kill him.[196]

---

[192] An apsara. Usually, Vishvamitra is associated with the apsara Menaka.

[193] The word used is tata. Lakshmana is senior, though not in age. Therefore, 'father' is more likely than 'son'.

[194] The nakshatras are the wives of the moon, but the moon loves Rohini (Aldebaran) more than the others.

[195] Because of the way the numbers are written in the shloka, anything other than the one trillion can be interpreted in more than one way. Suffice to say that there were a large number of rakshasas. How could Tara possibly know this? The story goes that Vali told Angada and Tara overheard the conversation.

[196] Sugriva will not be able to kill Ravana without Rama's help. This is sometimes interpreted as Rama not being able to kill Ravana without Sugriva's help, but that interpretation seems forced.

Vali, the learned lord of the apes, said this. It is not evident to me how all of them assembled there.[197] I have only told you what I have heard. It is to help you that all the bulls among apes have been sent. A large number of apes, bulls among apes, are being summoned for the battle. That is the reason the lord of the apes has not ventured out to accomplish Raghava's objective. He is awaiting the arrival of those valiant and extremely strong ones. O Soumitri! Because of the good arrangements Sugriva had made earlier, all those extremely strong apes will arrive here today.[198] Crores and thousands of bears and hundreds of golangulas will present themselves before you today. O scorcher of enemies! Conquer your anger. O Kakutstha! There will be crores of apes who will blaze in their energy. On looking at your face, full of rage, and at your eyes, which seem to be wounded,[199] the wives of the best among the apes can find no peace. All of them are disturbed because of the first signs of fear.'[200]

Chapter 4(35)

Soumitri was gentle in nature. He heard these words spoken by Tara, full of dharma, and accepted the statement. When he accepted those words, the lord of the large number of apes cast aside his great fear of Lakshmana, like casting aside a wet garment. There was a large and colourful garland, with many qualities, around his neck. Sugriva, the lord of the apes, shredded this and forgot his intoxication. Sugriva, supreme among all the apes, delighted Lakshmana, whose strength was terrible, with these words. 'My prosperity, deeds and this eternal kingdom of the apes were destroyed. O Soumitri! It is because of Rama's favours that I got them back again. That god is famous because of his own deeds. O brave one! O destroyer of

---

[197] How so many rakshasas came to be in Lanka.

[198] We are subsequently told, in Chapter 4 (36), that a time limit of ten days has been set.

[199] As red as a wound.

[200] Or, former signs of fear, such as when Vali was destroyed.

enemies! With the valour that he possesses, who is capable of paying him back? Raghava, with dharma in his soul, will use his own energy to get Sita back and slay Ravana. I can only be an aide. Indeed, why does he need an aide? With a single arrow, he penetrated seven large trees and shattered a mountain and the earth. O Lakshmana! From the sound of his twanging the bow, the mountains and the earth tremble. Why does he need help? O bull among men! I will follow that Indra among men when he leads and advances to slay his enemy, Ravana. If I have transgressed in any way, out of trust and affection, a messenger must always pardon. I have committed no crime.'

When the great-souled Sugriva said this, Lakshmana spoke these words, full of love and affection. 'O lord of the apes! My brother always has a protector. O Sugriva! You are the protector, especially since you are humble. O Sugriva! Your powers and supreme purity are such that you deserve to enjoy this excellent prosperity of the kingdom of the apes. O Sugriva! There is no doubt that with you as an aide, the powerful Rama will soon slay the enemy in a battle. You know about dharma. You are grateful. You do not retreat from the field of battle. O Sugriva! What you have spoken is full of logic. O supreme among apes! With the exception of my elder brother and you, who else is capable of recognizing one's own taints and speaking in this way? In valour and strength, you are Rama's equal. O bull among apes! After a long time, destiny has supplied you as an aide. O brave one! Quickly leave this place with me. Go and comfort your friend, who is miserable because his wife has been abducted. I heard the words spoken by Rama, when he was overwhelmed with grief. O friend! Therefore, I addressed you in harsh words. Please pardon me.'

Chapter 4(36)

When the great-souled Lakshmana spoke to Sugriva in this way, he[201] spoke to his adviser, Hanumat, who was standing

[201] Sugriva.

next to him. 'Swiftly summon the apes who are there on the five mountains of Mahendra, Himalayas, Vindhya, the summit of Kailasa and the white summit of Mandara; those who are there in the mountain that is always radiant, with a complexion like that of the rising sun;[202] those who are there in the western direction, in the mountain that is always radiant beyond the ocean, the sun's abode, with the hue of evening clouds;[203] the terrible bulls among apes who reside in groves of lotuses and palm trees; the apes who reside in Mount Anjana, like elephants in their energy and with the complexion of dark clouds; the apes who are golden in complexion and reside in the cave known as Manahshila; those who reside on the slopes of Meru and Mount Dhumra; those apes, terrible in force, who reside on Mount Maharuna, which is like the rising sun in hue, and drink maireya liquor there; and those who dwell in large and extremely fragrant groves and everywhere in the beautiful extremities of the forests where there are ascetics. Quickly summon all the apes from all over the earth. Quickly send messengers to those apes and summon them with gifts and conciliation. First, sent my messengers, those who are extremely fast. After that, to make them hasten, send other apes. There are apes who procrastinate, addicted to desire. On my instructions, swiftly fetch all of them here. Those who do not follow my command and do not assemble within ten days, will be regarded as those who defile the king's command. Those evil-souled ones should be killed. On my instructions, let hundreds, thousands and crores of lions among apes depart. Let all those in the different directions follow my command. Let the best among apes, terrible in form, and like mountains and clouds, follow my command and leave for this place. Let them shroud the firmament. There are apes who know about the routes. Let all of them follow the paths to everywhere on earth. Let them swiftly follow my command and fetch all the apes here.'

Hearing the words of the king of the apes, Vayu's son[204] dispatched valiant apes in all the directions. In an instant, sent by

[202] Mount Udaya, the sun rises from behind this.
[203] Mount Asta, the sun sets behind this.
[204] Hanumat.

the king, the apes departed. They leapt up,[205] like birds and stellar bodies. They followed the footsteps of the valiant Vishnu.[206] To accomplish Rama's objective, those apes urged all the apes who were in the oceans, mountains, forests and lakes. The king of the apes was like Death, Destiny, or Kubera. Hearing Sugriva's command, they arrived. They were scared of Sugriva. Raghava was on a mountain[207] that had the complexion of a dark cloud. Three crores of extremely swift apes left from that place. There were those who were in that supreme mountain, with a complexion like heated gold, behind which, the sun sets.[208] Ten crores left from there. The summit of Kailasa is as radiant as a lion's mane. One thousand crores of apes arrived from there. There were those who resided in the Himalayas, surviving on fruits and roots. Ten trillion assembled from there. There were apes from Vindhya, terrible in their deeds and as terrible as Angaraka.[209] One thousand crores swiftly arrived from there. There were those who had homes on the shores of the milky ocean, dwelling in tamala groves. They survived on coconut fruit. Their numbers were unknown.[210] An extremely large army of extremely swift apes arrived from forests, caves and rivers. They seemed to drink up the rays of the sun.[211] Among all the apes, there were some brave apes who had swiftly gone to the Himalaya mountains. They saw a giant tree there. On that beautiful and supreme mountain, Maheshvara had performed a sacrifice in ancient times and that divine and lovely sacrifice had satisfied the minds of all the gods. From the resultant food,[212] fruits and roots were generated and the apes saw those there, as succulent as amrita. From the food, divine and agreeable fruits and roots were created. If one eats these, one is satisfied for a

[205] Into the sky.

[206] This is a reference to Vishnu's vamana (dwarf) incarnation, where Vishnu covered heaven, the earth and the nether regions in three steps.

[207] Prasravana.

[208] Mount Asta.

[209] Mars.

[210] That is, there were a large number, innumerable.

[211] They covered the sky and blanked out the sun.

[212] Offered at the sacrifice.

month.[213] The leaders of the apes, those who survived on fruit, collected those divine roots and fruits and the divine herbs. The apes went to the place where the sacrifice had been held and to bring pleasure to Sugriva, collected the fragrant flowers. All the apes urged the supreme among apes on earth to hurry and returned, ahead of the herds. The herds were extremely swift and in an instant, hastened and reached Kishkindha, where the ape Sugriva was. There were apes who had collected all the herbs, fruits and roots. They made him accept these and spoke these words. 'Following your command, all the apes on earth, all those who dwell in mountains, oceans and forests, are coming here to you.' Hearing these words, Sugriva, the lord of the apes, was delighted. Delighted, he accepted everything that they had brought.

Chapter 4(37)

He accepted everything that they had collected and brought. He comforted all the apes and gave them leave to go. He granted permission to all the brave apes who had accomplished their task. He thought that the immensely strong Raghava, and he himself, had become successful. He was supreme among all the apes and was terrible in his strength. Lakshmana spoke reassuring words to him and delighted Sugriva. 'O amiable one! If it pleases you, let us leave Kishkindha.' He heard the excellent words spoken by Lakshmana. Sugriva was extremely happy and replied in these words. 'I will abide by your instructions. Let us go then.' Sugriva said this to Lakshmana, who was auspicious in his signs. He took his leave of Tara and the other women. Sugriva addressed the best among the apes, 'Come here.' Hearing his words, the apes arrived quickly. All those who were allowed to see the women came there and joined their hands in salutation.[214] When they arrived, the king, whose

---

[213] One does not have to eat for a month.

[214] Everyone was not allowed in the presence of the royal women in the inner quarters.

radiance was like that of the sun, addressed them. 'O apes! Quickly ready my palanquin.' Hearing his words, the apes, swift in their valour, readied and brought a handsome palanquin. The lord of the apes saw that the palanquin had been brought. He told Soumitri, 'O Lakshmana! Quickly mount it.' Saying this, Sugriva, whose complexion was like that of the sun, ascended that golden vehicle with Lakshmana. It was carried by many apes. A white umbrella was held above his head. In every direction, he was fanned with white whisks. The bards greeted him with the sounds of conch shells and drums. Sugriva, the possessor of supreme royal prosperity, departed. He was surrounded by hundreds of apes, wielding sharp weapons in their hands. He left for the spot where Rama was.

Having reached that excellent region, frequented by Rama, with Lakshmana, the immensely energetic one descended from the palanquin. He approached Rama and stood there, his hands joined in salutation. The other apes also stood there, their hands joined in salutation. Rama saw Sugriva and that large army of apes, resembling a lake filled with lotuses and lilies.[215] He was delighted. The lord of the apes was prostrate at his feet, his head lowered. Raghava raised him up. Showing him a lot of respect and affection, he embraced him. Having raised him up, the one with dharma in his soul asked him to be seated. When he saw that he had seated himself on the ground, Rama addressed him in these words. 'O brave one! O supreme among apes! A true king is a person who apportions time out for indulging in dharma, artha and kama. If someone abandons dharma and artha and only indulges in kama, he is like a person who sleeps on the top of a tree and only wakes up when he falls down. A king who bases himself in dharma, is engaged in slaying enemies and is also engaged in collecting friends, enjoys the fruits of all the three objectives.[216] O slayer of enemies! The time for exertion has presented itself. O lord of the tawny ones! With the apes who are your ministers, think about what needs to be done.'

[215] They raised their hands up, joined in salutation, and those looked like lotuses and lilies.

[216] *Trivarga* (three objectives of life)—dharma, artha and kama.

Thus addressed by Rama, Sugriva replied in these words. 'O mighty-armed one! Prosperity, deeds and the eternal kingdom of the apes were destroyed. It is through your favours that I have got them back again. O god! O supreme among victorious ones! It is through your favours and those of your brother that I have got them back. Among men, a person who does not pay back a good deed is reviled. O slayer of enemies! There are hundreds of supreme apes. They have returned after collecting all the strong apes on earth. O Raghava! There are bears, apes and brave golangulas. They are terrible to behold. They know about desolate regions and impenetrable forests. These apes are the sons of gods and gandharvas and can assume any form at will. O Raghava! Surrounded by their own respective soldiers, they are advancing along the paths. O scorcher of enemies! There are hundreds, hundreds of thousands, crores, *ayutas* and *shankus* of brave apes. [217] There are arbudas[218] of apes in the centre and hundreds of arbudas at the extremities. The apes and the leaders of herds of apes are arriving from the other shores of the oceans. O king! They are arriving, like the great Indra in their valour. Their form is like the Meru and Mandara. They have made their homes in the Vindhya and Meru. They are arriving so as to slay the rakshasas and their relatives in the battle. After Ravana has been slain in the battle, they will bring Maithilee back.'

Following the instructions of the intelligent lord of the apes, the arrangements had been made. On seeing this, the son of the king[219] rejoiced. His eyes, which looked like blue lotuses, dilated.

Chapter 4(38)

Sugriva spoke to Rama, supreme among those who uphold dharma, in this way, joining his hands in salutation. He embraced

---

[217] An ayuta is ten thousand. Shanku is the same as *shamkha* and means one hundred billion.

[218] One hundred million.

[219] Rama.

him in his arms and replied, 'O scorcher of enemies! As long as
Indra showers down during the monsoon and does not make the
earth bereft of colours, as long as the sun, with the one thousand
rays, removes the darkness from the sky, as long as the moon
makes the earth amiable and sparkling with its amiable beams, till
such time, let friends like you repay their debts. O amiable one! O
handsome one! O Sugriva! But this is not extraordinary in someone
like you. I know you as someone who is always pleasant in speech.
O friend! With you as a protector, I will triumph over all enemies.
A well-wisher and friend like you deserves to help me. By abducting
Vaidehi, the worst of the rakshasas has brought about his own
destruction, just as Anuhlada did with Shachi, Puloma's daughter.[220]
I will soon slay Ravana with sharp arrows, just as Shatakratu, the
destroyer of enemies, killed Poulami's insolent father.'

At this time, a dust arose and spread over the sky, enveloping the
hot and fierce radiance of the one with the thousand rays. Because
of that dust, the directions seemed to be anxious and senseless.
The earth, with all its mountains, forests and groves, started to
quake. The entire earth was covered with apes. They were like giant
mountains, extremely strong and with sharp teeth. Those leaders of
the apes could assume any form at will. In an instant, hundreds of
crores of them covered everything. There were extremely strong apes
from rivers, mountains and oceans. There were others who roamed
around in the forest. They thundered like clouds. There were those
who were like the rising sun in complexion. There were others who
were as fair as the moon and still others with the complexion of
lotus stamens. There were those who had made residences on the
Shveta and Meru. Surrounded by crores and tens of thousands of
handsome apes, a brave ape named Shatabali[221] was seen. Tara's
valiant father[222] was seen, with a complexion like that of a golden
mountain, and surrounded by many crores and tens of thousands.

[220] Anuhlada (or Anuhrada) was Hiranyakashipu's son and Prahlada's (or Prahrada)
brother. Shachi, married to Indra, was Puloma's (a demon) daughter. She was known as
Poulami. With Puloma's consent, Anuhlada abducted Shachi. Indra killed Puloma.

[221] Literally, one with the strength of one hundred.

[222] Sushena.

Hanumat's handsome father, Keshari was seen. His complexion was like that of lotus fibres, his face had the complexion of the sun. This intelligent and supreme ape was foremost among all the apes. He was surrounded by an army that consisted of thousands of apes. There was Gavaksha, the great king of golangulas and terrible in his valour. He was seen, surrounded by thousands of crores of apes. From among the bears, there was Dhumra, terrible in his speed and the slayer of enemies. He arrived, surrounded by two thousand crores. There was a leader of the herds named Panasa. The immensely valorous one arrived, surrounded by three crore of terrible ones who had complexions like giant mountains. There was a leader of the herds named Nila, with a form and complexion like that of a mass of black collyrium. That immensely gigantic one was seen, surrounded by ten crores. There was a powerful leader of the herds named Darimukha. Surrounded by one thousand crore, he presented himself before Sugriva. Mainda and Dvivida, the two immensely strong sons of the two Ashvins, were seen. Each was surrounded by one crore of apes. Gandhamadana arrived and thousands of crores and hundreds of thousands of apes followed him at the rear. Prince Angada arrived and he was like his father in valour. He was surrounded by one thousand *padmas*[223] and one hundred shamkhas. The ape Tara[224] was terrible in valour and was like the stars in his radiance. He was seen from a distance, with five crore of apes. The brave ape Indrajanu, leader of herds, was seen. The lord was surrounded by eleven crore. Rambha, with a complexion like that of the rising sun, arrived. He was surrounded by hundreds of thousands of ayutas. There was the brave ape named Durmukha, the leader of herds. The powerful one was seen, surrounded by two crore. Hanumat was seen surrounded by a thousand crore of apes who were terrible in valour and like the summit of Kailasa in form. The immensely valorous Nala arrived. He was surrounded by a hundred crore and a hundred thousand of those who dwelt on trees. There were Sharabha, Kumuda and the ape Vahni. These and many

---

[223] One thousand billion.
[224] Not to be confused with Taaraa.

other apes could assume any form at will. They enveloped the entire earth, with its mountains and forests. The apes roared, leapt up and jumped down. They approached Sugriva, like a large mass of clouds around the sun. Supreme in their strength, they uttered many kinds of sounds. The Indras among apes lowered their heads and presented themselves before Sugriva. Other supreme apes arrived, as was proper. They approached Sugriva and stood with their hands joined in salutation.

Sugriva, the one who knew about dharma, stood with his hands joined in salutation. He quickly presented all those bulls among apes to Rama and said, 'O Indras among apes! Dwell happily in the mountainous waterfalls and all the forests. Once you have settled down properly, the one who knows about armies[225] desires to inspect the strength of the army.'

Chapter 4(39)

Sugriva, the lord of the apes, now possessed all the means to accomplish the objective. He spoke to Rama, tiger among men and the one who afflicted enemy armies. 'The powerful ones, who can assume any form at will, have come and have settled down. These Indras among apes, those who have the complexion of the great Indra, are the ones who reside in my kingdom. There are many thousands of apes who are terrible in their valour. These terrible apes have arrived and they are like the daityas and the danavas. These powerful ones have conquered all exhaustion and are renowned for accomplishing extremely difficult tasks. They are excellent in their enterprise and are famous for their valour. O Rama! They roam around the earth, in the water and on land. They are the residents of many mountains. Waves of crores of apes have come here and they are your servants. All of them are awaiting their commands. All of them are engaged in the welfare of their

---

[225] Rama.

seniors. O scorcher of enemies! They are capable of accomplishing whatever you desire. O tiger among men! The time has come to tell them what you think. These soldiers are under your command and you should instruct them. I know the truth about the task that you wish for. Even then, it will be appropriate for you to command them about the truth.'

When he was addressed by Sugriva in this way, Rama, Dasharatha's son, embraced him in his arms and spoke these words to him. 'O amiable one! O immensely wise one! We must find out whether Vaidehi is alive or not and about the place where Ravana resides. After we get to know about Vaidehi and Ravana's residence, when the right time arrives, in consultation with you, I will issue my commands then. O lord of the apes. For the task at hand, neither I, nor Lakshmana, is the master. O lord of the apes! You are the master of the task that needs to be accomplished now. O lord! Determining the nature of my task, you must issue the instructions. O brave one! There is no doubt that you know about my objective. You are brave and you are my second well-wisher.[226] You are especially wise about the time. You are engaged in our welfare. You are good in accomplishing the objective and you know the purpose well.'

When he was thus addressed, in Rama's presence and that of the intelligent Lakshmana, Sugriva spoke to the leader of the herd named Vinata. This energetic lord of the apes had the complexion of a mountain and thundered like the clouds. 'O supreme among apes! Go with the apes who are sons of Soma and Surya. You know about the time, the place and good policy. You know about what should be done and what should not be done. Surround yourself with one hundred thousand spirited apes. Go towards the eastern direction,[227] with its mountains, forests and groves. Follow the routes in impenetrable mountains, forests and rivers, to search out Sita Vaidehi and Ravana's residence. Explore the beautiful rivers Bhageerathee, Sarayu, Koushiki, Kalindi, Yamuna, the giant and

---

[226] Lakshmana being the first.
[227] This means the east of Jambudvipa and not the east of Kishkindha.

dark mountain,[228] Sarasvati, Sindhu,[229] Shona, with water that shines like jewels, Mahi,[230] Kalamahi, adorned with mountains and groves, Brahmamala, Videha, Malavat,[231] Kashi, Kosala, Magadha, with large villages, Pundra, Vanga, the habitations of the *koshakaras*[232] and the land where there are silversmiths. Search out everything everywhere. Look for Rama's beloved wife Sita, Dasharatha's daughter-in-law, in fathomless oceans, mountains and habitations. There are large places secreted in the valleys of the Mandara. Some have squashed ears there. Others have pierced lips and ears. There are terrible ones who seem to have faces made out of iron. Others are swift, though they only possess a single foot. There are men who have inexhaustible strength. Others eat the flesh of men. There are *kiratas*[233] who decorate their ears. Some have golden complexions and are pleasant to see. The kiratas who reside in the islands eat raw fish. It has been said that there are terrible tigers among men who reside inside the waters. Search out the residences of all these and the habitations of those who dwell in groves. Leap from one place to another and ascend the mountains. There is the island of Yava,[234] full of jewels and adorned with seven kingdoms. It is full of silver and gold. Once you pass beyond it, there will be the mountain named Shishira. It is populated by gods and danavas and the summit touches the sky. There are impenetrable mountains, waterfalls and forests there. Here and there, search out the route of Ravana and Vaidehi. You should see the extremely terrible island in the ocean. There are extremely gigantic asuras there and they always seize people by their shadows. Brahma ordained that they should remain hungry for a long period of time. Go to the tirtha in the

[228] Known as Kalinda or dark.

[229] Sarasvati does not belong on the eastern side. Neither does Sindhu, unless this refers to some other river Sindhu. The geographical sections in this and the next three chapters also occur in the Matsya Purana.

[230] River Mahi is also towards the west.

[231] If this is Malava, it does not belong here.

[232] The likeliest meaning is those who earn a living from silk. But it could also mean those who make scabbards for swords.

[233] Hunters.

[234] Identified as Java.

great ocean. It is populated by giant serpents that roar loudly. Their forms are like clouds of destruction. After this, there is the terrible ocean named Lohita, with water like blood.[235] Having gone there, you should see the giant silk-cotton trees.[236] Vainateya's[237] abode is there, decorated by many kinds of jewels. It is like Kailasa and was constructed by Vishvakarma. There are terrible rakshasas named Mandeha there and their complexion is like that of mountains. They have diverse fearful forms and hang downwards from the peaks of mountains. When the time for sunrise comes, they always fall down in the water. They are scorched by the sun and repeatedly hang downwards again.[238] There is the ocean named Kshiroda, with a complexion like that of a white cloud. O invincible ones! Having gone there, you must see the waves that are like necklaces made out of pearls. In the midst of this, there is the gigantic mountain named Rishabha, white in complexion. It is surrounded by silvery and blossoming trees with divine fragrances. There is the lake named Sudarshana, full of swans. There are silver-coloured lotuses there, with dazzling golden fibres. To cheerfully sport in that lake full of lotuses, gods, charanas, kinnaras and large numbers of apsaras go there. O apes! After passing beyond Kshiroda, you should see Jaloda. This is best among oceans and is fearful to all creatures. The great *hayamukha* fire is there, created from the energy of rage.[239] It is said to possess great force and devours all mobile and immobile objects. The loud shrieks of creatures who dwell in the ocean can be heard there, when they are rendered incapacitated on seeing the *vadavamukha* fire. There is a region that is thirteen yojanas to the north of those tasty waters. The extremely large mountain with a golden peak, named Jatarupa, is there. The thousand-hooded god,

[235] Lohita means red.

[236] Silk cotton is shalmali and this *dvipa* is named Shalmali dvipa.

[237] Vinata's son, Garuda.

[238] When the sun rises, the Mandehas try to obstruct the sun's path. When oblations of water are offered at the time of sunrise, the Mandehas are scorched by the sun and fall down in the water.

[239] This is the subterranean fire, known as hayamukha (horse's head/mouth) or vadavamukha (mare's head/mouth). It emerges at the time of the final destruction and devours everything. The fire was created from the anger and rage of the sage Urva.

Ananta, attired in blue garments and worshipped by all creatures, is seated on the summit of that mountain.[240] The great-souled one's standard is a three-headed palm tree. It has been established, with its foundation, on the summit of that mountain and is radiant. The gods have created this as a mark of the eastern direction.[241] After this, there is the supremely wonderful Mount Udaya, made out of gold. It is one hundred yojanas high and its peak touches the firmament. With its foundation, it dazzles. It is divine and is made out of molten gold. There are blossoming sala, tala, tamala and karnikara trees. These are divine and are made out of molten gold. They dazzle and are like the sun. There is a peak[242] that is one yojana wide and ten yojanas high. This is firm and is named Soumanasa. It is made out of molten gold. In ancient times, Vishnu Trivikrama[243] placed his first foot there. Purushottama placed his second foot on Mount Meru. The sun is repeatedly seen atop this giant peak.[244] It then circles Jambudvipa from the north. The radiant maharshis, named vaikhanasas and valakhilyas are seen there. Those ascetics have the complexion of the sun. The dvipa known as Sudarshana is ahead of that.[245] He[246] illuminates with his energy and provides eyesight to all those who are living. On the slopes of that mountain and in caverns and forests, here and there, search for the route taken by Ravana and Vaidehi. The golden mountain is suffused by the great-souled sun's energy and is seen to assume a reddish tinge at the time of sandhya. Beyond this, the eastern direction is barred by the gods and is impossible to penetrate. With the sun and the moon missing, it is enveloped in darkness. Janakee should be searched out in all the mountains, caves and forests I have mentioned, and even in the places I have not mentioned. O bulls among the apes! Apes are only capable of going up to this spot. We do not know about what is

[240] Vishnu lies down on the serpent named Ananta.
[241] The eastern direction ends beyond this.
[242] One of Mount Udaya's peaks.
[243] In his dwarf incarnation.
[244] Soumanasa.
[245] This is where the sun resides.
[246] The sun.

beyond. That is without the sun and beyond the boundaries. Having
reached Mount Udaya, you will search for Vaidehi and Ravana's
residence for a month and return after that. No one will stay for
more than a month. If anyone does that, he will be bound up in my
residence. Go and find Maithilee. Return after accomplishing your
objective. O apes! Use your skills to search that direction, loved by
the great Indra and adorned with forests and groves. Get back Sita,
loved by the descendant of the Raghu lineage. Return after that.
May you be happy.'

Chapter 4(40)

After sending that great army of apes, Sugriva, the brave leader
of large numbers of apes, desired to send apes to the southern
direction. He summoned Agni's son Nila, the ape Hanumat, the
great ape named Jambavat who was the grandfather's son, Suhotra,
Sharari, Sharagulma, Gaja, Gavaksha, Sushena,[247] Vrishabha,
Mainda, Dvivida, Vijaya, Gandhamadana, the two sons of Agni
named Ulkamukha and Ananga, Angada and other brave ones. They
possessed speed and valour and knew about the directions. He made
Angada the leader of that large force. He then instructed the brave
apes about searching the southern direction. The lord of the apes
told the best among the apes about some extremely impenetrable
regions in that direction. 'There is the Vindhya, with one thousand
peaks. It is covered with many trees and creepers. There is the
impassable river Narmada, populated by giant serpents. There is
the beautiful Godavari and the great river Krishnaveni. There is the
immensely fortunate Varada,[248] populated by giant serpents. There
is the region of Mekhala,[249] Utkala[250] and the city of Dasharna.

[247] This is a different Sushena, not the one who was Tara's father.
[248] Identified as Wardha.
[249] Amarakantaka, where the Narmada originates.
[250] This deviates from the geography, as do subsequent references to Vanga and
Kalinga.

Search everywhere in Avanti and Abhravanti, Vidarbha, Rishika and the beautiful region of Mahishaka. Search everywhere in Vanga, Kalinga and Koushika. Search all the mountains, rivers and caves in Dandakaranya. Look everywhere around the river Godavari. Go to Andhra, Pundra, Chola, Pandya, Kerala and Mount Ayomukha,[251] which is decorated with minerals. It has a beautiful peak, colourful with blossoming trees. Search out the routes on that giant mountain, with its forests full of sandalwood trees. Beyond this, you will see the river Kaveri. It has divine, auspicious and sparkling water and large numbers of apsaras sport there. Seated on the summit of Malaya, you will see the immensely energetic and supreme rishi Agastya, who is like the sun. When the great-souled one is pleased and grants you permission, cross the great river Tampraparni, full of a large number of crocodiles. It has many dense islands, which have groves of divine sandalwood trees. It is like a beautiful young woman, going to meet the beloved ocean. O apes! You must go and see Pandya. It has gates made out of gold, decorated with divine pearls and jewels. To accomplish your objective, you will then approach the ocean, with the handsome Mount Mahendra, supreme among mountains. It has a beautiful summit, made out of gold. Agastya had placed the base of this mountain inside the ocean and the peak can be seen above the great ocean. The mountain is decorated with many kinds of flowering trees and creepers. It is visited by gods, rishis, the best of yakshas and apsaras. It is extremely pleasant and is full of large numbers of siddhas and charanas. On every auspicious day, the one with the thousand eyes always goes there. There is an island on the other side of this and it is one hundred yojanas in expanse. It blazes and humans cannot penetrate it. You must search this out, everywhere. Search this place in particular for Sita's whereabouts, using every means at your disposal. This is the region of the evil-souled Ravana, who deserves to be killed.[252] The

---

[251] This is Mount Malaya. Literally, with iron at its mouth.

[252] This causes all kinds of problems. How did Sugriva know Ravana lived there? If he knew, why did he tell Rama he did not know where Ravana dwelt? Why did he send the apes off to other directions? Since the instructions were given in Rama's presence, why didn't Rama react?

lord of the rakshasas resides there and he is like the one with the one thousand eyes in his radiance. There is a rakshasi who resides in the middle of the southern ocean. She is famous as Angaraka and devours shadows.[253] After you cross that prosperous place, at a distance of one hundred yojanas, there is a mountain named Pushpitaka in the ocean. It is populated by siddhas and charanas. Its radiance is like that of the sun and the moon and on all sides, it is surrounded by the waters of the ocean. The large and dazzling summit seems to be writing in the sky. One peak is golden and is loved by the sun. Another peak is silvery and is loved by the moon. An ungrateful person cannot see it. Nor can a cruel person, or a non-believer. O apes! Bow your heads down and search out that mountain. After passing beyond this, at a distance of fourteen yojanas, there is the impenetrable mountain named Suryavat. This is a path that is extremely difficult to traverse. Once one has passed beyond, there is Mount Vaidyuta. It has trees with fruits that yield all the objects of desire, pleasant in all seasons. Those best of roots and fruits deserve to be eaten. O apes! Eat them. Drink the excellent honey and proceed beyond. There is the mountain named Kunjara, desired by the eyes and the mind. Vishvakarma constructed this as Agastya's residence. This extends for one yojana and rises up ten yojanas. This divine and golden resort is decorated with many kinds of jewels. The city named Bhogavati, the abode of the snakes, is there. The broad roads are impenetrable and are protected on all sides. They are protected by terrible serpents, who have sharp fangs that are full of great poison. Vasuki, the extremely terrible king of the snakes, resides there. Search the city of Bhogavati. On emerging, pass over the region where there is the great Rishabha. The mountain named Rishabha is full of every kind of jewel. Divine sandalwood trees grow there—*goshirshaka*, *padmaka*, *harishyama* and *agnisamaprabha*.[254] See those sandalwood trees, but never touch them. A terrible gandharva named Rohita guards that grove. There are five lords of the gandharvas who are like the sun in their

---

[253] Also known as Simhika. She seizes the shadow and thereby devours the prey.

[254] These are four species of sandalwood, respectively, ochre yellow, leafy green, sky blue and fiery red.

radiance. They are Shailusha, Gramani, Bhikshu, Shubhra and Babhru. This is the impenetrable end of the earth and those who have conquered heaven reside there. After this, there is the extremely terrible world of the ancestors and we should not go there. This is the capital of Yama, full of hardships and enveloped in darkness. O brave bulls among apes! We are only capable of searching up to this point. We have no means of proceeding beyond this. Search all this and every other place that you can see. You must find out about Vaidehi's route and return. If a person returns within a month and tells me that he has seen Sita, he will enjoy affluence and pleasures that are like mine and will sport in joy. There will be no one who will be more loved by me, more than my own life. Even if he has committed many kinds of crimes, he will be my friend. You possess infinite strength and valour. You have extensive qualities and have been born in noble lineages. In addition, you have the qualities of your own manliness. Obtain the daughter of the king of men.'

Chapter 4(41)

When the apes had left for the southern direction, Sugriva summoned the extremely energetic leader of the herds named Sushena. He possessed intelligence and valour and was like Vayu in his speed. He was terrible in his valour. He was Tara's father and the king's father-in-law. He[255] prostrated himself, joined his hands in salutation and spoke the following words. 'Please help Rama. The time has come to repay him. Surround yourself with one hundred thousand spirited apes. O amiable one! O lord! Go to Varuna's western direction, to Surashtra, Bahlika, Shura[256] and Abhira. There are prosperous habitations and large and beautiful cities. The inner groves are full of punnagas, bakulas and uddalakas.[257] O bulls among apes! Search out the routes amidst

[255] Sugriva.
[256] The region around Mathura.
[257] Uddalaka means honey. So this is a tree from which honey can be obtained.

the dense growth of ketakas. Every river bears flows of cool and
auspicious water. There are forests frequented by ascetics and
desolate mountains. The western direction has unapproachable
routes that are encompassed by walls of mountains. You should
then reach and see the western ocean. O apes! The water there
is agitated by many whales and crocodiles. There are clumps of
ketakas and dense growths of tamalas. The apes can sport in the
groves of coconut trees. Search out Sita and Ravana's residence
there. There is the habitation of Marichi and the beautiful city of
Jati. There are Avanti[258] and Angalopa and the forest of Alakshita.
Here and there, there are large kingdoms and habitations. There is
a mountain at the confluence of the Sindhu with the ocean. There
is a giant mountain named Hemagiri, with hundreds of peaks and
large trees. On the beautiful slopes there, lions that can fly with
their wings can be found. Whales, fish and seals make their nests
there. The lions make their lairs on the summit of that mountain.
Proud and satisfied elephants are there, trumpeting like clouds.
They roam around in that extensive place, surrounded by water
everywhere. The summit is golden, with colourful trees, and seems
to touch the sky. The apes, which can assume any form at will, must
search all this quickly. Near the ocean, there is a golden peak that
is one hundred yojanas high. This is Pariyatra and it is extremely
difficult to see.[259] O apes! Go and see it. Twenty-four crores of
spirited gandharvas reside on that summit. They are terrible, as
radiant as the fire, and they can assume any form at will. Apes,
even if they are terrible in their valour, must not approach them.
The apes must not pluck any fruit from that region. Those brave
and spirited ones[260] are extremely strong and impossible to assail.
Terrible in their valour, they protect the fruits and the roots there.
Your task is to search out Janakee everywhere there. O apes! As
long as you do not follow them,[261] you have nothing to fear from
them. In the fourth part of the ocean, there is Mount Chakravat.

---

[258] This is not the Avanti mentioned earlier.
[259] Because it dazzles.
[260] The gandharvas.
[261] The gandharvas.

Vishvakarma constructed a chakra with a thousand spokes there. Purushottama slew Panchajana and the danava Hayagriva and obtained the chakra and the conch shell.[262] Here and there on that colourful summit and in the large caves, search for Ravana and Vaidehi. After sixty-four yojanas, there is the mountain named Varaha. It has an extremely large and golden summit. Varuna's fathomless abode is there. There is the city named Pragjyotisha there, made out of molten gold.[263] The evil-souled danava named Naraka used to dwell there. Here and there on that colourful mountain, and in the large caves, search for Ravana and Vaidehi. Once you pass beyond, there is an Indra among mountains. The inside of that mountain is made out of gold. The mountain is golden everywhere and there are innumerable waterfalls. There are elephants, boars, lions and tigers everywhere. They insolently roar all the time and the mountain itself seems to roar. That mountain is named Megha. The great and prosperous Indra, the chastiser of Paka and the possessor of tawny steeds, was crowned as the king of the gods there. This Indra among mountains is protected by the great Indra. Passing beyond, reach sixty thousand golden mountains. They have the complexion of the rising sun and are radiant everywhere. There are beautiful blossoming trees that are made out of molten gold. In their midst, there is the excellent Mount Meru, the king. In ancient times, Aditya[264] was pleased and granted the mountain a boon. He told the Indra among mountains, 'Because of my favours, everything that finds refuge in you will be golden, during the day and at night. The gods, gandharvas and danavas who reside in you will always have a reddish tinge and a golden complexion.' At the time of the western sandhya, the Adityas, the Vasus, the Rudras, the Maruts and the residents of heaven come to that excellent mountain, Meru. They worship the sun. Worshipped by them, the sun goes behind Mount Asta and can no longer be seen by any creature. The sun quickly

---

[262] Vishnu slew these two demons on Chakravat. He thus obtained the conch shell from Panchajana and the chakra from Hayagriva.

[263] Since Pragjyotisha is in the east, in Assam, this does not fit.

[264] The sun god.

traverses the distance of ten thousand yojanas[265] in one-and-a-half muhurtas[266] and approaches that tall peak. On the summit of that great peak,[267] there is a divine residence that is like the sun in complexion. This palace has many layers of storeys and was constructed by Vishvakarma. It is adorned with many colourful trees, full of diverse kinds of birds. This is the residence of the great-souled Varuna, with a noose in his hand. Between Meru and Asta, there is a large palm tree, with ten heads. It is handsome, made out of molten gold, and has a glittering and wonderful base. Here and there, everywhere in the impenetrable places, lakes and rivers, search for Ravana and Vaidehi. Meru Savarni is famous as being Brahma's equal. He knows about dharma and has cleansed himself through his austerities. He resides there. The maharshi Meru Savarni has a complexion like that of the sun. After you have bowed your head down on the ground in front of him, he can be asked about Maithilee's welfare and her whereabouts. When the night is over, the sun dispels darkness from the world of the living. But thereafter, he goes beyond Mount Asta. O bulls among apes! This is the point up to which apes are capable of going. We do not know about what lies beyond. That is without the sun and without boundaries. Having reached Mount Asta, you will find out about Vaidehi and Ravana's residence and return before an entire month is over. No one will stay for more than a month. If anyone stays for more, he will be bound in my residence. My brave father-in-law will go with you. You will listen to everything that he instructs and act accordingly. The mighty-armed one is a senior. The immensely strong one is my father-in-law. All of you are valiant and that is evident in all your deeds. Make him your leader and search the western direction. If we can find the wife of the infinitely energetic Indra among men, we will be able to repay the good deed that he has done for us. After this task has been accomplished, if there is any other task that can bring about his benefit, considering the time, the place and the objective, we will

---

[265] From Mount Meru to Mount Asta.
[266] One hour and twelve minutes.
[267] Mount Asta.

undertake later.' Sushena and the other foremost apes heard the accomplished words spoken by Sugriva. They took their leave of the lord of the apes and left for the western direction, protected by Varuna.

Chapter 4(42)

Sugriva sent his father-in-law to the western direction. The lord of the apes then summoned the brave ape named Shatabali. The king, supreme among all the apes and the one who knew everything, addressed him in these words, for his own welfare and for Rama's welfare. 'Surround yourself with one hundred residents of the forest who are like you. Go with your ministers and with Vaivasvata's[268] sons. O valiant one! Go to the northern direction, with the Himalayas as its crest. Search everywhere for Rama's unblemished wife. When we have accomplished this task, we will do something that will bring Dasharatha's son pleasure. O supreme among those who know the objectives! We will accomplish our task and be freed from our debt. The great-souled Raghava has performed an agreeable task for us. If we are able to pay him back, our being alive will have served its purpose. Use your intelligence to determine how Janakee can be found. That is your task and our pleasure and benefit lie in this. This supreme among men is revered by all creatures. Rama is the one who triumphs over the cities of enemies and this will bring us and him pleasure. You possess intelligence and valour. There are many forests, impenetrable areas and rivers inside the mountains. Search them. There are habitations of *mlechchhas*,[269] Pulindas, Shurasenas, Prasthalas, Bharatas, Kurus, Madrakas, Kambojas, Yavanas, Shakas, Bahlikas, Rishikas, Pouravas, Tankanas, Chinas, Paramachinas, Niharas and Daradas. Search them repeatedly and search the Himalayas. Search here and

---

[268] Yama's.

[269] A mlechchha is a barbarian, meaning that mlechchhas do not speak Sanskrit and are not *aryas*.

there in the clumps of *lodhra*[270] and padmaka trees and in the *devadaru*[271] forests for Ravana and Vaidehi. Go to Soma's hermitage, frequented by the gods and the gandharvas. Then go to the large mountain named Mount Kala. Search the giant peaks, caves and caverns for Rama's immensely fortunate and illustrious wife. Pass beyond that large mountain, with gold in its womb. Passing beyond that Indra among mountains, you should go to the mountain named Sudarshana. Here and there, in the groves, clumps, caves and caverns, search for Ravana and Vaidehi. When you pass beyond this, there is an expanse that extends for one hundred yojanas in every direction. There is nothing but the sky there. There are no mountains, rivers or trees. All living creatures avoid it. Swiftly pass over this desolate plain that makes the body hair stand up. You will then reach the white Mount Kailasa and will be delighted. This has the complexion of white clouds and is embellished with molten gold. Kubera's beautiful palace was constructed by Vishvakarma there. There is a large lake there and it is full of lotuses and lilies. It is full of swans and karandavas and is frequented by a large number of apsaras. The prosperous King Vaishravana,[272] the king of the yakshas, the granter of riches and worshipped by all creatures, is there, sporting with the guhyakas. Here and there, in the mountain caverns that are as radiant as the moon, search for Ravana and Vaidehi. Reach Mount Krouncha and its extremely impenetrable tunnel. Enter it carefully, because it is said to be extremely difficult to enter. Welcomed by the gods, the great-souled maharshis reside there. They are themselves like the gods in form and are like the sun in their resplendence. Here and there, search the other caves of Krouncha, the summits, the peaks, the caverns and the flanks. Here and there, search Krouncha's summit too. Search Mount Kama, which is without any trees, and Manasa, the abode of birds. Creatures cannot go there. Nor can gods or rakshasas. Search every place there, the summits, the slopes and the plains. After you pass beyond Mount Krouncha, there is the mountain named Mainaka.

---

[270] The lotus bark tree.

[271] Species of pine. Devadaru literally means tree of the gods.

[272] Kubera.

The danava Maya's residence is there and he constructed it himself.
Search Mainaka, its peaks, slopes and caves. Here and there, there
are the abodes of women who have faces like mares.[273] After passing
over that region, there is a hermitage frequented by the siddhas.
Siddhas, vaikhanasas and the ascetic valakhilyas are there. Worship
the ascetic siddhas, who have used austerities to cleanse themselves
of all sins. Humbly, you can ask them about Sita's welfare and
whereabouts. There is lake Vaikhanasa, covered with golden
lotuses. Sparkling swans that are like the rising sun roam around
there. Kubera's mount is known as Sarvabhouma. That elephant
always goes to that place, accompanied by she-elephants. When you
cross that lake, the sun or the moon can no longer be seen. The sky
will be bereft of the large number of nakshatras. There will be no
clouds. Nor will there be any sound. However, that region will be
illuminated by rays that are like those of the sun. Siddhas full of
austerities rest there and they are like the gods. They illuminate with
their own radiance. Once you cross that region, there is the river
named Shailoda. Along both its banks, there are bamboos named
kichaka. The siddhas use these to cross over to the other bank and
return. The land of Uttara Kuru is for those who have earned merits.
There are thousands of rivers there. The water is full of lotuses and
the lotuses are golden in complexion. The leaves of the lotuses are
as blue as lapis lazuli. The forests are full of red lotuses with golden
hues. There are waterbodies that are as radiant as the rising sun.
The leaves are made out of expensive gems and the filaments are
golden in complexion. That region is surrounded everywhere by
colourful groves of blue lotuses. The banks of the river are made out
of molten gold, fashioned with extremely expensive jewels and
pearls that cannot be weighed. The valleys in those supreme
mountains are wonderful, with jewels everywhere. There is molten
gold that is like the fire in its radiance. The trees there are always
laden with flowers and fruits and are thick with birds. They[274] are
divine to the smell, taste and touch and satiate all the objects of

---

[273] Kinnaras, the feminine of the species.
[274] The flowers and fruit.

desire. The fruits of other excellent trees yield many forms of clothing. They yield colourful pearls, lapis lazuli and ornaments suitable for both men and women. In all seasons, they happily savour the fruits of other excellent trees. During the winter, there are other excellent trees that yield extremely expensive beds and wonderful spreads of different types. Other trees yield garlands that are loved by the heart and many kinds of expensive drinks and diverse types of fruit. The women possess all the qualities and are seen to possess beauty and youth. Gandharvas, kinnaras, siddhas, nagas and *vidyadharas*[275] sport with women who dazzle in their resplendence. All of them have performed good deeds. All of them are engaged in carnal pursuits. To pursue kama and artha, all of them reside with women. There are the sounds of singing and the playing of musical instruments. Wonderful sounds of laughter are heard there at all times and these are agreeable to all creatures. There is no one there who is not happy. There is no one there who loves falsehood. From one day to the next day, the agreeable qualities of that place increase. When one passes beyond Uttara Kuru, there is a body of water. In its middle, there is the giant Mount Soma, made out of gold. Those who have gone to Indra's world, those who have gone to Brahma's world, those who have gone to heaven, and the gods can see this king of mountains from up there. Though that region is without the sun, a radiance illuminates it.[276] Though the radiance of the sun cannot be seen, it is as if the sun is radiating heat. The illustrious one who is the soul of the universe,[277] Shambhu, who is the soul of the eleven,[278] and Brahma, the lord of the gods, reside there, surrounded by brahmana rishis. You should never go to the region that is beyond Uttara Kuru. Other creatures are also not permitted to travel there. Even the gods find it extremely difficult to travel to the mountain named Soma. Having seen it, you should quickly return. O bulls among apes! That is the point up to which apes are capable of travelling.

[275] Vidyadharas are semi-divine, occupying the region between heaven and earth.
[276] From the radiance of Mount Soma.
[277] Vishnu.
[278] Shiva, eleven being a reference to the eleven Rudras.

There is no sun beyond that. There are no boundaries beyond that. We do not know about what is beyond. Search everything that I have mentioned and use your intelligence to search everything that I have not mentioned. Thereby, perform a greatly desired task for Dasharatha's son and it will be a task that will be even more agreeable for me. O those who are like the wind and the fire! Perform the task of seeing Videha's daughter. When you are successful with your relatives, I will honour you with all the agreeable qualities.[279] O apes! With your enemies pacified, you will roam all over the earth. With your beloveds, you will have offspring.'

Chapter 4(43)

To accomplish the objective, Sugriva specifically spoke to Hanumat. He had decided that in accomplishing the objective, he was the best among the apes. 'O bull among the apes! I do not see who can bar your entry on earth, the firmament, the sky, the abode of the gods, or in water. You know about all the worlds, the oceans and the mountains, the asuras, the gandharvas, the serpents and the gods. O great ape! O brave one! Your speed, force, energy and dexterity is like that of your father, the extremely energetic wind god. There is no creature on earth who is your equal in energy. Therefore, you should think about how Sita can be got back. O Hanumat! You possess strength, intelligence and valour. You conduct yourself in accordance with the time and the place and good policy. You are learned about good policy.'

Hanumat was about to leave on the task. Knowing this, Raghava thought about Hanumat. 'The lord of the apes has determined that Hanumat will certainly be able to accomplish the objective. It has been decided that in accomplishing the task, Hanumat is superior to the others. That determination must be based on his former deeds. In ensuring the fruits of the action, he has been clearly chosen by

---

[279] With objects that possess those qualities.

his master.' On considering the conduct of the extremely energetic ape, he[280] was delighted and thought that his task had already been accomplished. His senses and heart became cheerful. Delighted, the scorcher of enemies gave him his ring, with his name inscribed on it, so that the princess[281] would accept it as a sign of recognition.[282] 'O best among the apes! Through this sign, Janaka's daughter will recognize that you have come from me and will not look upon you with anxiety. O brave one! Your conduct, your spirit, your valour and Sugriva's instruction to you are conveying to me that you will be successful.' The best among the apes joined his hands in salutation. He accepted it and placed it on his head. Having worshipped at his feet, the supreme among apes departed. As if dragging that large army of the apes, the brave ape who was the son of the wind god leapt up into the sky. He was like the sparkling lunar disc, when the clouds have disappeared, adorned with a large number of nakshatras. 'O ape! O one who is supreme in valour! O one who is not limited in valour! O extremely strong one! I am depending on your strength. O son of the wind god! O Hanumat! Act so that you go wherever Janaka's daughter happens to be.'[283]

Chapter 4(44)

Understanding the fierce command of their master, the bulls among the apes enveloped the earth, like a swarm of locusts. With Lakshmana, Rama continued to dwell in Prasravana. He waited for the one month designated for Sita to be found. The king of the mountains[284] was spread across the beautiful northern

[280] Rama.

[281] Sita.

[282] This is not a very convincing reason. No such signs were given to the apes who headed towards the north, the east or the west, reinforcing the hypothesis that it was known that Ravana was towards the south, in Lanka. Nor is the reason for giving the ring to Hanumat, as opposed to Angada, very clear.

[283] This is Rama addressing Hanumat as he left.

[284] The Himalayas.

direction. With great force, the brave ape Shatabali headed there. Vinata, the leader of the apes, left for the eastern direction. With Tara, Angada and the other apes, the son of the wind god and the leader of the apes left for the southern direction, where Agastya once travelled. Sushena, the lord of the apes and tiger among the apes, left for the terrible western direction, harshly protected by Varuna. The king had respectively urged them in all the directions. Having dispatched them in this way, the brave commander of the army of the apes was delighted, happy and cheerful. The king thus urged all the leaders of the apes and they swiftly left towards their own respective directions. The apes shouted, screamed and roared. As those supreme among apes proceeded, they bellowed, 'We will kill Ravana and bring Sita back. If I come across him, I will single-handedly slay Ravana in the battle. I will violently agitate the one who abducted Janaka's daughter. Even if I tremble because of exhaustion, I will now remain steady. I will single-handedly bring Janakee back, even if it happens to be from the nether regions. I will shatter these trees. I will splinter these mountains. I will cleave the earth. I will agitate the oceans. There is no doubt that I will leap over one yojana. I will leap over one hundred yojanas. I will do more than one hundred. No one can obstruct my path on the surface of the ground, in the ocean, in mountains, in forests and even in the middle of the nether regions.' In the presence of the king of the apes, each of those apes, intoxicated with valour, spoke these and other words.

Chapter 4(45)

When the Indras among apes had left, Rama asked Sugriva, 'How do you know everything about the globe that is the earth?'[285] Sugriva bowed down and replied to Rama. 'Listen to my words. I will tell you everything in detail. There was a danava

---

[285] The word used is *mandala* and this means round, circular, globe.

named Dundubhi, in the form of a buffalo. In the region near Mount Malaya, Vali fought against him. The buffalo entered a cave inside Malaya and desiring to kill him, Vali also entered Malaya.[286] I was asked to humbly wait at the entrance to the cave. But though one year had passed, Vali did not emerge. That cave was then filled with a flood of blood. On seeing this, I was astounded and the poisonous sorrow on account of my brother afflicted me. I deduced it was evident that my senior had been killed. I covered the entrance to the cave with a boulder that was like a mountain, so that the buffalo would find it impossible to emerge and would be destroyed. I had no hopes of his remaining alive and came to Kishkindha. I obtained the extremely large kingdom, with Tara and Ruma. I resided there with my friends, devoid of all anxiety. However, after having killed the bull among danavas, Vali returned. Honouring him and driven by fear, I returned the kingdom to him. But Vali's senses were distressed. The evil-souled one wished to cause me injury. As I fled with my advisers, in his rage, he pursued me. As I was chased by him, I fled over many kinds of rivers and saw forests and cities. I saw the earth, like a reflection on the surface of a mirror. I saw some places that were like a circle of fire, and others that were like the hoof print of a cow. I first went to the eastern direction and then sought refuge in the southern direction. Scared, I next went to the western direction. Thereafter, I went to the northern direction. Then Hanumat addressed me in these words. "O king! I have just remembered how Vali, the lord of the apes, was cursed by Matanga. If Vali enters the circle of his[287] hermitage, his head will be shattered into one hundred fragments. We can dwell there happily and will not suffer from any anxiety." O son of a king! That is the reason why, though he reached Mount Rishyamuka, Vali was terrified of Matanga and did not enter. O king! I have thus directly experienced everything in the earth's globe. After that, I went to the cave.'[288]

---

[286] There is an inconsistency. We have earlier been told that Vali killed Dundubhi in Kishkindha, whereas a cave in Mount Malaya is being mentioned now.

[287] Matanga's.

[288] In Rishyamuka.

Chapter 4(46)

Commanded by the king of the apes, all the elephants among the apes did as they had been asked and energetically departed, searching for Vaidehi. They searched everywhere, in lakes, rivers, slopes, the sky, cities, impenetrable fortifications in the rivers and mountains. All the leaders of the apes had been commanded by Sugriva. They searched the regions, with the mountains, forests and groves. Determined to find Sita, they searched throughout the day. At night, the apes assembled together on the ground. Irrespective of the season and the place, every day, when it was nightfall, the apes would find trees with fruit and make those their beds. The first day of the stipulated month was the day they left Prasravana. When the month was over, the elephants among the apes despaired and returned to the king of the apes. As had been asked to, with his advisers, the immensely strong Vinata had searched the eastern direction and returned without seeing Sita. The brave and great ape, Shatabali, searched everywhere in the northern direction and returned with his soldiers. With the other apes, Sushena hopefully searched the western direction. However, when the month was over, he returned to Sugriva. With Rama, Sugriva was seated on the slope of Prasravana. They approached him, greeted him and said, 'We have searched all the mountains, forests, cities, rivers, the extremities of the ocean and habitations. We have searched all the caves that you had mentioned. We have searched the giant thickets and creepers that spread around everywhere. We have repeatedly searched impenetrable, impassable and uneven regions and desolate spots. We have sought out extremely large creatures in the course of the search and have killed them. The great-souled one[289] is noble in birth and broad in spirit. That Indra among the apes will see Maithilee. Sita has certainly gone to the southern direction and that is where Hanumat, Vayu's son, went.'

[289] Hanumat.

Chapter 4(47)

With Tara and Angada, the ape proceeded towards the region that had been indicated by Sugriva. All those supreme among apes reached that distant spot. They searched the caves and desolate spots in the Vindhyas,[290] the summits of the mountains, the rivers, the impenetrable areas, the lakes, the large trees, the thickets of trees, the many mountains and the forests of trees. All the apes searched in all the directions. But those brave ones could not see Maithilee, Janaka's daughter. They ate the many kinds of roots and fruits. Those invincible ones dwelt there and searched here and there. But that region was difficult to search. There were large and deep caves. All those leaders of apes then abandoned that region. Without any fear, they entered another impenetrable region. The trees were sterile there and did not yield any fruit. There were no flowers, nor any leaves. The rivers had no water and roots were extremely difficult to obtain. There were no buffaloes there, nor any deer or elephants. There were no tigers and birds, nor others that can be seen in forests. There were flowering lotuses and lilies that grew in lakes and on the ground. With gentle leaves, these were worth seeing and were fragrant. However, the bees shunned them. The immensely fortunate Kandu was truthful in speech and was a store of austerities. This maharshi adhered to rituals. But he was also supremely intolerant and was impossible to control. His son was a child when he was lost in that forest. He was only ten years old and lost his life there. Thereupon, the great sage was angered. The great-souled one cursed that entire large forest. The forest would become impenetrable and would be shunned by animals and birds. However, controlling themselves, they did search the extremities of the forests, the mountains, the caverns, the waterfalls and the rivers. But those great-souled ones, wishing to bring pleasure to Sugriva, did not see Janaka's daughter there, or her abductor, Ravana.

They entered another terrible forest, covered with creepers and shrubs. There, they saw an asura who had no fear of the gods and was cruel in his deeds. The apes saw that terrible one standing

---

[290] This establishes that the Vindhyas were to the south of Rishyamuka.

in the forest, resembling a mountain. On seeing the one who was like a mountain, all of them girded their loins. The powerful one shouted at the apes, 'Remain there. All of you will be destroyed.' He angrily rushed towards them, doubling up his fists. When Angada, Vali's son, saw that he was descending violently, he took him to be Ravana and slew him with a slap of his palm. Struck by Vali's soon, he started to vomit blood from his mouth. Like a mountain that had been overturned, the asura fell down on the ground. When he ceased breathing, the apes, desiring success, entered and searched all the caves in the mountain. They next searched all the forests and entered another terrible cave in a mountain. Having searched again, they were saddened. They emerged and assembled together, seating themselves at a lonely spot under a tree, miserable in their minds.

Chapter 4(48)

Angada, the immensely wise one, was exhausted. But he comforted all the apes and addressed them in these words, speaking slowly. 'We have searched everywhere in the forests, mountains, rivers, impenetrable and desolate places and caverns and caves in the mountains. But nowhere have we been able to see Janakee. Nor have we seen the rakshasa who has abducted Sita, who is like the daughter of a god. A long period of time has elapsed and Sugriva is fierce in his rule. Therefore, together, let all of us search again. Let us abandon our lassitude and sorrow. Let us wake up from our sleep. Let us search for Sita, so that we can see Janaka's daughter. Persistence, skills and a mind that refuses to give up are said to be the reasons behind success in any course of action. That is the reason I am speaking to you in this way. O residents of the forest! Let us search this impenetrable forest yet again. Let us cast aside our exhaustion. Let all of us search this forest again. The fruits of this action will certainly be seen to materialize. Enough of this dejection that has come upon us. This lassitude of ours cannot be pardoned. O apes! In his anger, King Sugriva will chastise us severely. We

should always be frightened of him and the great-souled Rama. I
have said this for our welfare. If it pleases you, act in accordance
with it. O apes! This is proper and appropriate for all of us.'

Gandhamadana was suffering from thirst, exhaustion and
dejection. Hearing Angada's words, he uttered these indistinct
words. 'What Angada has spoken is indeed worthy of him. These
words are beneficial and appropriate. Let us act accordingly. Let
us collectively again search out the route in the mountains, caves,
boulders, desolate groves and the mountainous waterfalls, every such
place. This is what the great-souled Sugriva instructed, to search all
the forests and the impenetrable parts of the mountains.' At this, the
extremely strong apes raised themselves again. They searched the
southern direction, full of forests everywhere in the Vindhyas. The
apes ascended a handsome silvery mountain that was like autumn
clouds, with peaks and caverns. There was a beautiful grove of lodhra
trees[291] there. There were groves of saptaparna trees too. Desiring to
see Sita, the supreme apes searched all these spots. Though extensive
in their valour, when they ascended the peak, they were exhausted.
However, they could not see Vaidehi, Rama's beloved queen. The
apes looked around everywhere. As they descended, they cast their
eyes on the many caves on that mountain, as far as the eye could
see. Exhausted and senseless, they descended on the flat ground. For
a while, they stayed there, near the root of a tree. For a while, they
suspended their exertions and comforted themselves. Then they rose
up again and searched all the routes in the southern direction. With
Hanumat as the foremost, the bulls among the apes started again.
Beginning with the Vindhyas, they searched in all the directions.

Chapter 4(49)

With Tara and Angada, the ape Hanumat searched the caves
and the desolate spots of the Vindhyas. In every direction,

[291] The lotus bark tree.

there were caves full of lions and tigers. There were uneven places on that king of the mountains and giant waterfalls. While they resided there, the time elapsed.[292] With large caves and impenetrable spots, that region was extremely difficult to search. However, Vayu's son[293] searched everywhere on that mountain. Gaja, Gavaksha, Gavaya, Sharabha, Gandhamadana, Mainda, Dvivida, Hanumat, Jambavat, Prince Angada and Tara, who roamed around in the forests, were not together. But they were not far from each other either. The routes along that spot in the southern direction were covered with a range of mountains. Hungry, thirsty and exhausted, they wished for some water. Then they saw a large cave that was shrouded with creepers and trees. Curlews, swans and cranes emerged from inside this. There were chakravaka birds, wet with water, their limbs red with pollen from lotuses. They approached that fragrant cave, which was extremely difficult to reach. The bulls among apes were amazed, but also anxious in their minds. Though those excellent, immensely strong and energetic apes were delighted,[294] they were also suspicious of drawing near that cave. Hanumat, the son of the wind god, possessed the complexion of a mountain peak. He was accomplished about caves and desolate plains. He told the terrible apes, 'The routes in this region of the southern direction are covered with a range of mountains. All of us are exhausted and we have not been able to see Maithilee. From every direction, swans, curlews, cranes and chakravakas wet with water are emerging. There is undoubtedly water here, from a well or from a lake. That is the reason there are gentle trees at the entrance to this cave.'

Thus addressed, all of them entered that cave, which was covered in darkness. The apes saw that there was no moon or sun there and this made their body hair stand up. That impenetrable cave was full of many kinds of trees. Holding on to each other, they entered one yojana inside. Their senses were disturbed. They were thirsty and frightened, craving water. Attentive, for some time, they leapt around inside that cave. The faces of the apes were lean and distressed. They were exhausted. As those brave ones lost hope of remaining alive,

---

[292] The time set by Sugriva for the search.
[293] Hanumat.
[294] Because there was water inside the cave.

they saw a light. The amiable ones approached that region, where the forest was devoid of darkness. They saw some golden trees that blazed like a flaming fire. There were sala, tala, punnaga, vanjula, dhava, champaka, nagavriksha and flowering karnikara trees. They seemed to be like sacrificial altars made out of lapis lazuli, resembling the rising sun. There were lakes full of lotuses that had the complexion of blue lapis lazuli, teeming with birds. The place was surrounded by large golden trees that were like the rising sun in complexion. There were fish and large turtles that were made of molten gold. They saw lakes full of lotuses, with sparkling water. There were mansions made out of gold and silver. These had windows fashioned out of molten gold, covered with nets of pearls. There were many storeys made out of gold and silver, decorated with lapis lazuli and gems. Everywhere there, the apes saw the best of residences. The trees were covered with flowers and fruits that had the complexion of coral and jewels. There was honey in every direction, with golden bees. There were colourful and large couches and seats made out of gems and gold. In every direction, they saw extremely expensive vehicles. There were heaps of vessels, made out of gold, silver and brass. There were heaps of divine aloe and sandalwood. There was auspicious food, roots and fruits. There were extremely expensive drinks and succulent honey. There were piles of extremely expensive and divine garments. There were colourful carpets and piles of deerskin. They searched here and there in that extremely radiant cave. Not very far away, the brave apes saw a woman. On seeing her, clad in bark and black antelope skin, they were extremely terrified. The ascetic lady was restrained in her diet and blazed because of her energy. Hanumat, with a complexion like that of a mountain, joined his hands in salutation and honoured the aged one. He asked, 'Who are you? Whom do these residences, the cave and the jewels belong to? Tell us.'

Chapter 4(50)

The immensely fortunate ascetic, clad in black antelope skin, was one who acted in accordance with dharma. Having spoken,

Hanumat spoke to her again. 'We suddenly entered this cave, enveloped in darkness. We were hungry, tired and exhausted and suffering in every possible way. Thirsty, we entered this gigantic hole in the ground. There are many kinds of attributes here and many kinds of wonderful signs. On seeing these, we are distressed and scared, deprived of our senses. Whom do these golden trees, which are like the rising sun in complexion, belong to? There is auspicious food, roots and fruits. There are golden vimanas and houses made out of silver. The windows are made out of molten gold and are covered with nets of jewels. Whose energy has led to these trees that are fashioned out of molten gold? They are sacred, with excellent fragrances. They bear flowers and fruit. Golden lotuses have been generated in the sparkling waters. How did it happen that golden fish and turtles are seen to roam around? Whose strength of austerities has resulted in this? Is it your own? We do not know anything about this. You should tell us everything.'

The ascetic lady who followed dharma was addressed by Hanumat in this way. Engaged in the welfare of all creatures, she replied to Hanumat. 'There is an immensely energetic bull among danavas named Maya.[295] He is accomplished in maya. He used his maya to construct everything in this golden forest. Earlier, this foremost among danavas was like Vishvakarma. He is the one who has fashioned these golden, divine and excellent mansions. In the great forest, he tormented himself through austerities for one thousand years. He obtained a boon from the grandfather that he would obtain all the riches of Ushanas.[296] Using all his strength, the lord[297] then arranged for all the objects of desire. For some time, he dwelt happily in this great forest. When that bull among danavas was engaged with an apsara named Hema, the lord Purandara used the valour of his vajra to slay him. Brahma then bestowed this excellent forest, with its eternal objects of desire and pleasure and these golden residences, on Hema. I am Svayamprabha and I

---

[295] The architect of the demons, just as Vishvakarma is of the gods.

[296] The grandfather is Brahma. Ushanas is Shukracharya, the preceptor of the demons. Thus, Brahma gave Maya the boon that we would be able to take away the riches of the preceptor of the demons.

[297] Maya.

am the daughter of Meru Savarni. O excellent ape! I guard Hema's residence. Hema is my beloved friend and is accomplished in singing and dancing. She granted me a boon that I should protect her great residence.[298] What is your task? What is the reason why you have come to this desolate region? How did you notice this impenetrable forest? Eat this auspicious food, the roots and the fruits. Drink. Thereafter, you should tell me everything.'

Chapter 4(51)

When all the leaders of the apes had rested, the ascetic lady, who single-mindedly followed dharma, addressed them in these words. 'O apes! If your exhaustion has been destroyed after eating these fruits, if you think I am capable of listening to it, I wish to hear about your account.'

Hearing her words, Hanumat, the son of the wind god, started to honestly tell her about the truth. 'Rama is the king of all the worlds and he is like the great Indra and Varuna. He is handsome and is Dasharatha's son. With his brother, Lakshmana, and his wife, Vaidehi, he entered Dandaka forest. Using his strength, Ravana abducted his wife from Janasthana. His[299] friend is the ape, King Sugriva. He is foremost among the apes and that king has sent us here, towards the southern direction, traversed by Agastya and protected by Yama. There are other foremost apes with us, Angada and the others. Ravana and all the rakshasas can assume any form at will. He[300] instructed all of us to collectively find out the route that Sita has taken. We have searched everything in the southern direction. Since all of us were hungry and exhausted, we sought refuge near the root of a tree. With pale faces, all of us started to meditate. Despite being thus immersed, we could not reach the other shore in this great ocean

---

[298] Though not stated clearly, Hema must have gone away to heaven after this. Indeed, she may have been sent by Indra to seduce Maya.

[299] Rama's.

[300] Sugriva.

of our thoughts. As we cast our eyes around, we saw this great cave. It was shrouded in creepers and trees and was enveloped in darkness. Swans, kingfishers, cranes and other birds were emerging from it. They were wet and their feathers were covered with drops of water. I told all the apes, "Let us enter." All of them had also deduced that this was a right course of action. Having decided to enter, we speedily set about our task. Clutching to each other's hands, we descended into the deep cave. We suddenly entered this cave, enveloped in darkness. In accomplishing our task, this is how we have managed to come here. Extremely distressed and hungry, that is how we arrived before you. Following the dharma towards a guest, you gave us roots and fruits. Suffering from hunger, we have devoured all of this. We were about to die from hunger and you have saved all of us. Tell us. What can we apes do in return to possibly pay you back?'

Svayamprabha knew everything and was thus addressed by the apes. She replied to all the leaders among the apes. 'I have followed my dharma and there is nothing that needs to be done for me. I am content that the spirited apes have been satisfied.'

Chapter 4(52)

The ascetic lady, full of dharma, addressed them in these auspicious words. Thereupon, Hanumat spoke to the one with the unblemished sight in these words. 'O one who follows dharma! All of us are seeking refuge with you. The great-souled Sugriva set a time period for us. While we have been roaming around inside this cave, that period has passed. You should rescue us from this cave. Even otherwise, since we have transgressed Sugriva's words, our lifespans are over. We are suffering from fear on account of Sugriva and you should save us. O one who follows dharma! There is a great task that we have to perform. We will not be able to perform that task if we are constrained to reside here.'

Addressed by Hanumat, the ascetic lady replied in these words. 'I think that a person who has entered cannot possibly return alive.

However, I have earned great powers because of my austerities and rituals. Using these, I am capable of saving all the apes from this cave. O bulls among apes! Close your eyes. I am incapable of saving you as long as your eyes are open.' All of them closed their eyes and covered them with their delicate fingers and hands. Desiring to leave, they cheerfully closed their eyes instantly. The great-souled apes had covered their faces with their hands. In the twinkling of an eye, they were raised out of the cave. The ascetic lady, the one who followed dharma, spoke to all of them and comforted them, after they had been taken out of that uneven region. 'This is the handsome Vindhya mountain, covered with many trees and creepers. There is the great Mount Prasravana and there is the great ocean.[301] O bulls among apes! May you be fortunate. I will return to my residence.' Saying this, the beautiful Svayamprabha entered the cave.

They saw the terrible ocean, Varuna's abode. Full of terrible and turbulent waves, it raged and the other shore could not be seen. The king had set a time period of one month. But in searching in the mountainous caves and the cave constructed through Maya's maya, this period had elapsed. At the foot of Mount Vindhya, there was a flowering tree. The great-souled ones sat down there and were immersed in their thoughts. They saw trees that were typical of the spring season and were filled with fear and dread. They were laden with flowers and the tops were covered with hundreds of creepers. They told each other that the spring season had arrived.[302] Realizing that the time for conveying the news was over, they fell down on the ground. The prince, the ape Angada, was immensely wise, with thick and long arms and shoulders like that of a lion or a bull. He spoke these words. 'All of us followed the instructions of the king of the apes and left. O apes! Do you not realize that we spent an entire month inside the cave? Meanwhile, the time that Sugriva had himself set has elapsed. All of us, who reside in the forest, should now undertake

---

[301] Both could be seen from the spot where they emerged.

[302] Deductions are possible about the timeline. Sugriva summoned the armies in Margashirsha, November–December. The month of Pushya, December–January, was fixed for their return. They spent around one month, January–February in the cave. Hence, the spring season is near.

an act of praya. Sugriva's nature is innately fierce and he has now obtained the status of our lord. Since we have committed a crime, he will not pardon all of us. Since we have not brought back tidings of Sita, he will certainly commit this injury. Therefore, it is better that we now engage in praya. Before we return and the king kills all of us, let us abandon our sons, our wives, our riches and our residences. This death is like being killed and is superior to that act. I have not been consecrated as the heir apparent by Sugriva. Rama, Indra among men and the performer of unblemished deeds, has consecrated me. The king is already tied to me with bonds of enmity. On seeing that I have transgressed, he will make up his mind to fiercely chastise me and kill me. When my life comes to an end, what is the point of my well-wishers witnessing my hardships? I will resort to praya on the shores of this auspicious ocean.' The prince, the heir apparent, spoke these words. Hearing this, all the best among apes addressed him in these piteous words. 'Sugriva is fierce in nature and Raghava is devoted to his beloved. We have been unable to see Vaidehi and the time set for seeing her has elapsed. Since we have been unable to accomplish what would have brought Raghava pleasure, there is no doubt that we will be killed. When we reach the side of our master, our crime will not be pardoned.' The apes were afflicted by fear. On hearing their words, Tara said, 'Enough of this misery. If it appeals to all of you, let us enter the cave and reside there. This has been constructed by Maya and is extremely difficult to penetrate. There are many trees and there is a lot of water. There is plenty to eat and drink. There is no fear here, not even from Purandara, nor from Raghava and the king of the apes.' Hearing these words, which were similar to what Angada had said, all the apes accepted this and said, 'This is a means whereby we will not be killed. Let us act in this way now.'

Chapter 4(53)

When Tara spoke in this way, Hanumat thought that this was tantamount to Angada robbing the kingdom of Tara's radiant lord.[303] Hanumat thought that Vali's son possessed the eight kinds of intelligence, the four kinds of forces and the fourteen qualities.[304] He was always full of energy, strength and valour. His prosperity waxed, like that of the moon from the first day of shukla paksha. He was Brihaspati's equal in intelligence and his father's equal in valour. He was now listening to Tara, like Purandara had once done to Shukra.[305] Though he was accomplished in all the sacred texts, he was now exhausted in an attempt to accomplish his master's objective. Therefore, Hanumat started to placate him. Using his wealth in the use of words, from among the four modes, he used the third one of bheda to wean away all the other apes.[306] When all the others were weaned away, he used the fourth mode to scare Angada. He addressed him in many terrible words that were filled with rage. 'O Tara's son! You can bear burdens and you are more capable than your father in fighting. You are certainly capable of firmly bearing the burden of the kingdom of the apes, just as your father was. O bull among apes! Apes are always fickle in their understanding. Separated from their sons and their wives, they will not tolerate your commands for a long time. They will not follow you and I am telling you what is evident. That is what will happen with Jambavat, Nila and the great ape, Suhotra. Nor will I follow you. Using the qualities of sama, dana and qualities like danda, you will not be able to wean us away from Sugriva. It is said that a

---

[303] Taaraa's radiant lord, that is, Sugriva. Hanumat thought that this was tantamount to Angada challenging Sugriva's authority as a king.

[304] The eight kinds of intelligence are attentiveness, capacity to listen, capacity to grasp, capacity to remember, ability to discriminate, ability to ascertain the truth, deep understanding and a capacity to distinguish between good action and bad action. The four kinds of forces are usually infantry, cavalry, elephants and chariots. But here, it probably means the capacity to selectively use sama, dana, bheda and danda. The fourteen qualities are knowing about time and place, fortitude, endurance, capacity to think of all the consequences, skill, self-defence, an ability to keep one's counsel secret, avoidance of pointless debates, courage, a capacity to identify the strengths and weaknesses, faith, an ability to shelter those who seek refuge, the ability to show anger at the right time and a capacity to steadfastly pursue a course of action.

[305] The preceptor of the demons.

[306] He used dissension to wean away all the other apes from Angada's decision. He then used the fourth one of danda to frighten Angada.

person who is weak should not take on someone who is stronger. Protect yourself and do not listen to these weak ones. You think and you have been told that this cave in the ground is safe. Lakshmana's arrows are easily capable of shattering it. In ancient times, it was created when Indra lightly hurled his vajra at it. Lakshmana's sharp arrows will shatter it, like a cup made out of leaves. Lakshmana possesses many kinds of sharp and iron arrows. O scorcher of enemies! If you decide to settle down here, all the apes will make up their minds to desert you. They will always remember their sons and their wives and will be anxious and hungry. They will regret it and sleep in misery. They will turn their backs on you. You will then be deprived of your well-wishers and the friends who desire what is beneficial for you. You will be extremely anxious and will tremble, even at the sight of a blade of grass. A person whom Lakshmana's terrible arrows cannot injure hasn't been born. They are extremely forceful and impossible to withstand. When they seek to kill, one cannot step aside. If you return with us and present yourself humbly and tell Sugriva everything that has happened, from the beginning, he will establish you in the kingdom. Your uncle loves dharma. He is firm in his vows and desires to be affectionate. He is pure and truthful to his pledges. He will let you live and will not kill you. He is affectionate towards your mother and wishes to do what is agreeable to her. He is alive only for her sake. He has no offspring other than you. O Angada! Therefore, let us go to him.'

Chapter 4(54)

He heard Hanumat's polite words, which were in conformity with dharma and were full of respect towards their lord.[307] However, Angada spoke these words. 'Stability in every respect of one's being, purity, non-violence, uprightness, valour and patience are not discernible in Sugriva. When his elder brother was still

[307] Sugriva.

alive, his beloved queen and wife, following dharma, was like
a mother to him. But he desired her and seized her as his own.
When his brother was fighting inside the hole and instated him
at the entrance, he abandoned him. How can such an evil-souled
one know dharma? Grasping his hand in a pledge of truth, the
immensely illustrious Raghava performed a good deed for him.
He forgot that. What other good deed will he remember? The
coward has not been scared of adharma. He has commanded us to
seek out Sita's path because he was terrified of Lakshmana. How
will he follow dharma? He is wicked and ungrateful. He and his
memory are both fickle. Which person, born in a noble lineage,
who wishes to remain alive, will trust him as one who is noble?
A son must be established in the kingdom, whether he possesses
qualities or does not possess qualities. Therefore, how can Sugriva
permit someone like me, born from his enemy, to remain alive?
My advisers have been weaned away.[308] I have committed a crime.
Who is as inferior in strength as I am? Even if I reach Kishkindha
and remain alive, I will be weak and without a protector. He may
punish me in secret ways. He may bind me up. For the sake of the
kingdom, Sugriva can be deceitful, cruel and violent. Resorting to
praya is superior to bondage and suffering. O apes! All of you
have my permission to return to your houses. I am informing all
of you that I will not return to the city. I will resort to praya here.
That kind of death is superior for me. First greet the king and ask
about his welfare. Then speak to my younger father, Sugriva, the
lord of the apes. Speak words to my mother, Ruma, and first ask
her if she is well. You should then ask about my mother, Tara, and
reassure her. That ascetic lady naturally loves her son and will not
be angry. On hearing that I have been destroyed, it is evident that
she will also not remain alive.' He spoke these words to the aged
ones and greeted them. Distressed in his mind, Angada lay down
on the darbha grass that was spread around there. When he lay
down there, the bulls among the apes started to weep. Since they
were miserable, warm tears started to flow from their eyes. They

[308] From the idea of living in the cave.

censured Sugriva and praised Vali. All of them surrounded Angada
and decided to engage in praya. The bulls among the apes got to
know the words that Vali's son had spoken. All of them touched
water and sat down, facing the eastern direction. The tips of the
darbha faced the southern direction and they were on the shores
of the water. Those apes, who were like the peaks of mountains,
lay down there, having traversed many mountains and stepped
through many caverns inside them. The salty ocean roared, like
terrible thunder clouds.

Chapter 4(55)

On the slope of the mountain, all the apes sat down in an act of
praya. At that time, a king of the eagles arrived at the spot.
His name was Sampati and he was a bird who lived for a long
time.[309] He was handsome and renowned because of his strength
and manliness. He was Jatayu's elder brother. He emerged from
a cave in the great mountain of Vindhya. He saw the apes seated
there. Cheerful in his heart, he spoke to them. 'Destiny decides and
all men in this world have to follow destiny. I have been waiting
for food for a long time and destiny has presented itself before me.
I will eat these apes one after another, as they progressively die.'[310]
Having spoken these words, the bird glanced at the apes. The bird
desired food and on hearing his words, Angada became supremely
anxious. He spoke to Hanumat. 'Behold. As if on Sita's command,
Vaivasvata Yama seems to have presented himself before us. He
has arrived at this spot to cause a calamity to the apes. We have
not accomplished Rama's task. We have not followed the king's
instructions. While we did not know it, this calamity for the
apes has suddenly presented itself before us. Jatayu, the king of
the eagles, performed a good deed in a desire to bring pleasure

[309] Alternatively, lived for ever.
[310] Alternatively, kill them one after another, as opposed to their dying naturally.

to Vaidehi. We heard the complete details about it there. All creatures, even those born as inferior species, are doing what brings pleasure to Rama and are giving up their lives, just as we are about to. We have abandoned all thought of our lives and are exhausted, trying to accomplish Raghava's objective. We traversed through all the desolate areas, but did not see Maithilee. The king of the eagles who was slain by Ravana in the battle is happy. Freed from all fear of Sugriva, he has attained the supreme destination. After the destruction of Jatayu and King Dasharatha, and Vaidehi's abduction, all the apes face an uncertain situation.[311] Rama and Lakshmana resided in the forest with Sita. Raghava killed Vali with an arrow. All the rakshasas were slain because of Rama's rage.[312] Because of the boon given to Kaikeyee, all these catastrophes have come about.'

Hearing the words that had emerged out of Angada's mouth, the eagle with the sharp beak uttered these words in a loud and rumbling voice. 'Who has spoken these words, making my mind tremble? I love my brother, Jatayu, more than my own life. Who has announced his death? How did this encounter between the rakshasa and the eagle happen in Janasthana? I have heard my brother's name mentioned today, after a long period of time. He is younger to me and possesses all the qualities. His valour is praiseworthy. O bulls among the apes! That is the reason I wish to hear about his destruction. My brother, Jatayu, was a resident of Janasthana. How is Dasharatha, my brother's friend? His eldest son, Rama, loves his seniors and the people, and is loved by him.[313] Since my wings have been scorched by the rays of the sun, I am incapable of stretching them.[314] O destroyers of enemies! Therefore, I wish that you should lower me from this mountain.'

[311] There are several implicit statements in the argument. Had Dasharatha not died, Rama might have been recalled from the exile. Had Jatayu not died, he might have been able to prevent Ravana, or at least tell the apes about where Ravana had taken Sita. Had Sita not been abducted, none of this would have happened.
[312] In Dandakaranya.
[313] Dasharatha.
[314] The story follows later.

Chapter 4(56)

The leaders of the apes heard his words, which wavered because of his sorrow.[315] Though they honoured his words, they were unsure about their course of action.[316] Seated in the act of praya, the apes saw the eagle. They then decided, 'This terrible one will not devour all of us. In any event, if he eats us, we are seated in praya in every possible way. What is going to occur will happen and we will speedily obtain success.' Having made up their minds in this way, all the bulls among the apes lowered the eagle from the peak of the mountain.

Angada spoke to him. 'There was a powerful Indra among the apes and his name was Riksharaja.[317] O bird! The noble king had two sons who were devoted to dharma. These sons were Sugriva and Vali and they possessed intelligence and strength. King Vali, famous in the worlds because of his deeds, was my father. There is a maharatha in the lineage of the Ikshvakus and he is the king of the entire earth. This is the handsome Rama, Dasharatha's son, and he entered the forest of Dandaka, with his brother, Lakshmana, and his wife, Vaidehi. He did this because of his father's command and because he always resorts to the path of dharma. His wife was forcibly abducted from Janasthana by Ravana. The king of the eagles, named Jatayu, was the friend of Rama's father. He saw that Sita Vaidehi was being abducted through the sky. He deprived Ravana of his chariot and rescued Maithilee. However, he was exhausted and aged and was slain in the battle by Ravana. This is the way the eagle was killed by a stronger Ravana. After Rama performed his funeral rites, he reached the supreme destination. After this, Raghava contracted an act of friendship with my uncle, the great-souled Sugriva, and killed my father. Since he had acted against my father, he had bound up Sugriva and his advisers. However, having slain Vali, Rama consecrated him as the king. Sugriva was

---

[315] At the news of Jatayu's death.
[316] In case the eagle ate them.
[317] Here, the text uses the word Raksharaja.

instated in the kingdom, as the lord of the apes. The king, foremost among the apes, dispatched all of us. Having been thus engaged by Rama, we thus searched the routes here and there. But we could not find Vaidehi, just as the radiance of the sun is unreachable during the night. Controlling ourselves, we searched everywhere in Dandakaranya. In our ignorance, we entered a cave that extended inside the ground. We searched in that cave, constructed by Maya through his use of maya. The month that the king had decreed for us passed in that way. All of us are engaged in acting in accordance with the commands of the king of the apes. Since the contracted period was over, we were terrified and have resolved to fast and undertake praya. Kakutstha, Sugriva and Lakshmana will be angry with us if we return there. Therefore, no purpose is served by us remaining alive.'

Chapter 4(57)

The apes, who were ready to give up their lives, spoke these piteous words. The voices of the apes choked with tears. The eagle replied in a loud voice. 'O apes! My brother, named Jatayu, is younger to me. He is the one who has been spoken about, as having been killed by a stronger Ravana in the encounter. Though I cannot tolerate what I have heard, I am aged and do not possess any wings. I do not possess the strength now to save my brother from his enemy. Earlier, when Vritra was killed, the two of us wished to rival each other.[318] We approached the sun, blazing in its garland of rays. With a terrible speed, we travelled through the sky and covered it, reaching the sun at midday. Jatayu began to suffer. I saw that my brother was suffering because of the rays of the sun and became extremely anxious. Out of affection, I covered him with my wings. O bulls among the apes! When my wings were burnt, I fell down on the Vindhyas. While I resided here, I

[318] Sampati and Jatayu had a friendly contest about who could fly closer to the sun.

no longer noticed what my brother was up to.' Sampati, Jatayu's brother, said this.

The immensely wise Prince Angada replied. 'If Jatayu was your brother, you have heard what I have said. If you know about the residence of that rakshasa, tell us about it. Ravana, the lord of the rakshasas, does not possess foresight. Whether he lives nearby, or far away, if you know, tell us.'

Jatayu's elder brother was immensely energetic. Thus addressed, he spoke words that were worthy of him and delighted the apes. 'O apes! I am an eagle whose wings have been burnt. My valour has been lost. But even then, through my words, I will render excellent help to Rama. I know the world of Varuna and that of Vishnu of the three strides.[319] I know about the clash between the gods and the asuras and the churning of amrita.[320] I am the first one who will perform a task in accomplishing this objective of Rama's. However, I am aged and am robbed of my energy. My breath of life is ebbing away. I saw a young lady being abducted by the evil-souled Ravana. She was beautiful and was adorned in all the ornaments. The beautiful one shrieked, "Alas, Rama! Rama! Alas, Lakshmana!" As she writhed, she flung away the ornaments from her limbs. Her excellent silken garment was like the dazzle of the sun on the summit of a mountain. On that dark rakshasa, she was as radiant as lightning on a cloud. Since she spoke of Rama, I think that she must have been Sita. Listen, as I tell you where the residence of that rakshasa is. He is the son of Vishravasa himself and Vaishravana's[321] brother. The rakshasa named Ravana rules over the city of Lanka. This island[322] is in the ocean and is a full one hundred yojanas from here. The beautiful city of Lanka was constructed by Vishvakarma. The miserable Vaidehi, attired in

[319] A reference to the dwarf incarnation. Vishnu's third stride was in the nether regions.

[320] Amrita was obtained through the churning of the ocean, and the gods and the demons fought over it.

[321] Kubera's.

[322] The word used is dvipa. While dvipa does mean island, it is also a term that can be used for any geographical region.

silken garments, resides there. She is confined to Ravana's inner quarters and is guarded well by rakshasis. You will see Maithilee, King Janaka's daughter, there. On all sides, Lanka is protected by the ocean. When you reach the shores of the ocean, it is a full one hundred yojanas from there. When you reach the other side of the southern shore, you will see Ravana. O apes! You should hurry and quickly exhibit your valour. Through my knowledge, I can see that you will return. The first path is for *kulinga*s and others who live on grain.[323] The second is for those who survive on leftovers of sacrifices[324] and those who eat the fruits of trees.[325] The third is travelled by predatory birds, curlews and ospreys. Hawks reach the fourth level and eagles travel along the fifth. The sixth path is for swans that possess strength and valour and also have youth and beauty. However, the descendants of Vinata can go beyond this. O bulls among apes! All of us have been born from Vinata. The one who survives on flesh has perpetrated a reprehensible deed. From here, I can see Ravana and Janakee. Golden ones like us possess the divine power of eyesight. O apes! Therefore, because of our food, valour and lineage, we can always see anything up to one hundred yojanas, as if it is right in front of us. For those born in our lineage, it has been ordained that our subsistence should be through what is far away. For those who fight with their feet,[326] it has been ordained that their subsistence will be found near their feet. Think of a means so that you can leap over the salty waters. You will then reach Vaidehi and be successful in accomplishing your objective. I desire that you should convey me to the ocean, Varuna's abode. I wish to offer the water rites to my great-souled brother who has gone to heaven.'

At this, the extremely energetic apes took Sampati, whose wings had been burnt, to a spot near the shore of the lord of the male and female rivers. After this, they again brought the lord of the birds

---

[323] The first level of flight, lower down. Kulingas are sparrows and shrikes.
[324] Specifically, leftovers of meat offerings, such as crows.
[325] Like parrots.
[326] Like cocks.

back to the original spot. The apes were delighted on realizing that they might be successful.

Chapter 4(58)

The words of the king of the eagles were like a taste of amrita. On hearing his words, the bulls among the apes were delighted and rejoiced. With Jambavat, foremost among the apes, all the apes quickly arose from the ground and spoke to the king of the eagles. 'Where is Sita? Who saw her? Who abducted Maithilee? Tell us everything and thereby offer an indication to us, those who reside in the forest. Who will be brought down by the arrows of Dasharatha's son, which possess the force of the vajra? Who will be singled out by the valour of Lakshmana's own releases?' The apes had collectively composed themselves, wishing to hear about Sita.

He was delighted at this and again reassuring them, he addressed them in these words. 'Listen to how I heard about Vaidehi's abduction and about who told me where the large-eyed one is. For a long time, I have been on this impenetrable mountainous region that extends for many yojanas. I fell down. I am aged. My valour and breath of life have decayed. When I attained this state, my son named Suparshva, supreme among birds, sustained me by providing me food at the right time. Gandharvas are fiercely addicted to desire. Serpents are fiercely addicted to rage. Deer are fiercely addicted to fear. Like that, we are fiercely addicted to hunger. On one occasion, I was afflicted by hunger and desired some food. The day was over and the sun had set. But my son did not bring me any flesh. Because of sentiments associated with age, I censured him in my rage. I was overwhelmed by hunger and thirst. I was deprived of food and suffering. But my son, supreme among birds and the extender of my delight, entreated me. He told me the truth and addressed me in these words. "O father! In search of flesh, at the right time, I did fly up into the sky. I stationed myself

properly at the entry to Mount Mahendra. There are thousands of
creatures there, roaming around the shore of the ocean. With my
glance lowered, I stationed myself there, obstructing one of those
paths. At that time, I saw something that was like the radiance of
the sun when it rises. Seizing a woman, he was advancing, like a
mass of broken collyrium.[327] On seeing the two of them, I made up
my mind that they could be food. However, using conciliation and
humility, he pleaded that I should provide a path for them. There
is no one on earth who strikes those who resort to conciliation, not
even those who are inferior people. How could someone with limbs
like mine not have yielded? With his energy and force, he departed,
as if flinging the sky aside. At this, the creatures who roam around
in the sky and on earth approached me and praised me. O father!
The maharshis told me, 'It is through good fortune that Sita is alive.
The wife has been taken away in some way. But there is no doubt
that she will be safe.' The siddhas, supremely handsome, addressed
me in this way. They also told me about Ravana, the king of the
rakshasas. They showed me the ornaments that Janaka's daughter,
the wife of Rama, Dasharatha's son, had flung away, with her
dishevelled silken garments. She had been vanquished by the force
of her grief. With her hair loose, she had wailed, mentioning the
names of Rama and Lakshmana. O father! That is the reason the
time passed." Suparshva, supreme among those who are eloquent
in the use of words, told me everything about all this. Even after I
heard this, my mind did not turn to thoughts of exhibiting valour.
How can a bird like me, without any wings, undertake any such
endeavour? Possessing the qualities of speech and intelligence, I
have done all that I am capable of doing. Having heard what I have
told you, you must now resort to your virility. With my speech and
my intelligence, I have done what should bring you pleasure. You
have a task to perform for Dasharatha's son and there is no doubt
that it is mine too. You are supreme in intelligence. You are strong
and spirited. That is the reason the king of the apes has sent you.

---

[327] We have earlier been told that it was Sampati himself who saw Ravana and
Sita. This chapter makes it a second-hand account, through Suparshva. There are other
inconsistencies too.

Even the gods will find it impossible to withstand you. Rama and Lakshmana's sharp arrows are shafted with the feathers of herons. They are sufficient to save, or chastise, the three worlds. Dashagriva is indeed addicted to desire and he possesses energy and strength. However, you are capable and there is nothing that you will find difficult to accomplish. We have spent enough time together. Now make up your minds about what is to be done. Intelligent people like you should not delay in accomplishing the task.'

Chapter 4(59)

The eagle offered the water rites and bathed. On that beautiful mountain, the leaders of the apes surrounded him from every direction and seated themselves. Angada was seated, with all the apes surrounding him. Delighted that he had won their trust, Sampati spoke again. 'O apes! Be silent and listen attentively to me. I will recount the truth about how I came to know about Maithilee. O unblemished one![328] Earlier I fell down on the summit of Vindhya. My limbs suffered because of the heat of the sun and I was burnt by the rays of the sun. Though I regained my senses after six nights, I was unconscious and senseless. I glanced in all the directions, but could not identify anything. On looking at the oceans, mountains, all the rivers and lakes and the regions in the forests, I got my intelligence back. The caves inside the mountain were filled with a large number of cheerful birds. I made up my mind that this was Vindhya, on the shores of the southern ocean. There was a sacred hermitage there, extremely revered by even the gods. It belonged to the rishi named Nishakara, who was fierce in his austerities. Nishakara, who knew about dharma, went to heaven. But even without the rishi, I resided there for eight thousand years. Through that uneven terrain, I slowly descended from the summit of Vindhya with difficulty. I found my way through the

---

[328] In the singular, therefore, specifically addressed to Angada.

sharp darbha grass with hardship and again reached the ground. I desired to see the rishi and was therefore full of great misery. Jatayu and I had gone to him on several occasions. Many kinds of fragrant breezes blow through the spot where his hermitage is located. Trees without flowers are never seen there, nor those without fruits. I reached the sacred hermitage and found refuge at the foot of a tree. I waited there, desiring to see the illustrious Nishakara. From a distance, I saw the rishi, blazing in his energy. After performing his ablutions, the unassailable one was returning, his face turned towards the north. Bears, antelopes, tigers, lions and many kinds of reptiles surrounded him and followed him, like living beings follow the granter of life.[329] On knowing that the rishi had returned, all the creatures followed him, just as all the ministers and soldiers follow when a king returns. On seeing me, the rishi was content and entered his hermitage again. However, he emerged in an instant and asked me the reason why I was there. "O amiable one! I can see that you are disabled and your body hair cannot be seen. Your wings have been burnt by the fire. There are wounds on your skin. I have seen two eagles earlier and they were like the wind god in their speed. Those two brothers could assume any form at will and were kings among the eagles. O Sampati! You were the elder and Jatayu was your younger brother. You used to assume the form of men and touch my feet. What disease has come over you? How did your wings fall off? Who has punished you in this way? Tell me everything that I have asked you about.'"

Chapter 4(60)

'At this, I told the sage about the extremely terrible act, extremely difficult to accomplish, that I had done in my rashness, about the attempt to follow the sun. "O illustrious one! I am wounded. I am ashamed and my senses are distracted. I

[329] Brahma.

am exhausted and am incapable of addressing you in words. I and Jatayu were confounded and insolent, seeking to compete against each other. Wishing to test our valour, we flew a long distance up into the sky. In front of the sages who were there on the summit of Kailasa, we had staked a bet. We would follow the sun, until it set behind the giant Mount Asta. Together, we flew up and could see the surface of the earth below, with separate cities that looked as large as the wheels of chariots. We could hear musical instruments being sounded in some places, chants of the brahman in others. We heard women singing. They looked like fires in their red garments. We rose quickly up into the sky and stationed ourselves in the path of the sun. We could see the forest, as if it was just a patch of grass. The earth, with its tall mountains, was seen to be covered, as if with pebbles. The earth was covered with rivers, as if threaded with strings. The Himalayas, Vindhya and the extremely gigantic mountain of Meru could be seen on the surface of the earth, resembling serpents inside a waterbody. We sweated profusely and were filled with repentance and fear. We were overwhelmed with confusion and suffered from terrible unconsciousness. We could not make out the Yamya, Agneya or Varuni directions.[330] We seemed to be consumed by the fire, like the worlds being destroyed at the end of a yuga. After I made a great deal of effort, I could make out the radiance of the sun again. The sun appeared before us, with a size that was like that of the earth. Without taking my leave, Jatayu fell down on the ground. On seeing him do this, I too quickly freed myself from the sky. Since I protected him with my wings, Jatayu was not burnt. However, due to my carelessness, I was burnt and fell down, following the path of the wind. I suspected that Jatayu had fallen down in Janasthana. I was numbed and my wings were burnt. I fell down on the Vindhyas. I was deprived of my kingdom, my brother, my wings and my valour. I desired death through every means and flung myself down from the summit of the mountain.'"

---

[330] Yamya is the south, Yama's direction. Agneya is the south-east, Agni's direction. Varuni is the west, Varuna's direction.

Chapter 4(61)[331]

'Weeping and extremely miserable, I told the best among sages this. Having reflected for a while, the illustrious one spoke to me. "You will again have small wings to replace your wings. You will also possess eyesight, the breath of life, valour and strength. In ancient times, I have heard about an extremely important task that must be accomplished. I have witnessed this through my austerities. I have heard about this and know about this. There is a king named Dasharatha and he is the extender of the lineage of the Ikshvakus. He will have an extremely energetic son named Rama. With his brother, Lakshmana, he will go to the forest. With truth as his valour, he will be appointed by his father to do this. The *nairitta*[332] named Ravana will abduct his wife from Janasthana. That Indra among rakshasas cannot be killed by gods or danavas. He will tempt Maithilee with objects of pleasure, food and succulent meals. However, immersed in her grief, the illustrious and extremely fortunate one will not enjoy any of this. Knowing this, Vasava will give Vaidehi supreme food. That food will be like amrita and even the gods find it extremely difficult to obtain this. On obtaining this food and on knowing that it has come from Indra, Maithilee will first place a little bit of it down on the ground, as an offering to Rama. 'If my husband is alive, with the lord Lakshmana, and even if he has attained divinity, let this food be rendered to them.' The apes, Rama's messengers, will be dispatched here. O bird! You must then tell them about Rama's queen. In any event, you must not leave this place. In this state, where will you go? If you wait for the right time and place, you will get your wings back. If I am so inclined, I can get you your wings back even now. However, you should remain here, to accomplish a task that will bring benefit to the worlds. You will indeed perform that task for those two princes, for the brahmanas, the gods, the sages and Vasava. I too wish to see the brothers,

---

[331] This entire chapter doesn't quite belong.
[332] Demon.

Rama and Lakshmana. However, I do not wish to remain alive for a long time and will give up my body."'333

Chapter 4(62)

'The one who was eloquent in the use of words spoke many other words. Encouraging me and instructing me, he entered his own hermitage. Extremely slowly, I crept down the caves on the mountain. I ascended Vindhya and waited for you to arrive. From then to now, a full one hundred years have passed.334 Imbibing the sage's words in my heart, I have waited for the right time and place. After Nishakara went to heaven on his great journey, I have been tormented by remorse and have debated many kinds of things. My mind turned to killing myself, but the sage's words restrained me. The intelligence that he granted me made me preserve my life. That dispelled the grief, like a blazing flame of fire dispels darkness. I know about the valour of the evil-souled Ravana. That is the reason I did not use words to censure my son about not having saved Maithilee, when Sita was separated and he heard her lamenting. He did not do this, despite knowing about my affection for Dasharatha and about the beloved sons that had been born to him.'

As he spoke to the apes who were assembled around him, while those who roamed around in the forest looked on, his wings sprouted. He looked at the new wings sprouting on his body, with red feathers and obtained unmatched delight. He told the apes, 'This is because of the powers of maharshi Nishakara, immeasurable in his soul. The wings that were burnt down by the rays of the sun have reappeared again. I possessed valour in my youth. I can feel that strength and virility now. Make every kind of effort to search out Sita. The gain of my wings convinces me that you will also be successful in your objective.' Sampati, supreme among birds,

---

333 Though not stated explicitly, Nishakara gave up his life.
334 This is inconsistent with the one thousand years mentioned earlier.

said this to all the apes. He then flew up from the summit of that mountain, as if to test whether he could still fly up into the sky. Hearing his words, the tigers among the apes were delighted in their minds. They became eager to test their valour. The supreme among apes, with valour like that of the wind god, got their virility back. They were eager to search out the route travelled by Janaka's daughter. Desiring to head in that direction, they waited for the right moment.

Chapter 4(63)

Having been told by the king of the eagles, the apes leapt around. Like lions in their valour, they were filled with joy and roared. The apes had heard those undecaying words about Ravana from Sampati. Desiring to see Sita, they joyfully arrived at the ocean. Terrible in their valour, they travelled and arrived at that spot. It[335] was stationed there, like a giant mirror of the entire world. They approached the southern ocean from the northern direction. Together, the supreme among apes settled down there. There were many kinds of gigantic and malformed creatures that were sporting in the water. They were extremely large in form, with gaping mouths. It was turbulent with waves. It seemed to be asleep in parts, while other parts seemed to be sporting. In some places, there were masses of water that were as large as mountains. It was full of Indras among the danavas and those who resided in the nether regions. It made the body hair stand up and on seeing this, the elephants among the apes were distressed. The apes saw that the ocean was like the sky and was impossible to cross. All of them were instantly filled with grief and spoke about what could be done. Beholding the ocean, the army was miserable. Seeing that the apes were afflicted by fear, the supreme among apes[336] reassured them. 'Our task is not to grieve

---

[335] The ocean.
[336] Angada.

in our minds. Sorrowing is a grave sin. Grief destroys a man, just as an angry serpent destroys a child. If valour presents itself before a person, he cannot tolerate despair. A man who is inferior in his energy will not be able to accomplish his objective.'

With the apes, Angada spent the night there. Having met the aged apes, he again held consultations with all of them. The radiant standards of the apes surrounded Angada. It was as if an army of Maruts had surrounded Vasava. Who in that army of apes was capable of achieving the task, other than Vali's son, or Hanumat? Showing his respect to the aged apes and the soldiers, the handsome Angada, scorcher of enemies, spoke words that were full of meaning. 'Which immensely strong one can leap over the ocean now? Who will accomplish the task for Sugriva, the scorcher of enemies who does not deviate from his objective? O apes! Which brave one can leap across one hundred yojanas? Among all the leaders here, who is capable of freeing us from this great fear? Through whose favours will we accomplish our objective and return happily, seeing our wives, sons and homes again? Through whose favours will we cheerfully approach Rama, the immensely strong Lakshmana and the immensely strong Sugriva? If there is any ape who is capable of leaping across the ocean, let him quickly grant us the sacred dakshina of freedom from fear.' Hearing Angada's words, no one said anything. Everywhere, that army of apes seemed to be numbed. Angada, supreme among apes, again spoke to the apes. 'All of you are best among those who are strong. You are firm in your valour. You have been born in faultless lineages and have been repeatedly worshipped. No one has ever been able to restrain you from going anywhere. O bulls among apes! You should tell me. Who possesses the strength to travel there?'

Chapter 4(64)

All the supreme apes heard Angada's words. One by one, each of them spoke about the respective distances that they were capable of travelling—Gaja, Gavaksha, Gavaya, Sharabha, Gandhamadana, Mainda, Dvivida, Sushena and Jambavat. Gaja said, 'I can leap across ten yojanas.' Gavaksha said, 'I can leap across twenty yojanas.' The ape Gavaya told the apes who were there, 'O apes! I can travel thirty yojanas.' The ape Sharabha told the apes who were there, 'There is no doubt that I can travel forty yojanas.' The immensely energetic Gandhamadana told the apes, 'There is no doubt that I can travel fifty yojanas.' The ape Mainda told the apes who were there, 'I am capable of leaping across sixty yojanas.' The immensely energetic Dvivida replied, 'There is no doubt that I can travel seventy yojanas.' Sushena, supreme among apes, told the supreme among the apes, 'O bulls among apes! I can leap across eighty yojanas.' As they conversed, the eldest, Jambavat, showed all of them his respect and replied, 'Earlier, I possessed the valour required to travel. However, I have now reached the other shore of my age. Why should we be unable to go and ignore the task at hand? That is the task for which the king of the apes and Rama have made up their minds. Listen to the distance that I am capable of travelling now. There is no doubt that I can travel ninety yojanas.' Jambavat again spoke to the best among the apes. 'Indeed, I no longer possess the valour to travel beyond this point. Earlier, at the sacrifice of the great Bali, when the eternal Lord Vishnu was in his Trivikrama form, I once circumambulated him. But I am now aged and the valour of my leaps has been weakened. In my youth, my supreme strength was unmatched. Right now, there can be no dispute that I do not possess the capability to go beyond this point. Therefore, I am incapable of accomplishing the task beyond this point.'

Angada paid his respects to the immensely wise and great ape, Jambavat. He replied in words that were great in their import. 'I can travel this great distance of one hundred yojanas. However, I am not certain that I will possess the strength to return.' Jambavat, best among apes and accomplished in the use of words, told him, 'O supreme among apes and bears! Your strength in travelling is known. Why one hundred? If you so desire, it has been said that you are destined and capable of travelling one thousand yojanas and returning. O son![337] But the master must always send and never go himself. O supreme among apes! We are the ones who should be sent by you. You are instated as our master and we are the ones who must be protected by you. O scorcher of enemies! The roles of the master, those who have to be protected and the soldiers have been earmarked. O son! You must always protect those who have to be protected. O scorcher of enemies! You are the foundation for the task that has to be accomplished. The foundation of any task must be protected. That is good policy. When the foundation is tended to and possesses the qualities, flowers and fruits result. O one for whom truth is valour! You are the means to accomplish the task. O scorcher of enemies! You are the source. You possess intelligence and valour. O supreme among apes! You are my senior and are also the son of my senior. Seeking refuge in you, we are capable of accomplishing the objective.' The immensely wise and giant ape, Jambavat, spoke these words.

Vali's son, Angada, replied in these words. 'If I do not go and nor does any other bull among the apes, we will again have to undertake the task of praya. We cannot return to the intelligent lord of the apes with the message that we have been unsuccessful. In that event, I do not see any means of protecting our lives. The lord of the apes is excessive in his favours and his rage. If we go with the message that we have failed, we will head towards our destruction. There is no means other than to accomplish the task that is at hand. You should therefore think of a means whereby success can be brought about.' The brave bull among apes was addressed by Angada in this way. In reply, Jambavat spoke these excellent words to Angada. 'O brave one! This task of yours will not suffer in any way. I will urge the one through whom success can be ensured.' The best among the apes saw that Hanumat, supreme among the apes, was happily seated alone. The best among the apes urged him.

[337] The word used is tata.

Chapter 4(65)

The many hundreds and thousands of soldiers in the army of the apes were distressed. Jambavat saw this and spoke to Hanumat. 'O brave one! In the world of the apes, you are supreme in your knowledge of all the sacred texts. O Hanumat! Why are you seated alone, silent? Why are you not saying anything? O Hanumat! You are the equal of Sugriva, king of the apes. You are Rama and Lakshmana's equal in energy and strength. The immensely strong Garuda is the son of Arishtanemi and Vinata. He is famous and is supreme among all the birds. The immensely illustrious bird is immensely forceful. On several occasions, I have seen the immensely strong one pluck serpents out of the ocean. The strength of your arms is like the strength of his wings. You are not his inferior in valour and force. O supreme among apes! Among all creatures, you are special in your strength, intelligence, energy and spirit. Why are you not understanding this? The apsara Punjikasthala is famous and is best among all the apsaras. She is famous as Anjana, the wife of the ape Kesari. O son![338] She could assume any form at will.[339] But she was cursed that she would be born as a female ape. She was born as the daughter of the great-souled Kunjara, Indra among apes. As a female ape, she was beautiful in all her limbs. On one occasion, capable of assuming any form at will, she adopted the form of a woman, excellent in her youth. She roamed around on the summit of a mountain, like a streak of lightning in a cloud. She was adorned in wonderful garlands and ornaments, attired in extremely expensive silken garments. The large-eyed one's garments were yellow and sparkling, tinged with red. While she was located on the summit of the mountain, the wind god gently robbed her of those. The wind god saw her uncovered thighs, which were well formed. Her round breasts clung close to each other. Her face was beautiful and fashioned well. The illustrious one was slender at the waist, with wide hips. On seeing all her auspicious limbs, the

---

[338] The word used is tata.

[339] Punjikasthala was cursed that she would be born as Anjana.

wind god was confounded by desire and used force. The wind god embraced her with his long arms. Overcome by desire, he immersed himself in the limbs of that unblemished one. Terrified at this, the one who was excellent in conduct spoke these words. "Who wishes to destroy my vow of being the wife of a single husband?" Hearing Anjana's words, the wind god replied, "O one with the beautiful hips! I will not injure you. O immensely fortunate one! Do not be scared. O illustrious one! I have entered you and embraced you with my mind. You will have a son who is valiant and is full of intelligence." Later, when you were a child, you saw the rising sun in the great forest. Desiring to seize what you took to be a fruit, you leapt up into the sky. O great ape! You travelled for three hundred yojanas. But its[340] energy hurled you down and you were full of sorrow. O great ape! On seeing that you were swiftly reaching the sky, the intelligent Indra was filled with rage and hurled the vajra at you. When you fell down on the summit of the mountain, your left cheekbone was shattered. Because of this, you have been known by the name of Hanumat.[341] On seeing that you had been struck, Vayu, the bearer of scents, was himself extremely enraged and the wind ceased to blow in the three worlds. All the gods were terrified and the three worlds were agitated. The lords of the worlds sought the favours of the enraged wind god. When the wind god was placated, Brahma granted you a boon. O one who has truth as your valour! O son! Through the use of a weapon, you cannot be killed in a battle. The one with the one thousand eyes saw that though you had been brought down by the vajra, you were not wounded. Therefore, delighted in his mind, he had granted you an excellent boon. O lord! Your death will occur only when you wish for it. Kesari is terrible in his valour and you have been born in his field. You are the biological son of the wind god and you are his equal in your energy. O child! You are Vayu's son and are his equal in leaping. We now no longer possess any breath of life left. Among us, you are the one who possesses skill and valour. You are like another king of the birds.

[340] The sun's.

[341] One with a cheekbone (*hanu*), that is, one with a broken cheekbone.

O son! At the time of Trivikrama, I have circumambulated the entire earth, with its mountains, forests and groves, twenty-one times. On the instructions of the gods, we[342] have gathered the herbs that were crushed for the sake of amrita and that conferred great strength on us. However, I am aged now and my valour has decayed. At the present time, among all of us, you are the one who possesses all the qualities. O valiant one! You are excellent in leaping. Therefore, prepare yourself. All these soldiers in the army of the apes desire to witness your valour. O tiger among apes! Arise and leap across the great ocean. O Hanumat! Your capacity to travel is greater than that of all creatures. All the apes are distressed. O Hanumat! Why are you ignoring this? In your valour and great force, you are like Vishnu Trivikrama.' He was urged by Jambavat in this way. The ape who was the son of the wind god realized his own force. The army of the brave apes rejoiced when he[343] assumed a gigantic form.

Chapter 4(66)

Praised, the immensely strong Hanumat extended his size. Filled with joy and strength, he lashed his tail. All the bulls among apes praised him. Filled with energy, he assumed a supreme form. He was like a strident lion yawning in a mountain cave. Like that, Marut's biological son started to yawn. As he yawned, the intelligent one's face was radiant. He was like a blazing frying pan, or like a smoke without fire.

From the midst of the apes, he raised up his joyful body. Hanumat greeted the aged apes and spoke to them. 'The wind, the friend of the fire, breaks down the summits of mountains. Vayu's strength is immeasurable and he travels through the sky. I am Marut's biological son and the great-souled one is swift in speed. I am also swift in speed and am his equal in leaping across. The

---

[342] Though 'we' is used, this really means 'I'.
[343] Hanumat.

extensive Mount Meru is like a picture engraved in the sky. I am
interested in circling around it one thousand times. With the force
of my arms, I am interested in penetrating the ocean and raising the
waters to flood the worlds, with the mountains, rivers and lakes.
Such a great force will arise from my thighs and calves that the
giant crocodiles will be raised up from the ocean that is Varuna's
abode. I am capable of circling around Vinata's son[344] one thousand
times, while he flies through the sky, populated by birds, in search
of serpents to eat. The sun, with its garland of blazing rays, leaves
from Mount Udaya and returns to Mount Asta. O bulls among
apes! With my great and terrible force, I am interested in following
him and returning, without having touched the ground in the
process. I am interested in overtaking all those who course through
the sky. I will agitate the ocean and shatter the earth. O apes! I
will leap on the mountains and make them tremble. As I leap, the
force of my thighs will rob the great ocean of its waters. When I
now leap through the sky, all the creepers, herbs, flowers and trees
will follow my trail. My path will be like Svati's[345] path through
the sky. My leap up into the sky will be terrible and as I descend,
all the creatures and all the apes will witness it. O apes! You will
see me extend, like the great Meru. I will envelop the firmament
and proceed, as if I am swallowing the sky. I will dispel the clouds
and make the mountains tremble. As I control myself and leap, I
will agitate the ocean. My strength is like that of Vinata's son or
the wind god. With the exception of the king of the birds[346] or the
immensely strong wind god, no creature will be able to see or follow
me as I leap. In a twinkling, I will pass through the sky, which needs
no support. I will descend suddenly, like lightning arising inside a
cloud. When I leap across the ocean, my form will be like that of
the striding Vishnu in the course of the valour of his three strides.
O apes! Rejoice. Through my intelligence, thoughts and efforts, I
can see that I will be able to see Vaidehi. My force is like that of

---

[344] Garuda.

[345] The nakshatra Svati, Arcturus. When Svati is in the ascendant, it rains and there
is a harvest of crops. Hence, there is an image of the effort yielding fruit.

[346] Garuda.

the wind god. My speed is like that of Garuda. It is my view that I can travel ten thousand yojanas. Through my sudden valour, I will bring the vajra from Vasava's hand and amrita from the hand of Svayambhu Brahma. It is my view that I can go and bring back Lanka itself.' Infinitely energetic, the best among apes roared in this way.

Jambavat, supreme among apes, was extremely delighted. He said, 'O brave one! O son of Kesari! O forceful one! O son of the wind god! O son! You have destroyed the great misery of your relatives. The foremost among the apes have assembled, desiring your welfare. They will control themselves and perform all the auspicious rites required to bring about success in the objective. Through the favours of the rishis, the support of the aged apes and the favours of your seniors, you will leap across the great ocean. Each one of us will stand on one foot until you return. The lives of all the residents of the forest are dependent on your journey.'

The tiger among apes spoke to the residents of the forest in words of assent. 'Who in this world is capable of bearing the force of my leap? The summit of Mount Mahendra is stable and large. This mountain is full of boulders and cliffs. The best among birds place their feet here. If I place my feet there, it will be able to bear me when I leap across one hundred yojanas.' The ape was like the wind god. He was the son of the wind god. The scorcher of enemies climbed Mahendra, supreme among mountains. It was covered with many kinds of trees and grass that deer grazed on. There were obstructions of creepers and flowers. There were trees that were always laden with flowers and fruits. Lions and tigers roamed around there. The place was frequented by crazy elephants. The turbulent waters were full of flocks of maddened birds. The gigantic summit of Mahendra rose up. The immensely strong one, best among apes, like the great Indra in his valour, climbed up. The giant mountain was crushed by the great-souled one's feet and shrieked, like a giant elephant that has been injured by a lion. Waterbodies and heaps of boulders were dislodged, disturbed and hurled away. The animals and deer were terrified. The large trees trembled. There were many gandharva couples, intoxicated after having indulged in bouts of drinking. The birds flew up, as did large numbers of vidyadharas. Giant serpents that had hidden inside the great mountain slithered away. Hills, peaks and boulders were uprooted on that great mountain. Hissing, serpents stretched out their hoods as they emerged partially from their holes, and it seemed as if the mountain was radiant with flags. The rishis were terrified and abandoned all those peaks. The mountain seemed to suffer, like a traveller abandoned by his companions on a desolate plain. The forceful one, supreme among apes and the slayer of enemy heroes, invoked the force in himself. The extremely great one controlled his mind. The spirited one made up his mind to go to Lanka.

This ends Kishkindha Kanda.

CHAPTER FIVE

Sundara Kanda

Chapter 5(1)

Sita had been taken away by Ravana along a path that the charanas travelled on. The afflicter of enemies[1] sought to search her trail along these. There were pastures of grass, with the complexion of lapis lazuli and these looked like still bodies of water. Happily, the immensely strong one travelled along these. The intelligent one frightened the birds and uprooted trees with his chest. Like a striding lion, he also killed many deer. Like an elephant, the ape stood in a lake there. This was decorated with colourful and natural minerals on the rocks—blue, red, yellow, green like leaves, black and white. With their companions, there were yakshas, kinnaras, gandharvas who were like the gods and serpents there, capable of assuming any form at will. There were tens of thousands of elephants on the slope of that supreme mountain. Making up his mind to leave, he joined his hands in salutation before Surya, the great Indra, the wind god, Svayambhu and the elements. Facing the east, he joined his hands in salutation before the wind god, from whom, he had been born. He then turned towards the south, increasing his size and ready to travel towards the southern direction. Watched by the best among the apes, he had made up his mind to leap. To enhance the prospect of Rama's success, he increased his size, like the ocean on days of the full moon. Desirous of leaping across the ocean, his body

[1] Hanumat.

became immeasurably large. He pressed against the mountain with his arms and his feet. Suffering from the ape's action, for a while, the beautiful and immobile mountain wavered. All the flowers showered down from the tops of the young and blossoming trees. Showers of extremely fragrant flowers were dislodged from the trees. The mountain was covered with this everywhere and dazzled, as if it was made out of flowers. His supreme valour crushed the mountain and water started to ooze out, as if from a crazy elephant in musth. The strong one made Mount Mahendra suffer. Streaks of gold, silver and collyrium appeared. Boulders were dislodged. There were large rocks and rocks that were filled with sulphur. The mountain suffered and in turn, caused suffering to everything. Creatures hidden inside caves howled in hideous voices. Because of the suffering caused to the mountain, screams arose from the large creatures. This filled the earth, the directions and the groves. There were snakes with large hoods, the mark of the *svastika* identifiable on them. They vomited terrible fires and bit the rocks with their fangs. Stung by the poison filled with rage, the great rocks blazed like flaming fires and shattered into thousands of fragments. Clumps of herbs were generated on that mountain. However, even these were incapable of countering the poison released from the venom of the serpents.[2] The ascetics on the mountain thought that it was being shattered by demons. With large numbers of their women, the terrified vidyadharas flew away. They left behind liquor in golden vessels meant for storing liquor, extremely expensive vessels and golden pots. There were superior and inferior kinds of *lehya* and *bhakshya*.[3] There were many kinds of meat. There were shields made out of oxhide and swords with golden handles. They[4] were intoxicated, with garlands around their necks. They wore red garlands and were smeared with red paste. Their eyes were red. Their eyes were like red lotuses and they took to the sky. The women wore necklaces, anklets, armlets and bangles. Surprised, they stood in the sky with their loved ones and smiled. The vidyadharas and

[2] These were medicinal herbs.
[3] Respectively, food that is licked and eaten.
[4] The vidyadharas.

maharshis exhibited their great skills. Together, they stood in the sky and looked towards the mountain.

At that time, the rishis, cleansed in their souls, heard a sound, uttered by the charanas and siddhas who were located in the sparkling sky. 'This Hanumat is the son of the wind god and is like a mountain. Using his great force, he wishes to cross the ocean, the abode of *makaras*.[5] For Rama's sake and for the sake of the apes, he desires to perform this extremely difficult task. He wishes to reach the other shore of the ocean, which is extremely difficult to reach.'

He[6] shook his body hair. The one who was like a mountain, shook himself. He roared extremely loudly, like an extremely large cloud. His tail, covered with hair, was completely rolled up. Ready to leap, he raised it, like the king of the birds[7] raises a serpent. His tail was curled around at the back and because of the force, looked as though a large serpent was being carried away by Garuda. His arms were like gigantic clubs and he used these to support himself. The ape bent at the waist and contracted his feet. The handsome one drew in his arms and his head. The valiant one immersed himself in his energy, spirit and prowess. Concentrating his sight, he glanced at the path and the distance he would have to travel. He looked at the sky and held the breath in his heart. The elephant among apes planted his feet firmly. The immensely strong Hanumat drew in his ears. The supreme among apes addressed the apes in these words. 'Like an arrow released by Raghava, with the valour of the wind, I will go to Lanka, ruled over by Ravana. If I do not see Janaka's daughter in Lanka, with the same speed, I will go to the abode of the gods. Despite making these efforts, if I do not see Sita in heaven, I will bind Ravana, the king of the rakshasas, and bring him here. I will be successful in every way, with Sita, or I will uproot Lanka and bring it here, with Ravana.'

Hanumat, supreme among apes, spoke to the apes in this way. He leapt up with force and started to travel with great force. Because

---

[5] A mythical aquatic creature, which can be loosely translated as shark or crocodile.

[6] Hanumat.

[7] Garuda.

of the force of his leap, all the trees that grew on the mountain were drawn in and uprooted in every direction. There were blossoming trees with plump lapwing birds hanging on to them. Because of the force of his thighs, these were uprooted and trailed him as he proceeded through the sky. Uprooted by the force of his thighs, the trees followed the ape for some time, like relatives and kin follow someone who is leaving on a long journey. Uprooted by the force of his thighs, sala and other excellent trees followed Hanumat, like soldiers behind a lord of the earth. The ape Hanumat, who was like a mountain, was extraordinary to behold, with those many flowering trees. As if terrified of Mount Mahendra, those solid trees then sank into the salty waters of the ocean, Varuna's abode. The ape was himself covered with many kinds of flowers, shoots and buds. Like a mountain, he was as radiant as a mountain illuminated with fireflies. Because of the force, the trees shed their flowers. When their well-wisher departed, they then fell down into the water. Trees with many kinds of flowers were lightly raised because of the gust the ape created and fell down into the ocean. It was wonderful. Flowers of many kinds of hues stuck to the ape's body and he was as radiant as a cloud in the sky, tinged with flashes of lightning. The flowers raised up by that force could be seen and the water looked resplendent, like the firmament with stars in it. When he took to the sky, his arms were seen to stretch out and looked like five-headed serpents that had emerged from the summit of a mountain. The great ape was seen, as if he was drinking up the great ocean and its waves, as if he was drinking up the sky. As he followed the path of the wind, his eyes dazzled like lightning, or like two fires on a mountain. He was foremost among those with tawny eyes and the circles of his tawny eyes were large. The two eyes shone, fixed like the sun and the moon. His mouth and nose were copper coloured. His face looked like the solar disc when it is touched by the evening. As he leapt, the dazzling tail of Vayu's son was raised up in the sky, like Shakra's standard when it has been raised. The wind god's son had teeth that were white and the tail formed a huge circle. The immensely wise one was as radiant as the sun with its disc. The great ape's copper-coloured behind was radiant and looked like a large and shattered mountain, exuding ochre-hued minerals. As the lion among apes leapt across the ocean, the wind seemed to be roaring inside his armpits. The elephant among apes looked like a trailing meteor that has been dislodged from the northern sky. The large and radiant ape stretched out, like a bird that has covered the sky. He increased his size, like an elephant when it has been tied with a rope. Though his body was above, the ape cast a shadow, immersed in the ocean, and this looked like a boat being driven along by the wind. Whichever spot in the ocean the great ape advanced along, that part seemed to be maddened because of the force of his thighs. The net of waves in the ocean were like mountains and the great ape struck them with his chest, as he leapt across them with great force. There was the gust raised by the powerful ape. There was the gust released from the clouds. The ocean trembled severely and roared terribly. In his great force, he crossed over the waves, as if dragging along the net of large waves in that salty ocean. The serpents who had abodes in the ocean saw the tiger among apes leap through the sky and thought that he was Suparna.[8] The shadow of the lion among apes was beautiful in the water, ten yojanas wide and thirty yojanas long. The resplendent shadow was stretched across the salty water and it seemed as if a mass of white clouds were following Vayu's son. They saw him leap. As he swiftly leapt, the gods, the gandharvas and the danavas showered down flowers. As the lord among the apes leapt, the sun did not scorch him. To accomplish Rama's objective, the wind wafted gently. As he leapt through the sky, the rishis praised him. The gods and the gandharvas chanted praises to the immensely energetic one. On seeing that the supreme among apes suddenly lost all exhaustion, all the nagas, the yakshas, the rakshasas, the gods and the birds praised him.

When Hanumat, tiger among apes, was leaping in this way, to show respect to the Ikshvaku lineage, the ocean thought, 'If I do not act to help Hanumat, Indra among the apes, all those who wish to speak ill of me will find reason. I was extended by Sagara,

[8] Garuda.

the protector of the Ikshvaku lineage. This adviser of the Ikshvaku lineage should not suffer from exhaustion. Therefore, I must find a means so that the ape can rest. After having rested on me, he can happily take the remaining part of the leap.' Having had this virtuous thought, the ocean, the store of water, spoke to Mainaka, with a navel made out of gold and supreme among mountains. 'O best among mountains! The king of the gods has set you up here, as a barricade against the large number of asuras who reside in the nether regions.[9] You are stationed here, enveloping the immeasurable gate to *patala*[10] and preventing those who are born valiant[11] from rising up again. O supreme among mountains! O mountain! You have the capacity to increase your size, upwards, downwards and diagonally. Therefore, I am urging you to rise up. This valiant tiger among apes, Hanumat, is performing a terrible deed to accomplish Rama's objective and is leaping through the sky, above you. I should aid in the task of someone who follows the Ikshvaku lineage. Those of the Ikshvaku lineage are worshipped by me and they are worshipped even more by you. Therefore, help us, so that our task is not unsuccessful. If a task that should be performed is not performed, the virtuous become angry. Rise up above the water, so that the ape can rest on you. The supreme among apes is our guest and must be worshipped by us. O one with the large and golden navel, frequented by gods and gandharvas! Having rested on you, Hanumat can then travel the rest of the distance. On witnessing Kakutstha's non-violence, Maithilee's exile and the exertion of the Indra among the apes, you should raise yourself up.' Mainaka, with the golden navel, heard the words of the salty waters. With innumerable large trees and creepers, he swiftly arose from the water. He arose, piercing the waters of the ocean, just as the blazing rays of the sun pierce through a cloud. There were peaks made out of molten gold, full of kinnaras and large serpents. Like the rising sun, they arose and seemed to write in the sky. When the

[9] Patala, a general term for the nether regions. More specifically, there are actually seven nether regions—*atala, vitala, sutala, rasatala, talatala, mahatala* and patala.

[10] One of the seven nether regions.

[11] The asuras.

mountain arose, there were summits made out of molten gold. With the golden radiance, the sky looked like a weapon.[12] Made out of molten gold, the peaks were radiant with their own resplendence. The supreme mountain looked like one hundred suns.

Hanumat saw it rise suddenly, in front of him and in the midst of the salty waters. He decided that this was an obstruction. Having decided this, with great force, the great ape used his chest to bring down what had risen, like the wind god brings down a cloud. The supreme among mountains was thus brought down by the ape. Realizing the ape's force, he was delighted and rejoiced. He assumed the form of a man and stood on his own peak, presenting himself before the brave one who was travelling through the sky. Delighted and happy in his mind, the mountain addressed the ape in these words. 'O supreme among apes! You have performed an act that is extremely difficult to accomplish. Descend on my peaks and happily rest. The ocean was born in Raghava's lineage and extended by them.[13] That is the reason the ocean is worshipping you, as someone who is engaged in Rama's welfare. It is eternal dharma that one must pay back someone who has done a good deed. It truly wants to pay back. Therefore, you must respect it. With a great deal of respect, I have been urged by it. "When the ape has leapt over one hundred yojanas, before he travels the rest of the distance, let him rest on your peaks."[14] O tiger among apes! Rest on me and then travel. There are many fragrant and tasty tubers, roots and fruits here. O best among apes! Taste them. Rest and then travel. O best among apes! That apart, there is a relationship between you and me. It is famous in the three worlds and is accepted by those who possess the great qualities. O son of the wind god! O elephant among apes! I think you are foremost among the apes who are forceful and can leap. Indeed, even ordinary people, who seek to practise dharma, know that a guest must be honoured, not to speak of one who is as great as you. O elephant among apes!

---

[12] The image is of a sword, with the blue of the sky as the blade and the golden peaks as the handle.

[13] This is a reference to King Sagara.

[14] The ocean speaking to Mainaka.

The great-souled wind god is best among the gods and you are his son, his equal in force. O one who knows about dharma! If you are worshipped, the wind god is also worshipped. That is the reason you must be worshipped. But listen to another reason too. O son![15] Earlier, in *krita yuga*, mountains possessed wings. With the speed of Garuda and the wind, they travelled in all the directions. When they travelled around in this way, the large number of gods, with rishis and the creatures, were scared that they might fall down. At this, the thousand-eyed Shatakratu became angry and used his vajra to instantly sever the wings of thousands of mountains. Angry, the king of the gods also approached me, with his vajra raised. But the great-souled wind god violently flung me aside. O supreme among apes! I was thus flung into the salty waters. I was protected by your father and all my wings were preserved. That is the reason I revere the wind god and revere you. O foremost among the apes! This relationship between you and me possesses great qualities. O great ape! This being the case, it is your task to please me and the ocean and make our minds rejoice. O supreme among apes! Free yourself of your exhaustion and accept our worship. Accept our great respect cheerfully. I am delighted that I have been able to see you.'

Thus addressed, the best among apes spoke to the excellent mountain. 'I am delighted that you have shown me hospitality. Let there be no anger between us. It is time to make haste. The day is passing. I have given my pledge that I will not stop in between.' Saying this, the bull among apes embraced the mountain with his hands. As if smiling, the valiant one went up into the sky and continued to travel. The mountain and the ocean glanced at him with a great deal of respect. They worshipped the son of the wind god and showered him with blessings. Having taken his leave of the mountain and the great ocean, he rose far up. Resorting to the path followed by his father, he travelled through the sparkling sky. He went still further up and glanced down at the mountain. Without any support, the son of the wind god travelled through the sparkling sky. All the gods, the siddhas and the supreme rishis

---

[15] The word used is tata.

saw the extremely difficult task that Hanumat was performing
and praised him. The gods and the thousand-eyed Vasava were
delighted at the act performed by the one with the golden and
excellent navel.[16] Shachi's intelligent consort himself spoke to the
best among mountains, the one with the excellent navel, in words
that were indistinct because he was so satisfied. 'O one with the
golden navel! O Indra among mountains! I am greatly satisfied
with you. I am granting you freedom from fear! O amiable one!
Remain at ease. You have helped Hanumat, who is fearlessly
performing this extremely great task of travelling one hundred
yojanas, though there is reason to be afraid. He is going as the
messenger of Rama Hari, Dasharatha's son. I am content that you
have firmly performed this good deed.' On seeing that Shatakratu,
the lord of the gods, was content, the supreme among mountains
obtained unmatched delight. The mountain was granted a supreme
boon[17] and remained there.

In an instant, Hanumat travelled over the ocean. At this, the
gods, the gandharvas, the siddhas and the supreme rishis spoke to
Surasa, the mother of the nagas and like the sun in resplendence.[18]
'The handsome son of the wind god is leaping over the ocean.
For a while, become an obstruction before Hanumat. Assume the
form of an extremely terrible rakshasa that is like a mountain,
with horrible fangs and coppery eyes. Assume a face that rises up
into the firmament. We wish to ascertain his strength and valour
and know whether he can overcome you, or will be overcome by
sorrow.' The goddess was thus addressed by the gods and honoured
by them. In the midst of the ocean, Surasa assumed the fearful form
of a rakshasa. It was disfigured, malformed and fearful everywhere.
She obstructed the leaping Hanumat and said, 'O bull among the
apes! The gods have said that you are my food. I will devour you.
Enter my mouth.' Thus addressed by Surasa, the bull among apes
joined his hands in salutation. With a cheerful face, the handsome
one replied, 'Dashratha's son, named Rama, entered Dandaka

[16] Mainaka.
[17] By Indra.
[18] This attempt to test Hanumat through Surasa is strange.

forest with his brother, Lakshmana, and his wife, Vaidehi. Tied
with his enmity towards the rakshasas, when he was engaged in
another task, his illustrious wife, Sita, was abducted by Ravana.
On Rama's instructions, I am going to him as his messenger. O one
who resides in his dominion![19] You should help Rama. Listen to
my truthful pledge. Otherwise, for the sake of Rama, the performer
of unblemished deeds, after I have seen Maithilee, I will come and
enter your mouth.' Surasa, who could assume any form at will,
was thus addressed by Hanumat and said, 'My boon is that no
one can transgress me.' Thus addressed by Surasa, the bull among
apes became angry and said, 'Make your mouth so that you can
obstruct me.' Surasa became enraged at being addressed in this way.
She appeared before Hanumat with a mouth that was ten yojanas
wide and twenty yojanas long. Surasa's mouth was like a cloud, ten
yojanas wide and twenty yojanas long. On seeing this, Hanumat
became wrathful and became thirty yojanas long. Surasa made her
mouth forty yojanas high. The brave Hanumat became fifty yojanas
high. Surasa made her mouth sixty yojanas wide. At this, the brave
Hanumat became seventy yojanas high. Surasa made her mouth
eighty yojanas long. Like a foremost mountain, Hanumat rose
up ninety yojanas. Surasa made her mouth one hundred yojanas
long. Vayu's intelligent son saw that gaping mouth, with Surasa's
extremely terrible and long tongue resembling hell. Maruti[20] was
like a cloud, but contracted his form. In an instant, Hanumat
became as small as a thumb. With great speed, he swiftly descended
into the mouth. Emerging and stationed in the sky, the handsome
one spoke these words. 'O Dakshayani![21] I bow down before you.
I have entered your mouth. I will now go where Vaidehi is. Your
words have also come true.' She saw that he had been freed from
her mouth, like the moon from Rahu's mouth. Assuming her own
form, the goddess Surasa spoke to the ape. 'O best among apes! O
amiable one! Go cheerfully and accomplish the desired objective.
Bring Vaidehi before the great-souled Raghava.' Witnessing

---

[19] Rama's dominion.
[20] Hanumat.
[21] Daksha's daughter, Surasa being one of Daksha's daughters.

Hanumat's deed, which was extremely difficult to accomplish, all the creatures praised the ape.

Like Garuda in his force, he passed through the unassailable ocean, Varuna's abode. He then entered the sky and proceeded through it. There were clouds there and it was populated by birds. Those who were skilled in music and dancing[22] travelled there and it was frequented by Airavata.[23] Sparkling and ornamented vimanas were swiftly moving there, with lions, elephants, tigers and serpents as mounts. Their[24] forms were like the fire and they clashed like thunder and lightning. They were meant for immensely fortunate ones who had performed auspicious deeds and were decorated by those who had conquered heaven. Frequented by the fire god, many kinds of oblations were carried along. It was decorated by planets, nakshatras, the moon, the sun and a large number of stars. The place was full of a large number of maharshis, gandharvas, serpents and yakshas. It sparkled and was empty.[25] It was frequented by Vishvavasu.[26] This was the path travelled by the elephants of the king of the gods. This was the auspicious path of the moon and the sun. It was like a canopy spread over the world of the living, constructed by Brahma. There were many groups of excellent and brave vidyadharas there. Without any difficulty, the ape proceeded through the large clouds. He entered the net of clouds and repeatedly emerged again. He entered and emerged repeatedly, like the radiance of the moon amidst monsoon clouds.

There was a rakshasi named Simhika who could assume any form at will.[27] On seeing him leap, in her mind, she thought that she would extend her size. 'After a long period of time, my food has come before me. After a long period of time, this great being has come under my control.' Thinking this in her mind, she seized the

---

[22] Gandharvas.

[23] Indra's elephant.

[24] That of the vimanas.

[25] Not populated by humans.

[26] The king of the gandharvas.

[27] Sometimes, Simhika is also referred to as Angaraka.

shadow.[28] When his shadow was seized, the ape started to think. 'I am being violently seized and my valour has been disabled. It is as if a giant boat in the ocean is being pulled back by a contrary wind.' The ape looked around, up, down and diagonally. He saw a great spirit arising from the salty waters. He thought, 'This is the spirit, extraordinary to behold, that the king of the apes spoke about. There is no doubt that this is the extremely valorous one that seizes shadows.' The intelligent ape arrived at the right conclusion, that this was Simhika. Like a cloud during the monsoon season, he extended his gigantic form. On seeing that the giant ape was increasing his size, she extended her mouth, until it looked like patala stretched across the sky. The intelligent and great ape saw her extend her extremely large mouth, until her mouth was as large as his form. He also saw her inner organs. The immensely strong one repeatedly contracted himself and descended. The siddhas and the charanas saw him descend into her mouth. It was like the moon being swallowed on the night of the full moon by Rahu. With his sharp nails, the ape tore into her inner organs. After that, with a speed like that of thought, the valiant one flew up. On seeing that Simhika had quickly been brought down by the ape, the creatures who roam around in the sky spoke to the supreme among the apes. 'By slaying this great creature today, you have performed an extremely terrible deed. O supreme among apes! An extremely desired objective has met with success. O Indra among apes! If a person possesses four traits, perseverance, foresight, intelligence and skill, like you do, he will never falter in any task.' The revered ape was thus honoured by them. Determined to accomplish his objective, he entered and travelled through the sky, like the one who feeds on serpents.[29]

Having reached the other shore, he looked around in all the directions. At the end of the one hundred yojanas, he saw a clump of groves. He descended and saw many kinds of ornamented trees. The best among apes saw the dvipa and groves around Malaya. There was a bay near the ocean and in that bay, there were trees.

---

[28] Simhika devoured her prey by seizing their shadows.
[29] Garuda.

He saw the best among the wives of the ocean.[30] The one in control of himself looked at his own self, like a giant cloud that was obstructing the sky. The intelligent one thought, 'The rakshasas will see my enlarged form and my force.' The great ape thought, 'They will become curious about me.' Therefore, he contracted his body, which was like a large mountain. Like one who has been freed from a delusion, the one in control of his soul again assumed his natural form. He was capable of assuming many beautiful forms that others would find it impossible to replicate. He reached the other shore of the ocean and considering the objective, looked at his own self. In the ocean, there was a mountain named Lamba, with many wonderful peaks. The great-souled one, who was like a mass of clouds, alighted on a peak. There were many ketaka, uddalaka and coconut trees there. The ocean was full of innumerable danavas and serpents and was full of garlands of gigantic waves. He crossed the great ocean with his strength and valour and descended on the shore. He saw Lanka, which was like Amaravati.[31]

Chapter 5(2)

The immensely strong one safely crossed the insurmountable ocean. He saw Lanka, located on the summit of Trikuta. As he stood there, the valiant one was radiant and seemed to be made of flowers, since the trees released showers of flowers over him. The handsome ape, excellent in his valour, had crossed one hundred yojanas without taking a breath or suffering from any exhaustion. 'I can progressively cross many hundreds of yojanas. What is there in travelling one hundred yojanas and coming to the end of the ocean?' Thus, the best among valiant ones and supreme among the apes powerfully crossed the great ocean and went to Lanka. There was blue grassland and fragrant groves. He passed through

[30] That is, rivers.
[31] Indra's capital, the city of the immortals.

boulders and mountains. There were mountains covered with trees and blossoming forests. Hanumat, the spirited bull among apes, travelled. He stood on the mountain. From the summit of the mountain, the son of the wind god saw forests, groves and Lanka. There were *sarala*s, karnikaras, flowering kharjuras, priyalas, *muchulinda*s, kutajas, ketakas, fragrant nipas, saptaparnas, asanas and blossoming karaviras.[32] They were bent down by the weight of flowers and buds. The trees were full of birds, with the tops bent down because of the wind. There were lotuses and lilies in the waterbodies, with swans and karandavas. These were surrounded by many kinds of trees, filled everywhere with blossoming flowers. The elephant among apes saw beautiful groves.

He reached prosperous Lanka, ruled over by Ravana. It was adorned with moats that were full of lotuses and lilies. Because Sita had been abducted, it was protected well by Ravana. On every side, rakshasas with fierce bows roamed around it. The great city was surrounded by golden and beautiful ramparts. There were hundreds of mansions decorated with garlands of flags and pennants. The gates were golden and divine, decorated with the marks of creepers. Hanumat saw Lanka and it was like a city of the gods in heaven. With its white residences, Lanka was located on the summit of the mountain. It was like a handsome city in the sky and the best among apes saw it. It had been constructed by Vishvakarma and was protected by the Indra among the rakshasas. The ape saw the beautiful city, which seemed to be situated in the sky. It was full of terrible rakshasas, resembling serpents in Bhogavati. Something as clear as this was unthinkable. In earlier times, it used to be ruled over by Kubera. It was protected by terrible rakshasas who were like venomous serpents inside a cave. They were brave and possessed many fangs, with spears and lances in their hands. The large body of water[33] was like a garment and the walls were like hips. The *shataghni*s[34] and spears were like the tips of the hair. The mansions were like earrings. Having reached the northern gate, the ape started

---

[32] Muchulinda is a lemon tree.

[33] In the moats and in the ocean.

[34] A shataghni is a weapon that can kill one hundred at one stroke.

to think. It was like the summit of Kailasa, like a painting etched out in the sky. With the excellent mansions rising up, it seemed to be held up in the sky. He saw that the great city was protected by the ocean. The ape thought about the terrible enemy, Ravana. 'Even if the apes come here, they will not be successful. Even the gods will find it impossible to conquer Lanka in a battle. Protected by Ravana, Lanka is impenetrable and fortified. Even if the mighty-armed Raghava reaches it, what will he do? There seems to be no prospect of approaching the rakshasas and using conciliation,[35] dana, bheda or fighting.[36] There are only four great-souled apes who can come here—Vali's son, Nila, I and the intelligent king.[37] I will think about this after I have found out whether Vaidehi is alive or not. Let me first see Janaka's daughter.'

For a while, the elephant among apes thought. Engaged in ensuring Rama's objective, he stood on the summit of the mountain. 'I am incapable of entering the city of the rakshasas in this form of mine. It is protected by cruel and powerful rakshasas. The rakshasas are fierce in their energy, immensely brave and powerful. In searching out Janakee, I must deceive all of them. I must enter the city of Lanka in the night, in a tiny form that can just about be seen. To accomplish the great objective, that is what I must do, enter at the right time.' He saw that city, which is impossible for even the gods or the asuras to assail. Hanumat thought about this repeatedly and arrived at this conclusion. 'What means can I use to see Maithilee, Janaka's daughter, so that I am not seen by the evil-souled Ravana, Indra among the rakshasas? How can the task of Rama, who knows about his soul, be accomplished? How can I manage to see Janaka's daughter alone? Even if a messenger is ready to accomplish the objective, he can be harmed and rendered incapacitated if he acts against the time and the place, like darkness dispelled by the rising sun. An intelligence that cannot distinguish between gain and loss is worthless. Messengers who are insolent about their learning can defeat the objective. How can the task be

[35] Sama.
[36] Danda.
[37] Sugriva.

accomplished? How will there be no suffering? How will leaping across the ocean not be rendered futile? Rama, who knows about his soul, desires to bring an end to Ravana. However, if I am seen by the rakshasas, that task will fail. Undetected by the rakshasas, I am incapable of going there, even in the form of a rakshasa, not to speak of any other form. It is my view that even the wind cannot go there undetected. There is nothing that is unknown to the strong rakshasas. If I remain here, shrouding myself in my own form, I will be destroyed. My master's task will also suffer. That being the case, when it is night, I will diminish my size. To accomplish Raghava's objective, I will thus enter Lanka. Ravana's city is extremely difficult to approach and I will enter it at night. I will search everywhere in the mansions and seek out Janaka's daughter.' The ape Hanumat thought in this way and waited for the sun to set. Anxious to see Vaidehi, the brave one thought in this way.

When it was evening, the valiant Hanumat quickly assumed an extraordinary form that was only the size of a gnat.[38] He entered the beautiful city, laid out and divided well through large roads. The mansions were like garlands, with pillars made out of gold and silver. With lattice work that was made out of molten gold, it was like a city of the gandharvas. In that great city, he saw seven-storeyed and eight-storeyed buildings. The floors were made out of crystal and were decorated with gold. There were nets made out of pearls and there was wonderful work of lapis lazuli and jewels. The floors of the mansions of the rakshasas were dazzling. There were colourful and golden gates protected by rakshasas. Everything in Lanka was decorated and illuminated. The great ape saw Lanka. It was extraordinary in form and impossible to think of. Anxious to see Vaidehi, he was both happy and distressed simultaneously. The place was surrounded by garlands of pale mansions. There were extremely expensive gates, made out of nets of molten gold. It was illustrious and was protected by Ravana's arms. It was full

[38] The Critical Edition uses the term *prishadamshaka,* something that bites or stings an antelope. Non-Critical versions use the term *vrishadamshaka,* something that bites or stings a bull. While a gnat or similar insect is possible, something like a cat or a dog is also not ruled out.

of demons who were terrible in their strength. As if to help him, the moon rose and was radiant amidst a large number of stars. The entire world was pervaded by this canopy of moonlight. The one with many thousands of beams arose. Its complexion was like that of a conch shell, as white as milk or the stalk of a white lotus. As it arose, it illuminated everything. The brave ape saw the moon, which looked like a swan swimming in a lake.

Chapter 5(3)

He stood on the summit of Lamba, which was like an elongated cloud.[39] The intelligent Hanumat, the son of the wind god, resorted to his own spirit. The greatly spirited one, elephant among apes, entered Lanka at night. The city was protected by Ravana and was full of beautiful groves and waterbodies. It was adorned with the best of mansions, resembling autumn clouds. A sound arose, as if from the ocean. A breeze that arose from the ocean blew through it. It was protected by extremely well-nurtured soldiers, like Vitapavati.[40] There were beautiful protected gates, with white gates and turrets. The auspicious place was protected, like Bhogavati is by serpents who roam around. The paths were illuminated by the light of stellar bodies and looked like clouds tinged with lightning. A gust of wind blew, as if in Indra's Amaravati. There were giant ramparts that were made out of molten gold. The place was adorned with flags and there was the sound of tinkling from nets of bells. Cheerfully, he quickly climbed up a rampart. As he looked everywhere in the city, his heart was filled with wonder. The gates were made of molten gold and the platforms were of lapis lazuli. There were jewels, crystals and pearls and the floors were encrusted with gems. There were decorations made out of molten gold, embellished with sparkling white silver. The floors and stairs

[39] The word *lamba* means long and there is a play on words.
[40] Another name for Alakapuri, Kubera's capital.

were of lapis lazuli, with sparkling and clear work of crystal inside. There were auspicious and beautiful assembly halls that seemed to be flying through the sky. There were the sounds of curlews and peacocks. The place was populated by swans. The sounds of trumpets and ornaments echoed everywhere. He saw the city, which seemed to have been fashioned only out of riches. Lanka seemed to be flying through the sky and the ape Hanumat was delighted. He saw the auspicious city of Lanka, which belonged to the lord of the rakshasas.

Its prosperity was supreme and the valiant one started to think. 'It is impossible for anyone to attack this city with force. Ravana's soldiers protect it, wielding upraised weapons. Kumuda, Angada, the great ape Sushena, Mainda and Dvivida may be able to penetrate this region. So can the son of the sun god,[41] the ape Kushaparva, the bear Ketumala and I.' Thinking about the mighty-armed Raghava's valour and the prowess of Lakshmana, the ape became delighted.

The city was like a beautiful and ornamented woman attired in red garments. The treasure houses were like earrings. The large stores of machines were like her breasts. The large houses were illuminated by radiant lamps that dispelled the darkness. The giant ape saw the city of the Indra among the rakshasas. The spirited one, the son of the wind god, entered the city at night. He travelled along the great road, decorated with pearls and flowers. In front of him, there were the sounds of laughter and the blare of trumpets. The beautiful city possessed houses that were as firm as the vajra, strong like clubs and ornamented with diamonds. The city looked like the sky, decorated with clouds. Lanka blazed, with the beautiful houses of large numbers of rakshasas. There were colourful and white houses of the *padma*, svastika and *vardhamana* types.[42] All of these were decorated well. Wishing to perform a good deed for the king of the apes and to accomplish Raghava's objective, the handsome one roamed around, looking at the wonderful garlands

[41] Sugriva.
[42] These are different types of houses and refer to forms of architecture.

and ornaments and delighted. He heard sweet songs, chanted in the three kinds of tones[43] by women intoxicated with liquor, sounding like apsaras in heaven. The great-souled one heard the tinkling of girdles and the sound of anklets on the stairs of the houses. Here and there, there were the sounds of roaring and the slapping of arms. He saw yatudhanas engaged in studying. He saw rakshasas assemble, roaring their praise of Ravana. There were large numbers of rakshasa soldiers along the royal roads. He saw many rakshasa spies in the midst of the contingents. There were those who had been initiated into studying. There were those with matted hair or shaved heads, attired in garments made out of cowhide. Darbha grass in their hands were like weapons. Their weapons were sacrificial altars to the fire. There were others with mallets and clubs in their hands. Others wielded rods as weapons. Some possessed one eye. Others possessed many ears. There were those whose stomachs and breasts hung low. Some had cruel and malformed mouths. Others were disfigured and dwarves. Some wielded bows, swords, shataghnis and clubs as weapons. Others had excellent bludgeons in their arms, with colourful and blazing armour. Some were not very fat, others were not very lean. Some were not tall, nor were they short. Some were malformed, others had many forms. Some were excellent in form and extremely radiant. Some had lances and trees as weapons. Others wielded javelins and vajras. The giant ape saw some of them wield nooses that could be flung. Some were garlanded and smeared with pastes. Others were adorned in the best of ornaments. There were immensely strong ones, wielding sharp spears and vajras. The ape saw a hundred thousand rakshasas attentively protecting the centre. The giant ape saw the extremities, surrounded by ramparts. It was like divine heaven and there were celestial sounds. There were the sounds of horses neighing and the tinkle of ornaments. There were chariots, vehicles and vimanas and auspicious elephants and horses. There were elephants with four tusks, resembling a mass of white clouds. The ornamented and beautiful gates were full of maddened animals

---

[43] Slow, medium and fast.

and birds. The ape entered the protected residence that belonged to the lord of the rakshasas.

Chapter 5(4)

The moon reached the midpoint in the sky.[44] The giant cascade of moonlight spread everywhere. The intelligent one looked at the radiant body in the sky,[45] resembling a crazy bull roaming around amidst a herd of cows. This was the one who destroyed the sins of the worlds and made the great ocean wax. It was the one who illuminated all creatures. He saw the one with the cool rays rise up. The prosperity that is there on earth in Mandara, in the ocean during the evening and in the water in Pushkara—all that radiant beauty existed in the moon. The radiant moon illuminated the sky like a swan inside a cage made out of silver, like a lion in a cavern in Mandara and like a brave and proud elephant. The radiant moon was full, without any horns.[46] It was stationed there, with the sharp-horned one with humps.[47] It was like a giant white mountain with tall peaks. It was like an elephant with tusks made out of molten gold. When the moon appeared, all the sins disappeared, including the sins caused by rakshasas who flourished by surviving on flesh. All the taints vanished from the minds of women.[48] The illustrious one illuminated the evening with a radiance that was like that of heaven. Sounds that were pleasant to hear started from stringed musical instruments. Women who possessed good characters slept with their husbands. The ones who wander around in the night, creatures who are terrible in their conduct, started to roam around.

[44] This entire chapter has a metre that is somewhat different. It is full of imagery and descriptions, with the metaphors sometimes sounding forced and artificial.

[45] The moon.

[46] Meaning that there were no crescents.

[47] A reference to the mark on the moon, in the shape of a bull.

[48] This is a reference to playful quarrels between women and their lovers, which now vanished.

The intelligent ape saw houses that were full of maddened and intoxicated people and places where chariots, horses and excellent seats were kept. There were brave and prosperous people. They[49] lunged excessively at each other, nudging each other with their thick arms. They were intoxicated and spoke excessively to each other. Since they were intoxicated, they abused each other. The rakshasas beat their chests and hurled themselves on the bodies of women. He saw beautiful women smear themselves with unguents before sleeping. Large elephants trumpeted. The virtuous ones were honoured properly. The radiant and brave ones sighed, like serpents hissing in a lake. There were those who were intelligent, indulging in beautiful speech. There were faithful ones, foremost in the world. There were those who possessed many kinds of beautiful names. He also saw such yatudhanas in the city. He rejoiced when he saw the ones with beautiful forms. They possessed many qualities, qualities that were worthy of them. They were radiant in those forms. However, he also saw some who were malformed. Among them, there were extremely generous women, extremely pure in their sentiments and best among beautiful ones. They were devoted to their loved ones and addicted by nature to drinking. He saw some extremely radiant ones who were like stars. There were prosperous women, blazing in their ornaments. In the middle of the night, they were engaged in intercourse. He saw some women who clung to their loved ones, like birds cling to flowers. There were yet others who were seated on the floors of the mansions, happily lying down in the laps of their beloveds. They loved their husbands and were devoted to dharma. The intelligent one saw some who were in the throes of love. There were naked women with golden complexions. There were some with complexions of refined gold, meant for others.[50] There were also those who were like the moon in complexion. Some with beautiful complexions in their limbs were separated from their beloveds. He saw women who obtained their handsome beloveds and were filled with great

[49] The rakshasas.
[50] This probably means courtesans.

delight. The best among apes saw such extremely beautiful women, happy in their homes. There were garlands of faces that were like the moon. There were garlands of beautiful eyebrows and curved eyelashes. He saw garlands of ornaments and beautiful garlands that were like lightning. However, the extremely noble Sita, based on a virtuous path and born in a royal lineage, wasn't there. Born in a virtuous lineage, she was like a blossoming creeper. But he did not see the slender one, born through mental powers.[51] She was established on the eternal path of looking towards Rama, filled with desire for him. The beautiful one was always established in her husband's mind. She was supreme among women and special. She was afflicted by the heat[52] and her throat was choked with tears. Earlier, she wore extremely expensive and excellent jewels around her throat. She was born with beautiful eyelashes and a sweet voice. She was like a female peacock[53] that was no longer dancing in the forest. It was as if the marks on the moon were indistinct marks. It was as if a mark made with gold was covered with dust. It was like the mark left by an arrow in a deep wound. It was as if the lines made by clouds had been dispelled by the wind. He did not see Sita, the wife of Rama, lord of men and supreme among eloquent ones. For some time, the ape was therefore filled with distress and for some time, he was numbed.

Chapter 5(5)

The one who could assume any form at will roamed around the mansions, but did not find what he desired. Full of dexterity, the ape wandered around Lanka. He approached the prosperous residence of the Indra among the rakshasas. It was surrounded by radiant ramparts that possessed the complexion of the sun. It was

[51] Through Brahma's mental powers.

[52] Of separation from Rama.

[53] The text uses the word *nilakantha*. This means a peacock/peahen with a blue neck.

protected by terrible rakshasas, the way a great forest is protected by a lion. Having looked at the residence, the elephant among apes climbed up. It was decorated with silver and the colourful gates were adorned with gold. There were wonderful chambers, surrounded by beautiful gates. There were brave elephant riders on elephants, devoid of exhaustion. There were horses with attendants and chariots with drivers. There was armour for the body, made out of the skins of lions and tigers and decorated with ivory, gold and silver. Chariots always roamed around, making wonderful sounds. There were many jewels there and excellent seats and vessels. There were maharathas there, giant chariots and large seats. Here and there, extremely beautiful animals and birds could be seen. In every direction, the place was full of many thousands of these. It was protected well by rakshasas and the guards for the inner quarters were humble. In every direction, the place was full of foremost and excellent women. There were happy gems among women in the residence of the Indra among the rakshasas. The sound made by excellent jewellery was like the sound that arose in the ocean. There was excellent and supreme sandalwood, possessing qualities that could be used by a king. There were the sounds of tambourines and drums. The noise of conch shells resounded. The rakshasas always worshipped it[54] on every auspicious day of festivities, offering oblations. It was as deep as the ocean and made a sound like that of the ocean. The great-souled one possessed a great residence. It was full of great jewels and garments. The great ape saw that it was filled with great people. Full of elephants, horses and chariots, its form was radiant. The great ape thought that this was like Lanka's jewel. The ape roamed around from one house to another house and in the groves of the rakshasas. Without any fear, he wandered around everywhere in that palace. With great force, he leapt on to Prahasta's residence. With another leap, he went to the residence of the valiant Mahaparshva. Thereafter, the great ape leapt to Kumbhakarna's residence, which was like a cloud, and from there to Vibhishana's. He went to the houses of Mahodara, Virupaksha,

---

[54] Ravana's residence.

Vidyutjihva and Vidyunmali. The great ape then leapt to that of
Vajradamshtra. With great force, the intelligent leader of the apes
then went to the houses of Shuka, Sarana and Indrajit. The leader of
the apes went to the houses of Jambumali, Sumali, Rashmiketu and
Suryashatru. Hanumat, the son of the wind god went to the houses
of Dhumraksha, Sampati, Vidyutrupa, Bhima, Ghana, Vighana,
Shukanabha, Vakra, Shatha, Vikata, Hrasvakarna, Damshtra, the
rakshasa Romasha, Yuddhanmatta, Matta, Dvajagriva, Nadina,
Vidyutjihva, Indrajihva, Hastimukha, Karala, Pishacha, Shonita,
Kramamana and Krama. In those extremely expensive houses, the
great ape, the son of the wind god, saw their prosperity and wealth.
In every direction, he passed through all their houses and approached
the prosperous residence of the Indra among the rakshasas.

As he wandered around, the supreme among apes, tiger among
apes, saw rakshasis with malformed eyes sleeping near Ravana.
They held spears and clubs in their hands. They wielded javelins
and spikes. He saw many contingents of soldiers in the house of
the lord of the rakshasas.[55] There were extremely swift horses that
were red, white and black. There were handsome elephants born in
noble lineages, capable of taking on elephants of the enemy. These
elephants were skilled and trained, Airavata's equal in a battle. They
were capable of slaying the soldiers of the enemy and he saw them in
that house. Like clouds, they exuded musth. They exuded minerals
like mountains. They roared like clouds and the enemy found them
unassailable in a battle. There were thousands of *vahinis*[56] there,
decorated in molten gold. They were covered in nets of gold and
looked like the rising sun. He saw these in the residence of Ravana,
Indra among rakshasas. The ape who was the wind god's son saw
palanquins of different shapes. There were collections of colourful
creepers and chambers where paintings were kept. There were other
chambers for sporting, with mountains made out of wood. There
was a beautiful chamber for satisfying sexual desires and another

[55] The word used is *gulma*. The basic unit was a *patti*, with 250 men. Three pattis
constituted a gulma. Ten gulmas constituted a *gana*.

[56] A *sena* consisted of five hundred elephants and the same number of chariots. Ten
senas constituted a *pritana* and ten pritanas constituted a vahini.

chamber for the day. He saw these in the residence of Ravana, Indra
among the rakshasas. There was an excellent spot that was like the
plains of Mandara and it was full of pens for peacocks. He saw an
excellent house that was filled with standards and staffs. There was
an infinite quantity of jewels and everywhere, heaps of riches. Patient
and attentive supervisors tended to these, like in the residence of the
lord of the *bhuta*s.[57] The rays of these jewels indicated Ravana's
energy. Because of this, that residence was radiant, like the rays
of the one with the rays.[58] There were couches and seats made out
of molten gold. The leader of the apes saw sparkling vessels. The
bejewelled vessels were moist with madhu and *asava*.[59] Delightful
and without obstructions, it was like Kubera's residence. There was
the tinkling of anklets and the sound of girdles. There was the noise
of drums and the clapping of hands. The many chambers in the
palace were filled with hundreds of jewels among women. Hanumat
entered that large residence, with many extensive chambers.

Chapter 5(6)

The powerful one saw that network of houses.[60] They had
windows that were decorated with lapis lazuli. It looked
like a giant net of clouds during the monsoon, penetrated with
lightning and mixed with a net of birds. There were many kinds of
houses and halls. There were major ones for storing conch shells
and weapons, halls for bows. He again saw pleasant and large
chambers above those houses, like attics. There were many kinds
of riches in those houses, extremely revered by gods and asuras.
They were devoid of all kinds of taints. The ape saw the strength

[57] Meaning Kubera.
[58] Meaning the sun.
[59] Both are forms of liquor, asava probably made through a process of distillation.
[60] In this chapter, as well as in some others, the beauty is in the cleverness of the
poetry and the play on words. Translated, the content sometimes sounds artificial and
forced. The similes and metaphors are impossible to capture in a translation.

they had accumulated for themselves. He saw the houses of the lord of Lanka, constructed with a great deal of care and effort, as if by Maya himself.[61] It possessed all the excellent qualities on earth. He then saw an excellent house that had no comparison. It rose up loftily, like a cloud. It was pleasant to see, with a beautiful form made out of gold. This belonged to the lord of the rakshasas and was similar to his own strength. It was spread out like a heaven on earth. It blazed in prosperity and was filled with many kinds of jewels. It was covered with flowers from many trees and was like the summit of a mountain, covered with pollen. It dazzled, like an excellent woman. It was like a cloud, being worshipped by the lightning. It blazed with prosperity, like a vimana in the sky meant for the performers of good deeds, being borne along by excellent swans. It was like the summit of a mountain, colourful with many minerals. It was like the firmament, coloured with planets and the moon. He saw it and it was like a colourful cloud. He saw the jewel among vimanas, coloured with many gems.[62] The earth was created so that it could be full of mountain ranges. The mountains were created so that they could be full of arrays of trees. The trees were created so that they could be full of arrays of flowers. The flowers were created so that they could be full of filaments and petals. The white houses were also created and so were the lakes, full of excellent flowers. There were also lotuses with filaments and colourful and superb groves. The great ape saw a great vimana there, radiant and named Pushpaka. It was large and radiant with jewels. It was taller than the excellent houses. Birds made of lapis lazuli were in it and also birds made of silver and coral. There were colourful serpents made out of many kinds of riches. There were steeds from noble breeds, auspicious in their limbs. The wings of the birds were of coral, molten gold and flowers. Without any water, the wings were curved. The wings were as radiant as Kama[63] himself. These birds, with excellent faces and excellent wings, were

[61] Lanka was built by Vishvakarma, but as if by Maya.

[62] Descriptions of the residence are interspersed with descriptions of Pushpaka vimana.

[63] The god of love.

constructed. The goddess Lakshmi was fashioned,[64] seated on a lotus, with excellent hands and with a lotus in her hand. She was worshipped by elephants with excellent trunks, holding lotuses with filaments in their trunks. The house was beautiful in this way. He wondered at its beauty, which was like that of a beautiful mountain. He again looked at it, extremely fragrant and extremely beautiful, like a mountain with beautiful caverns during the spring. The ape approached and wandered around that revered city, protected by the one with ten faces and arms.[65] However, he did not see Janaka's extremely revered daughter, vanquished by the force of the qualities her husband possessed, and became extremely miserable because of this. Therefore, the one with the cleansed soul thought in many ways. He had made up his mind to search out Janaka's daughter. Unable to see her, his mind became extremely miserable. The great-souled one roamed around, casting his glance here and there.

Chapter 5(7)

In the midst of those best among houses, Hanumat, the son of the wind god, saw an extremely large and excellent residence. It was half a yojana long and one yojana wide. This was the residence of the Indra among the rakshasas and had many mansions inside it. He was searching for the whereabouts of the large-eyed Vaidehi Sita. Hanumat, the slayer of enemies, wandered around everywhere. There were elephants with four tusks and with three tusks. It was extensive, without obstructions, and was protected by rakshasas wielding weapons. This was the residence of Ravana and his rakshasi wives. It was full of princesses whom he had abducted, using his force. It was like an ocean, turbulent because of the force of the wind and filled with crocodiles, makaras, fish and serpents. The prosperity that existed with Vaishravana[66] and with Indra with

---

[64] That is, an image of the goddess.
[65] In the text, 'ten' is an adjective for faces, not arms.
[66] Kubera.

the tawny steeds, all that always existed in Ravana's house, without any diminishing. Whatever prosperity existed with King Kubera, Yama or Varuna, such prosperity and more existed in the rakshasa's house. In the midst of those mansions, there was a residence that was constructed very well. The son of the wind god saw this, filled with many chambers. It was divinely constructed, fashioned in heaven by Vishvakarma for Brahma. This was the vimana named Pushpaka and it was decorated with every jewel. After performing supreme austerities, Kubera obtained this from the grandfather. Through his energy, the lord of the rakshasas defeated Kubera and obtained it. There were images of wolves, fashioned out of silver and gold. The pillars were constructed extremely well and blazed in their prosperity. It was like Meru or Mandara, etched out in the sky. It was decorated everywhere and was full of secret chambers that were auspicious in form. Vishvakarma had fashioned it well and it blazed like the fire and the sun. The stairs were made out of gold and the altars were beautiful and excellent. There were windows and ventilators made out of gold and crystal. The best of platforms were made out of jewels like blue sapphire and emeralds. The great ape climbed on to the divine vimana, Pushpaka. Fragrances arose from the drinks, food and rice stored there. A divine and beautiful fragrance could be smelt, blown along by the wind. Like a friend speaking to an excellent friend, that fragrance seemed to tell the great spirit,[67] 'Come here', summoning him to the spot where Ravana was. Hanumat left in that direction and saw a large and auspicious gallery, loved by Ravana's mind, like an excellent woman who is loved. The stairs were made out of jewels, embellished with golden nets. The floor was made out of crystal and there were images made out of ivory inside. There were a large number of pillars, decorated with pearls, coral, silver, gold and gems. These were even, upright and extremely tall, ornamented all over. Using those tall pillars, like a bird, it seemed to take off and leave for the sky. It was covered with a huge carpet, marked with all the signs of the earth.[68] The

---

[67] Hanumat.
[68] Rivers, oceans, mountains and forests were painted on the carpet.

residence of the lord of the rakshasas was marked by the calling of crazy birds, the scent of divine fragrances and the spreading out of supreme carpets. It was thick with the smoke and incense of aloe. It was as sparkling white as a swan. Colourfully decorated with flowers, it was as greatly radiant as the celestial cow. The agreeable colour generated delight in the heart. It destroyed sorrow and seemed to generate divine prosperity. Protected by Ravana, it satisfied like a mother, using excellent objectives of the five senses to cater to the five senses. The son of the wind god thought, 'This is perhaps heaven, the world of the gods. This is perhaps Indra's city. This is perhaps the supreme objective.' While thinking in this way, he saw golden lamps. He thought, 'There is the radiance of the lamps, Ravana's energy and the brilliance of the ornaments. It is as if in an act of gambling, a skilled gambler is being defeated by a gambler who possesses greater skills.'

He saw thousands of beautiful women, attired in many kinds of garments. With garments and garlands of many shades, they were seated on many kinds of seats. Midnight was over. They had fallen prey to drinking and sleep. After having sported, in the second half of the night, they were sleeping even more deeply. As they slept, their inner ornaments were radiant, but silent. It was like a great grove full of lilies, where the swans and the bees were quiet. The son of the wind god saw that their eyes were closed and their teeth were covered by their lips. He saw the faces of those excellent women, covered with the fragrance of lotuses. The faces were like lotuses that had bloomed during the day, but now that it was night and day was over, the petals of the lotuses had closed. It seemed as if crazy bees were incessantly hovering around those faces, which were like lotuses, as if seeking out blooming lotuses. The handsome and great ape reasoned it out in this way. He thought, 'In qualities, these faces are the equal of lotuses that bloom in the water.' With the radiance of those women, that pavilion was like the clear sky during the autumn, decorated by stars. The lord of the rakshasas was surrounded by those radiant ones and was like the handsome lord of the stars, surrounded by the stars. The ape thought, 'When their merit is exhausted, stars are dislodged from the sky. All these

assembled ones are like that.' From the radiance of the women, there
was an auspicious complexion in the palace. They clearly seemed
to be like large stars with auspicious rays. Their excellent garlands
and garments were scattered around and their heavy breasts were
revealed. After drinking and exertions, sleep had taken away their
senses. For some, the marks on the foreheads were smudged. For
some, the anklets had fallen off. For some other supreme women,
the necklaces had been placed to one side. Some wore necklaces
made of pearls. For some, the garments were displaced. Like young
female horses, for some, the noose of the girdle had been loosened.
There were some with excellent earrings, but their garlands were
torn. They were like creepers in a great forest, crushed by an Indra
among elephants. Some women slept like swans and between their
breasts, there were prominent necklaces, with a hue like that of the
moon's beams. Others had necklaces made of lapis lazuli and these
looked like kadamba birds. The golden threads of others looked
like chakravakas. Their radiant hips were like the banks of a river,
decorated by flocks of swans, karandavas and chakravakas. They
slept like the banks of an illustrious river, full of crocodiles, with
the large nets of gold like radiant lotuses. On some, the auspicious
marks left by the ornaments were themselves like ornaments on
their delicate limbs and on their nipples. The inhalation of breath
by some disturbed the ends of the garments of others and they
repeatedly breathed on each other's faces. There were many kinds
of dazzling and golden ornaments around the necks of those wives,
and radiant in form, they rose up like flags. As if with rays that
are auspicious, the earrings of some moved around, because of
the breath that was gently exhaled by those excellent women. The
breath was pleasant and fragrant because of the scent of liquor
made from molasses.[69] The breath from their faces seemed to
serve Ravana. Some of Ravana's women repeatedly inhaled the
fragrance from the mouths of their co-wives, mistakenly taking
those to be Ravana's face. The minds of those supreme women
were excessively attached to Ravana. They were not completely

[69] More literally, sugar.

independent, and therefore, acted agreeably towards their co-wives. Some were ornamented and slept using their own arms as pillows. Those beautiful women were decorated with garments and bracelets. Some slept on the bosom of another, some in the arms of another. Some slept in the lap of another, some on the thighs of another. They embraced the thighs, flanks, waists and backs of others. Others were intoxicated and overcome by affection, clung to each other. Some slender-waisted ones were delighted at being able to touch the limb of another. The women slept with their arms entwined with each other. It was as if a garland of women had been fashioned out of each other's arms. It was as radiant as a garland, with crazy bees hovering around it. Clinging to each other, they were like a garland made out of flowers adhering to each other, or like a blossoming creeper during a spring month, tended to by the breeze. As their shoulders clung to each other, they were like a grove, frequented by bees. Ravana's women were like a grove. Even if one tried, the ornaments, limbs, garments and garlands of those women couldn't clearly be distinguished from those of others. With many kinds of complexions, Ravana's women slept happily. When one looks without blinking, they were like blazing golden lamps. Those women were the daughters of royal sages, daityas and gandharvas, forced to surrender to the rakshasa's desire. There was no woman who had not been abducted, obtained through the qualities of valour. There was no one who had desired another man, or had indulged in intercourse with another. The only exception was the supreme lady, Janaka's daughter. There was no one who was not of noble birth. There was no one who was ugly. There was no one who was unaccomplished. There was no one who did not know how to serve. None of his wives was weak in spirit. There was no one who was not desired and loved. The lord of the apes thought, 'Just as the rakshasa king's wives are with their husband, it would have been good had Raghava's noble-born wife by dharma been with her husband.' Greatly distressed, he again thought, 'It is certain that Sita is superior to them in qualities. Though the lord of Lanka is great-souled, he has performed an extremely ignoble act.'

Chapter 5(8)

Hanumat looked around and saw excellent couches that were like divine ones, decorated with crystal and jewels. In one spot, he saw a white umbrella that was like the lord of the stars, decorated with garlands at the top. In every direction, there were whisks made of hair in their hands.[70] There were many kinds of fragrances and the scent of excellent incense. It[71] was covered with an excellent spread and the best of sheep hide was spread over it. In every direction, it was embellished with ropes that were made out of garlands. On that, he[72] was like a cloud, with blazing and excellent earrings. The mighty-armed one's eyes were red and his garments were made out of gold. His limbs were smeared with fragrant red sandalwood paste. He was like a cloud in the sky, with the qualities of lightning and as red as the evening. He wore divine jewellery and he was extremely handsome, capable of assuming any form at will. He was asleep and was like Mandara, with its trees and creepers. Having sported in the night, he was adorned in supreme ornaments. He was loved by the rakshasa maidens and brought happiness to the rakshasas. The great ape saw him lying down there, after a bout of drinking. The brave lord of the rakshasas was asleep on a radiant couch. Ravana was sighing like a serpent. The supreme among apes approached him, and then, anxious and scared, retreated. He ascended and resorted to another platform and from there, the great ape looked at the tiger among rakshasas, who was asleep. Lying down on that excellent couch, the Indra among the rakshasas was resplendent. He was like a giant waterfall, with a fragrant elephant inside it. The great-souled one saw that the Indra among rakshasas had spread out his arms, with golden armlets on them. They looked like Indra's standard. There were wounds from the tips of the tusks, created when Airavat had attacked him. His thick shoulders bore marks of being struck with

---

[70] Of the women attendants.

[71] A specific couch.

[72] Ravana.

the vajra and Vishnu's chakra. The shoulders were appropriate for such a strong one, thick and developed well. It was seen that the nails, thumbs, fingers and palms bore excellent marks. The arms were round, like the trunks of elephants. They were round, like clubs, with well-formed joints. As he slept on that sparkling couch, they were spread around, like five-headed serpents. The upper part of his body was smeared with sandalwood paste that was extremely cool and extremely fragrant, with a hue like that of a hare's blood.[73] He was the one who made yakshas, serpents, gandharvas, gods and danavas scream. Excellent women had massaged him and smeared those excellent unguents on him. The ape saw him lying there on that couch, with his arms spread out. He was like a giant and angry serpent, asleep inside Mandara. The full arms of the lord of the rakshasas were as radiant as a mountain, or like Mandara with its peaks. As the lion among the rakshasas lay down and exhaled, the excellent fragrance of mangoes, punnagas and supreme bakula emerged from his large mouth and filled that house. However, the scent of liquor dominated all this, mixed with juices from sweet rice. He had taken off his golden and radiant crown, dazzling with many kinds of pearls and jewels. Because of the earrings, his face blazed. He was ornamented by a necklace smeared with red sandalwood paste. It dazzled on his thick, broad and large chest. He was attired in a white silk garment and his eyes were like wounds.[74] An extremely expensive and yellow garment was tied well around him.[75] He was like a pile of black beans and sighed like a serpent. He was like an elephant sleeping in the great waters of the Ganga. He was illuminated from the four directions with four golden and blazing lamps. Thereby, all his limbs were like clouds tinged with lightning.

In the house of the lord of the rakshasas, at his feet, the extremely great-souled one saw his wives and his beloved wife. Their faces were like the moon and they were ornamented with the best of earrings. The leader of the apes saw that they were adorned

---

[73] The sandalwood was red.

[74] They were red.

[75] The yellow garment was tied on top of the white one.

with garlands and ornaments that did not fade. They wore excellent ornaments and were accomplished in dancing and the playing of musical instruments. The ape saw them sleeping, on the arms and lap of the Indra among the rakshasas. The tips of the ears of those women were embedded with diamonds. He saw their earrings and armlets, made out of molten gold. Their faces were like the moon and the delicate earrings sparkled. The mansion was resplendent, like the sky with a large number of stars. The women of that Indra among the rakshasas were exhausted and tired from drinking and exertions.[76] As soon as they found a chance, those slender-waisted ones fell asleep. One could be seen to be asleep, embracing her veena. She was like a lotus floating away on a great river and clutching to a boat. Like an affectionate mother attached to her infant child, another black-eyed and beautiful one slept embracing a drum. Another lovely one who was beautiful in all her limbs and possessed beautiful breasts embraced a war drum, as if she had got back her lover after a long time. Another lotus-eyed one slept while embracing a flute, as if a beautiful lady was embracing her lover and had been overcome by sleep. Another one possessed soft, thick and beautiful golden breasts. With intoxicated eyes, she slept while embracing a drum.[77] There was another unblemished one, with a flat stomach. Exhausted from lust, she slept while clutching a cymbal next to her arms and sides. Another embraced a small drum, as if she was attached to that small drum. The beautiful one slept, as if embracing her young child. Another lotus-eyed woman, intoxicated by desire, slept while clutching on to a drum with her arms, as if in the throes of passion. Another radiant and beautiful lady fell down in her sleep, while clutching a pot. She looked like a sparkling and speckled garland made out of flowers during the spring. Another clutched her own breasts, which were like golden pots, with her hands. Vanquished by the power of sleep, that weak one slept while embracing herself. There was another one with eyes like lotus petals, with a face that was like the full moon. The one

[76] Sexual exertions.

[77] Different types of drums have been named and we have translated all of them as drum.

with the beautiful hips was senseless with desire and slept while embracing another one. Those supreme women embraced different kinds of unknown musical instruments. While they slept, they crushed them with their breasts, like women full of desire embrace men full of desire.

Among all those women, asleep and spread out on a beautiful bed and alone, the ape saw another lady who was full of beauty. She was excellently adorned in ornaments made out of pearls and jewels. She seemed to be adorning that excellent residence with her own beauty. She was the desired one, with a golden complexion and fair. She was the mistress of the inner quarters. The ape saw Mandodari, beautiful in form, lying down on that bed. The mighty-armed son of the wind god saw that ornamented one and reasoned that this one, full of the wealth of beauty and youth, could be Sita. The leader of the apes was filled with great delight and rejoiced. He slapped his arms and kissed his tail. In his joy, he played, sang and walked around. He climbed pillars and fell down on the ground. He exhibited the nature of apes.

Chapter 5(9)

While he was there, the great ape dismissed such thoughts.[78] Thinking about Sita, he thought of something else. 'Separated from Rama, the beautiful one should not be able to sleep. She will not eat, decorate herself with ornaments or drink. If another man approaches, even if that happens to be the lord of the gods, she will not approach him. Even among the gods, there is no one who is Rama's equal.' He decided that the person who was there in that drinking hall must be someone else. Some were exhausted from sporting, others from singing. Others were exhausted from dancing and intoxicated with liquor. Some were resting on tambourines, drums and seats. There were other women who were lying down

---

[78] That the lady who was sleeping was Sita.

on the best of spreads. There were thousands of women who were
adorned in ornaments. They possessed good conduct and could
speak about beauty. They could converse about the meanings behind
the songs. They were accomplished about the time and the place.
They knew how to speak appropriate words. The leader of the apes
saw them sleeping, after their sexual pursuits. Amidst them, the lord
of the rakshasas was radiant. He was like a bull amidst a large
herd of cattle. The Indra among the rakshasas was dazzling, himself
surrounded by all of them. He was like a giant male elephant in the
forest, surrounded by female elephants. In the residence of the lord
of the rakshasas, the great-souled tiger among the apes saw a hall for
drinking, filled with all the objects of desire. In that hall for drinking,
he saw pieces of flesh from deer, buffaloes and wild boar, laid out.
In large golden vessels, the tiger among the apes saw half-eaten
bits of peacocks and cocks. Hanumat saw the meat of wild boar,
*vardhanasaka*s,[79] porcupines, deer and peacocks, preserved in curds
and salt. Many kinds of *krikara*s[80] had been cooked. There were
half-devoured *chakora* birds. The flesh of buffaloes, porcupines and
goats had been prepared. There were many kinds of superior and
inferior lehya, *peya* and *bhojya*.[81] There were sour and salty sauces
and many kinds of sweetmeats.[82] Extremely expensive necklaces,
anklets, armlets, vessels for drinking and eating, diverse types of
fruits and garlands made of flowers were strewn around, making the
place look even more prosperous. Here and there, couches and seats
were laid out properly. Even without a fire, the drinking hall was
seen to blaze. Meat had been prepared exceedingly well, seasoned
properly and was separately laid out in that drinking hall. There
were many kinds of divine and sparkling *sura*,[83] as if they had been
prepared by the gods. There was liquor made from sugar, asava,

[79] This can mean goat, a kind of bird, or a kind of deer.

[80] Partridges.

[81] The four types of food are those that are chewed (*charvya*), sucked (*choshya* or
chushya), licked (lehya) and drunk (peya). Bhakshya is the same as charvya and bhojya is
the same as choshya.

[82] A specific type of sweetmeat known as *ragashadava*, made from the juices of grapes,
pomegranates and black gram.

[83] Sura is a general term for liquor.

liquor made from honey, liquor made from flowers and liquor made from fruits. They had separately been flavoured with many kinds of powders. The floor was covered with many kinds of garlands and these made it radiant. The vessels and smaller pans were made out of gold and crystal. There were other smaller vessels that were made out of molten gold. The ape saw pots made out of silver and molten gold there and these were filled with copious quantities of excellent liquor. He saw golden pots that were encrusted with gems. The great ape saw silver vessels that were full. He saw some vessels from which the drinks had been half drunk, others from which the drinks had been completely drunk. There were some from which nothing had been drunk. In some places, there were many kinds of food. In other distinct places, there were many kinds of drink. As he roamed around, in some places, he saw half-eaten food. The smaller vessels had been shattered in some places. In others, the pots had been agitated. In some places, garlands, water and fruits were together. In some places, the couches were empty. In others, many women, supreme in beauty, were asleep, embracing each other. Some women were asleep, overcome by the strength of sleep. As they slept, they stole the garments of others and covered themselves with these. The wind from their breaths gently made the colourful garments and garlands on their bodies quiver, as if a gentle breeze was blowing. The wind blew in different directions, bearing along many kinds of scents—from the cool sandalwood, liquor, honey, juices and different kinds of flowers. Many kinds of fragrant scents blew everywhere in Pushpaka vimana then, from accompaniments used in baths, sandalwood and incense fumes. Some extremely beautiful women were not dark, others were dark. In that residence of the rakshasa, others were golden in complexion. They were senseless from acts of desire and had come under the subjugation of sleep. As they slept, their forms were like those of lotuses.

In this way, the extremely energetic ape searched everywhere in Ravana's inner quarters, but did not see Janakee. The great ape looked at all the women. However, a great thought came over him, about what was virtue and dharma. 'In the inner quarters, I have looked at the wives of someone else, while they were asleep. This will indeed make my dharma suffer severely. In this kingdom, I have looked at the wives of someone else. I have thus seen someone else's wives.' After this the spirited one again had a different thought. He was clear about what needed to be done and was single-mindedly devoted to that task. He decided, 'All of Ravana's wives were trusting and I could have looked at them with eyes of desire. However, there was not the slightest bit of agitation in my mind. The mind is the reason behind what all the senses do, be it in a fortunate situation or an unfortunate one. I am extremely well controlled. I am incapable of searching out Vaidehi somewhere else. When one searches for women, they are always found amidst other women. A creature can only be found among those who are similar in birth. One is capable of finding a lost woman amidst female deer. With a pure mind, I have searched everywhere in Ravana's inner quarters for Janakee, but have not found her.' The valiant Hanumat searched among the maidens of the gods, the gandharvas and the serpents, but did not see Janakee. The ape did not see her there, but saw the other beautiful women. The valiant one seriously thought about going elsewhere.

Chapter 5(10)

That residence was full of colourful chambers covered with creepers and chambers for sleeping. Anxious to see Sita, he wandered around inside it. However, he did not see the one who was beautiful to behold. Unable to see the one who was loved by the descendant of the Raghu lineage, the great ape thought, 'Wishing to see Maithilee, I have searched, but not seen her. It is certain that Sita is dead. The child, supremely interested in protecting herself and her good conduct, has remained on the noble path. There is no doubt that the foremost among the rakshasas, extremely evil in conduct, has killed her. The women of the king of the rakshasas are malformed. They are disfigured and are without radiance. They possess large faces and long and malformed eyes. On seeing them, the daughter of King Janaka has been destroyed from fright. I have spent a long period of time with the apes, but have not been able to see Sita, or establish my manliness. There is no way I can go to Sugriva. That powerful ape will chastise me with sharp punishment. I have searched everywhere in the inner quarters. I have seen all of Ravana's women. However, I have not seen the virtuous Sita. My exertions have been in vain. When I return and approach all the other apes, what will they say? "O brave one! Having gone there, what did you do? Tell us." Having not seen Janaka's daughter, what will I say? The time has passed. It is certain that they will ask me to resort to praya. I have come to the other shore of the ocean. When I return and meet the other apes, what will the aged Jambavat and Angada say? However, being indifferent[84] is the source of prosperity. Indifference is supreme happiness. Therefore, I must again search where I have not searched before. Indifference always accomplishes the objective in every possible way. A creature who acts ensures success from that action. Therefore, resorting to indifference, I will again make supreme efforts. In this region, protected by Ravana, I will search places I have not seen earlier. The drinking hall has been searched and the chamber full of flowers. The chambers with paintings have been searched and so have the chambers for sporting. All the paths in gardens and all the vimanas have been searched.'

Having thought this, he started to search again, in houses that were underground, in houses that were in sanctuaries and in houses that were far away from the main houses. He again started to leap up and leap down, stay and proceed. He opened doors and opened windows. He entered and emerged, climbed up and climbed down. The great ape roamed around in all the spaces. The ape went everywhere in Ravana's inner quarters and did not leave out any space that was more than four fingers in width. He searched the paths between the ramparts and went to the platforms and sanctuaries. He looked in all the wells. Hanumat saw many kinds of rakshasas there, malformed and disfigured. But he did not see Janaka's daughter. He saw excellent women from among the

---

[84] Indifferent to joy or unhappiness. Therefore, not yielding to despondency.

vidyadharas. Their beauty was unmatched in the world. However, Hanumat did not see the one who brought delight to Raghava. There were beautiful women from among the nagas. Their faces were like the full moon. Hanumat saw them there, but he did not see the slender-waisted Sita. The Indra among rakshasas had crushed naga maidens and forcibly abducted them. Hanumat saw them there, but did not see Janaka's daughter. The mighty-armed one saw those other excellent women there, but did not see her. The mighty-armed Hanumat, the son of the wind god, became depressed. The Indra among the apes, the son of the wind god, saw that his act of leaping across the ocean had become unsuccessful and was again immersed in thoughts. Hanumat, the son of the wind god, descended from the mansion. His senses afflicted by grief, he was immersed in thoughts.

Chapter 5(11)

The leader of the apes crossed the mansion and the ramparts. Hanumat resorted to a force that was like that of lightning in the clouds. Hanumat went beyond Ravana's residence. However, unable to see Janakee Sita, the ape spoke these words. 'Looking for Rama's beloved, I have again wandered around Lanka. However, I have not seen Vaidehi Sita, who is unblemished in all her limbs. I have searched everywhere on earth—pools, ponds, lakes, rivers, groves, marshes, impenetrable spots and mountains. But I have not seen Janakee. Sampati said that Sita is here, in Ravana's residence. That is what the king of the eagles said, but I have been unable to see her. How can Sita, Vaidehi, Maithilee, Janaka's daughter, even though she has been incapacitated, serve Ravana, evil in conduct? I think that the rakshasa must have been scared of Rama's arrows. When he abducted Sita and was flying swiftly, he must have dropped her down somewhere. Or perhaps, as she was being abducted along the path followed by the siddhas, I think the noble one must have seen the ocean and fallen down inside it. Her arms were crushed by the force of Ravana's thighs. Therefore, I think that the large-eyed and noble one has given up her life. As she was being progressively carried across the ocean, Janaka's daughter must have struggled and fell down in the ocean. Alas! While the ascetic Sita was trying to protect her chastity without a relative, has the inferior Ravana devoured her? The dark-eyed one is without any taints. Has she been eaten by the wives of the Indra among the rakshasas, who are wicked in their intent? She is like the full moon. Her eyes are like lotus petals. While she was meditating on Rama's face, she may have been distressed and has died. "Alas, Rama! Alas, Lakshmana! Alas, Ayodhya!" Lamenting in this way, Vaidehi Maithilee may have cast aside her body. Otherwise, in Ravana's residence, lamenting like a *sharika* bird that has been caged, she must certainly have died. Rama's slender-waisted wife has been born in Janaka's lineage. How can the one with eyes like lotus petals remain in Ravana's subjugation? Janaka's daughter has been destroyed or killed and is dead. How can one inform Rama about his beloved wife? What is better? There is a sin in informing him. There is a sin in not informing him. What should indeed be done? This seems to me to be a difficult choice. The time for performing the task is over. What is a better course of action?' In this way, Hanumat started to think again. 'If I go to the city of the Indra among the apes without having seen Sita, how will my manliness have been established? My feat of leaping across the ocean will be in vain. And so will the act of entering Lanka and seeing the rakshasas. When the apes return to Kishkindha, what will Sugriva and the two sons of Dasharatha say? If I go to Kakutstha and give him this extremely disagreeable news that I have not been able to see Sita, he will immediately give up his life. These will be harsh, terrible, cruel, sharp and extremely intolerable words about Sita. They will scorch the senses. Having heard them, he will no longer exist. On seeing him face this great hardship and making up his mind to die, the intelligent Lakshmana, who is extremely devoted to him, will also no longer exist. Hearing that the two brothers have been destroyed, Bharata will also die. On seeing that Bharata is dead, Shatrughna will no longer exist. There is no doubt that on seeing their sons dead, the mothers, Kousalya, Sumitra and Kaikeyee, will no longer exist. Sugriva, the lord of the apes, is grateful and fixed on the objective of truth. On seeing Rama face this state, he will give up his life. The ascetic Ruma will be distressed in her mind and will grieve. She will be miserable and unhappy. On account of sorrow over her husband, she will be afflicted and will give up her life. Afflicted by sorrow on account of Vali and afflicted by grief on account of the king[85] having died, Tara will also no longer exist. When his mother and father have been destroyed, and on account of hardship over Sugriva, how will Prince Angada be able to sustain his life? The residents of the forest[86] will be overcome by sorrow on account of their master. They will strike their heads with their palms and their fists. The apes have been comforted, favoured and respected by the illustrious king of the apes. They will give up their lives. The elephants among the apes will no longer assemble and sport in the forests, the mountains and the canopied areas. They will suffer hardship on account of their master. With their sons, wives and advisers, they will assemble on the summits of mountains and fall down on uneven terrain.[87] The apes will resort to poison, hanging, entering the fire, fasting and weapons.[88] Because of the destruction of the Ikshvaku lineage and because of the destruction of the residents of the forest, I think that there will be terrible lamentations. Therefore, I will not leave this place and go to the city of Kishkindha. Without Maithilee, I am incapable of meeting Sugriva. As long as I do not leave this place, the two great-souled maharathas and the spirited apes will sustain their lives on hope. As long as I am unable to see Janaka's daughter, I will reside in this region near the ocean. There are roots, fruits and water here. I will control myself and live near the root of a tree. I will resort to vanaprastha. I will generate a fire through the use of kindling sticks and enter that pyre. I will sit down and accomplish the task of fasting to death. My body will be eaten by crows and predatory beasts. It is my view that this kind of departure is approved of by the rishis. If I do not see Janakee, I will enter deep water. I have been born from a noble foundation. I am extremely fortunate. I am illustrious and possess a

---

[85] Sugriva.
[86] Meaning the apes.
[87] Killing themselves.
[88] Again, to kill themselves.

garland of deeds. If I do not see Sita, all these will be destroyed and it will be like a night that lasts for a long period of time. Perhaps I will become an ascetic, controlling myself and resorting to the foot of a tree. Without having seen the dark-eyed one, I will not leave this place. If I leave this place without knowing about Sita, Angada and all the other apes will no longer exist. However, there are many kinds of taints associated with dying. A person who is alive may be fortunate. Therefore, I should sustain my life. If one is alive, it is certain that a meeting may take place.' In this way, he repeatedly bore many kinds of sorrows in his mind. The elephant among the apes was not able to cross over to the other shore of this ocean of grief. 'I will kill the immensely strong Ravana Dashagriva. He abducted Sita because of his desire and this will be some kind of revenge. Perhaps I will seize him and progressively drag him across the ocean, presenting him to Rama, like an animal rendered to Pashupati.'[89] Having been unable to see Sita, he was filled with these kinds of thoughts. With his soul overcome by sorrow, the ape reflected. 'As long as I do not see Sita, Rama's illustrious wife, I will continue to repeatedly search the city of Lanka. If I convey Sampati's words to Rama, and Raghava does not see his wife, he will burn down all the apes. I will reside here, controlling my food and controlling my senses. Because of what I have done, all the men and all the apes should not be destroyed. There is the large grove of Ashoka, filled with giant trees. I will go to that. That has not been searched by me. I will bow to the Vasus, the Rudras, the Adityas, the Ashvins and the Maruts and go there, increasing the sorrow of the rakshasas. I will vanquish the rakshasas and give the queen, the delight of the Ikshvaku lineage, to Rama, like the fruits of asceticism.' With his senses afflicted, Hanumat thought in this way for some time.

After this, the mighty-armed son of the wind god arose. 'I bow down before Rama, together with Lakshmana. I bow down before the queen who is Janaka's daughter. I bow down before Rudra, Indra, Yama and Vayu. I bow down before the moon, the sun and the large number of Maruts.' The son of the wind god bowed

---

[89] The lord of the animals, Shiva.

down to them and to Sugriva. He glanced in all the directions and headed towards Ashokavana.[90] He first made up his mind to go to the auspicious Ashokavana. The ape, the son of the wind god, later thought about what was to be done. 'It is certain that the grove will be full of many rakshasas. Many kinds of excellent arrangements for Ashokavana will have been thought of. There is no doubt that guards have been earmarked and they will protect the trees. The illustrious one who is inside all creatures[91] will not blow very strongly there. For the sake of Rama and Ravana, I have contracted my size. The gods and the large number of rishis will bring me success here. The illustrious Svayambhu Brahma, the gods of all the directions, Agni, Vayu, Puruhuta,[92] the wielder of the vajra, Varuna, with the noose in his hand, Soma, Aditya, the great-souled Ashvins and all the Maruts will grant me success. The illustrious lord of all beings who ensures success for all creatures will grant me success. The others, who are unseen along the path,[93] will also grant me that. She has a high nose. She has white teeth. She is without any injuries. She has a beautiful smile and possesses eyes like lotus petals. She has a pleasing appearance and is like the lord of the stars[94] to behold. When will I see her? He is inferior and wicked, cruel in his deeds. He adorns himself with ornaments and garments that are extremely terrible. He abducted the ascetic lady with force. When will she come within my range of vision?'

Chapter 5(12)

The immensely energetic one thought for an instant. Making up his mind, he then leapt on to the wall of that residence.[95] With

[90] The Ashoka grove.
[91] The wind.
[92] Indra.
[93] Other minor divinities.
[94] The moon.
[95] Towards Ashokavana, which was outside the residence.

joy writ all over his limbs, the great ape based himself on the wall and looked at all the different kinds of blossoming trees at the advent of spring—salas, ashokas, beautiful blooming champakas, uddalakas, nagavrikshas and mangoes that had the colour of a monkey's face. Like an iron arrow shot from a bowstring, he then leapt into that grove of trees, which was full of mango trees and enveloped by hundreds of creepers. He entered that wonderful place, surrounded everywhere with silver and gold trees and resounding with the calls of birds. The grove was colourful because of the many kinds of birds and herds of animals. Hanumat, the ape, saw that it was like the rising sun. It was surrounded by many kinds of trees that yielded flowers and fruits. It was always populated by maddened cuckoos and bhringarajas. There were these animals and birds and it was also full of happy men. There were flocks of maddened peacocks and many other birds of diverse kinds. While the ape searched for the beautiful and unblemished princess, he woke up birds that were happily asleep. As the many birds flew up, the trees were struck by their wings and released showers of flowers of many different hues. Hanumat, the son of the wind god, was himself radiant, covered with flowers. In the middle of Ashokavana, he looked like a mountain made out of flowers. The ape rushed around in all the directions, having advanced amidst the trees. On seeing him, all the creatures thought that spring[96] had arrived. The earth was resplendent, separately covered by flowers that had showered down from the trees, and looked like an ornamented woman. The trees trembled because of the force of that spirited one. Thus, the ape lead to the showering down of many kinds of flowers. The tops of the trees were bare, shorn of flowers, fruits and leaves. They looked like defeated gamblers, who had flung away their garments and ornaments. The best of trees trembled because of Hanumat's force. Full of flowers, they swiftly shed their flowers, leaves and fruits. The birds on the trees were left with only the branches as refuge. It was as if all the trees had been stirred by the wind. The trees looked like a young maiden with her hair dishevelled and her sandalwood

---

[96] In its personified form.

paste smudged. It was as if someone had drunk from her lips, leaving teeth marks, as if she had been injured from nails and teeth. Crushed by his tail, hands and feet, Ashokavana itself looked like an excellent tree that had been shattered. With his force, the ape tore at the large creepers that were like bonds. He was like the wind during the monsoon, dispelling masses of clouds over the Vindhyas. As he roamed around there, the ape saw beautiful floors encrusted with jewels and silver. There were golden floors too. There were many kinds of ponds filled with excellent water. Here and there, there were flights of stairs, embedded with extremely expensive gems. There were golden trees along the colourful banks—the sand was made out of pearls and coral and the bottoms were made out of crystal and precious stones. There were clumps of blooming lotuses and lilies, with the sound of chakravakas. Flocks of aquatic birds, swans and cranes, called. In every direction, the river had tall trees alongside it. The canals were tended to properly, with auspicious water like amrita in them. There were hundreds of creepers and the region was shrouded with *santanaka* trees. The grove was enveloped with many kinds of shrubs and the interior had karavira trees. He saw a mountain with a lofty peak and it was like a cloud. In every direction, it was surrounded by peaks. There were caves in the mountain and it was enveloped with many kinds of trees. The tiger among apes saw one of the earth's beautiful mountains. The ape saw the mountain, with the river descending from it, like a beloved one arising from her beloved's lap and leaping down. Descending into the water, the tops of the trees were beautiful. They looked like an angry woman, being restrained by her beloved relatives. The great ape looked at the water in the river again. It was like a beloved who was happy, having reached her beloved again. Not very far from this,[97] Hanumat, tiger among apes, the son of the wind god, saw ponds filled with lotuses and with flocks of many kinds of birds. Though artificial, the pond was full of cool water. The steps were embedded with the best of gems and the beautiful sand was made out of pearls. There was a colourful grove, filled

[97] The mountain.

with many kinds of wonderful herds of animals. With the extremely large mansions, Vishvakarma had constructed this. Though the grove was artificial, it was ornamented everywhere. All the trees there yielded flowers and fruits. There were umbrellas and large platforms. All the smaller platforms were made out of gold. The great ape saw a single golden *shimshupa* tree.[98] It was covered with many kinds of creepers and shrouded in a large number of leaves. In every direction, it was surrounded by platforms made out of gold. He saw parts of the ground where fountains welled out from holes and many other golden trees that blazed like the fire. The brave and great ape thought, 'The radiance of these trees is like that of Meru. Though an ape, I have become golden in complexion.' Those large number of golden trees were fanned by the wind and there was the sound of hundreds of bells. On seeing this, he was overcome by wonder. With great force, he climbed up the shimshapa tree, which was full of leaves. The top was covered with beautiful young shoots and leaves.

He thought, 'From here, I will be able to see Vaidehi, who desires to see Rama. Afflicted by grief, she will roam here and there and come here, as she wills. The Ashokavana of the evil-souled one is firm and beautiful. It is ornamented with champaka, sandalwood and bakula trees. This beautiful pond is frequented by flocks of birds. It is certain that Janakee, Rama's wife, will come here. For Raghava, Rama's beautiful queen is always beloved. Skilled in roaming around in the forest, Janakee will certainly come here. She is the one with eyes like a fawn and is knowledgeable about this forest. Afflicted by thinking of Rama, she will come to this grove. Because of Rama, the beautiful-eyed queen is tormented by grief. She has always been attached to residing in the forest. The one who wanders around in the forest will come here. In earlier times, Rama's beloved wife, Janaka's daughter, always desired those who roamed around in the forest. The young Janakee, who is attached to the performance of sandhya rites, will certainly come here. The one

---

[98] Alternatively, shimshapa, the Indian rosewood. Indeed, the spelling should be shimshapa. Also used for the ashoka tree, which is what is probably meant here.

with the beautiful complexion will want the auspicious waters of
the river for the sake of sandhya rites. This auspicious Ashokavana
is worthy of her. Everything that is auspicious is revered by the one
who is the wife of Rama, Indra among kings. If the queen, whose
face is like the lord of the stars, is alive, she will certainly come here
for the sake of the auspicious waters of the river.' This was the view
of the great-souled Hanumat. He waited for the wife of the Indra
among men. He hid himself in the leaves, thick with blossoming
flowers, and looked at everything there.

Chapter 5(13)

Searching for Maithilee, he looked around. He looked at
everything that was on the ground. The trees were beautifully
adorned with santanaka creepers. They adorned everything there
and were full of divine fragrances and juices. Enveloped with
animals and birds, it was like Nandana. The ponds were decorated
with golden lotuses and lilies. There were many seats and carpets
and many underground houses. The trees were full of flowers from
all the seasons and beautiful fruit. The radiance of the blossoming
ashokas was like the shine of the rising sun. Maruti saw that
everything there seemed to be ablaze. Denuded of leaves, the
branches were unprepared for the birds that repeatedly descended
and perched there. However, the trees were covered with hundreds
of colourful flowers. All the way down to the roots, the ashokas, the
destroyers of sorrow,[99] were covered with flowers. The great burden
of flowers made the trees bend down, as if to touch the ground.
There were flowering karnikaras and kimshukas in bloom. Because
of their radiance, everything in that region seemed to be ablaze.
There were punnagas, saptaparnas, champakas and uddalakas.
These had many large and extended roots and were radiant with
flowers. Some possessed the complexion of molten gold. Some were

[99] There is a play on words, *a* + *shoka*, without sorrow.

like the flames of fires. Some were like blue collyrium. There were thousands of ashoka trees there. It was like many colourful groves—Nandana and Chaitraratha. It was superior to all of them and was unthinkable. It was divine and beautiful, surrounded by prosperity. It was like a second sky, with the flowers like a large number of stellar bodies. With hundreds of colourful flowers and jewels, it was like the fifth ocean.[100] The trees were full of flowers from all the seasons, with sweet and fragrant scents. In that beautiful grove, sounds arose from many kinds of animals and flocks of birds. Many kinds of auspicious scents were borne along and these fragrances were pleasant. There was a heap of fragrances that was like an Indra among mountains, like a second Gandhamadana. Not very far from there, in Ashokavana, the bull among apes saw a lofty place of worship.[101] It was as white as Kailasa and thousands of pillars stood in its centre. The stairs were made out of coral and the sacrificial altars were made out of molten gold. It blazed in its prosperity and its end could not be seen with the eyes. Sparkling and tall, it seemed to etch out a painting in the sky.

He then saw her, like the trace of the pure crescent moon at the beginning of shukla paksha. She was attired in a soiled garment and was surrounded by rakshasis. She was distressed and lean from fasting. She was sighing repeatedly. Her beautiful form and radiance could only be discerned slightly. She was like the flame of the fire when it has been enveloped in a net of smoke. She was attired in a single and excellent garment that was yellow in colour. She was without ornaments. She was like a lotus pond, covered in mud and without lotuses in it. The ascetic one was faded and ashamed, tormented by grief. She was like Rohini, afflicted by the planet Mangala. Her miserable face was full of tears. The fasting had made her emaciated. She was immersed in her thoughts. She was extremely miserable and always full of sorrow. She was unable

[100] The text uses the word *panchama*, meaning fifth. This could be a typo and perhaps *dvitiya*, meaning second, is intended. A second ocean makes perfect sense. There are seven oceans and in standard lists, the fifth is an ocean made out of sugar cane juice (*ikshu sagara*). This too makes sense, but less so.

[101] *Chaityaprasada.*

to see her dear ones and only saw the large number of rakshasis. She was like a doe separated from her own kin and surrounded by a pack of dogs. A single braid of hair, with a hue like that of a dark serpent, hung down, up to her hips. She deserved happiness, but was tormented by grief. She was not accomplished in handling hardships. He saw the large-eyed one, more faded and lean than normal. Because of various logical reasons, he decided that this must be Sita.

Her form, when she had been seen being abducted by the rakshasa who could assume any form at will, had been described and this woman's form was like that. Her face was like the full moon and her eyebrows were excellent. Her beautiful breasts were round. Through her radiance, the queen dispelled darkness from all the directions. Her hair was dark. Her lips were like *bimba* fruit.[102] She possessed a firm and slender waist. With eyes like lotus petals, Sita was like Manmatha's Rati.[103] She was desired by the entire world, like the radiance of the full moon. With her excellent body, she was seated on the ground, controlling herself like an ascetic. The timid one sighed a lot, like the terrified wife of an Indra among serpents. Since she was immersed in an extensive and large mass of grief, she was no longer radiant. She was like the flame of a fire, when it has been enveloped in a mass of smoke. She was like a memory that has been lost, or a prosperity that has been thrown away. She was like faith that has been shattered, like a hope that has been frustrated. She was like obstructions in the path of success, like an intelligence that has been tainted. She was like deeds that have suffered through calumny, though the act has not been done.[104] She was suffering because of the obstruction caused to Rama and was afflicted at having been abducted by a rakshasa. With eyes like those of a helpless fawn, she glanced around here and there. Her face was cheerless and her eyelashes, with sidelong glances, were filled with tears. With a miserable face, she sighed repeatedly. She was distressed and was covered in filth and dust. Though she deserved

---

[102] The fruit of *Momordica monadelpha*.

[103] Manmatha, also known as Madana or Kama, is the god of love and Rati is his wife.

[104] The calumny is false. The act of censure has not actually been done.

to be ornamented, she was without ornaments. She was like the radiance of the king of the nakshatras[105] at a time when it is covered by dark clouds. After having repeatedly glanced at Sita, his mind was unsure about the course of action. She was like learning that has turned lax because it has not been studied and used. With great sorrow, Hanumat accepted that this person without ornaments, like words that have meaning but are without polish, was indeed Sita. He looked at the large-eyed and unblemished princess. Because of various reasons, he debated and determined that this was Sita. Rama had described Vaidehi's limbs and hers were like that. The ornaments that should have enhanced the beauty of her body could not be seen. There used to be well-crafted earrings, in the shape of a dog's teeth, on her ears. There used to be colourful ornaments, made out of jewels and corals, on her hands. However, because she had worn these for a long time, there were dark marks where these used to be. He thought, 'I think these are the ones Rama described. I cannot discern the ones that are missing. But there is no doubt that the ones that are not missing are the ones that were described. She had flung aside her auspicious upper garment, with a yellow complexion like that of a golden plate. It had adhered to a tree and the apes had seen it there. Her excellent ornaments had been dropped on the ground. There were others that had been dropped, making a great sound. Having been worn for a long time, this garment has faded a lot. Even then, it is clear that this one's complexion and radiance are identical to those of the other one. This one with the golden complexion is Rama's beloved queen. She has not been destroyed. Nor has she been destroyed in his mind. She is the one because of whom Rama has been tormented in four ways—compassion, non-violence, sorrow and desire. The compassion was because his wife had disappeared,[106] the non-violence because she was one who sought refuge,[107] the sorrow because a wife had disappeared and desire because of a beloved. This dark-eyed queen's form and the elegance of her major and minor limbs are exactly like Rama's. This

---

[105] The moon.
[106] This is irrespective of whether the person was a wife or not, hence, compassion.
[107] And violence was caused to her.

queen's mind is vested in him and his is vested in her. It is because of her that the one with dharma in his soul is able to sustain his life even for an instant. Rama is mad with desire for her and has performed an extremely difficult task. Without Sita, the mighty-armed one has been able to remain alive for more than an instant.' Thus, seeing Sita, the son of the wind god was delighted. Mentally, he praised Lord Rama.

Chapter 5(14)

Sita deserved to be praised and the bull among apes praised her. He also praised Rama's delightful qualities and started to think again. For a short while, the spirited Hanumat reflected on Sita. He lamented and his eyes filled with tears. 'She is revered by Lakshmana. She is humble towards her seniors. She loves her seniors. If Sita is afflicted by grief, destiny is indeed very difficult to cross. However, like the Ganga at the onset of the monsoon, because of the efforts of Rama and the intelligent Lakshmana, the queen is not excessively agitated. She is his equal in good conduct, age and character. She is his equal in nobility of birth and signs. Raghava deserves the dark-eyed Vaidehi and she deserves him.' He saw her, golden in complexion, like Shri,[108] loved by the worlds. In his mind, he went to Rama and addressed him in these words.[109] 'It is for the sake of this large-eyed one that the immensely strong Vali has been slain, and Kabandha, who was Ravana's equal in valour, has been brought down. In the forest, Rama used his valour to slay the rakshasa Viradha, terrible in his valour, in a battle, like the great Indra bringing down Shambara. There were fourteen thousand rakshasas who were terrible in their deeds. With arrows that were like the flames of the fire, they were killed in Janasthana. Khara was killed in the battle and Trishira was brought down. Rama,

---

[108] Lakshmi.

[109] The subsequent sentences are more like Hanumat thinking aloud, rather than words addressed to Rama.

who knows about his soul, killed the greatly energetic Dushana. The wealth of the apes is extremely difficult to obtain and was protected by Vali. It is for her sake that Sugriva obtained it and is honoured by the world. It is for the sake of the large-eyed one that I have crossed the handsome ocean, the lord of the male and female rivers, and have examined this city. For her sake, if Rama whirls around this earth, with its frontiers in the ocean, and even does it to the entire universe, it is my view that this would be proper. If there is a comparison between the dominion of the three worlds and Sita, Janaka's daughter, all the *kala*s of the dominion of the three worlds falls short of one kala of Sita.[110] She is the daughter of the great-souled Janaka, the king of Mithila who follows dharma in his conduct. Sita is firm in her vows towards her husband. When the field was being ploughed, she split the earth and rose up, from the mouth of the plough. She was then covered by the auspicious dust from the field and these were like the pollen from lotuses. Dasharatha was valiant and noble in conduct. He never retreated from a battle. This illustrious queen is his eldest daughter-in-law. Rama knows his soul. He knows about dharma and is grateful. This is his beloved wife, who has now come under the subjugation of the rakshasis. Because of the strength of affection towards her husband, she gave up all the objects of pleasure and not thinking about the miseries, entered the desolate forest. She was attentive towards serving her husband and content with fruits and roots. She obtained great happiness in the forest, as if she was in her own residence. Her limbs are golden in complexion and she always smiles when she talks. This unfortunate one has to undergo this intolerable misery. She is good in conduct and Raghava desires to see her. Ravana is crushing her, like a thirsty person does to a store of water. Through getting her back again, Raghava will certainly find joy. That will be like a king, who has been dislodged from the kingdom, getting the earth back again. She has given up desire and the objects of pleasure. She has been separated from her relatives.

[110] There are sixteen kalas (parts) of the moon and this is extended to everything, the whole consisting of sixteen parts. All the sixteen parts of the three worlds fall short of one-sixteenth part of Sita.

She is sustaining her body only because she desires to meet him. She does not see the rakshasis, or these trees with their flowers and fruits. It is certain that single-mindedly, she only sees Rama. Among all ornaments, the husband is the greatest ornament for a woman. This one is separated from him. Though she deserves to be adorned, she is not adorned. Separated from her, Lord Rama is performing an extremely difficult task. He is sustaining his own body and is not sinking down in sorrow. The tips of her hair are black. Her eyes are like lotuses. She deserves happiness, but is miserable. Knowing this, my mind is also distressed. She is like the earth in her forgiveness. Her eyes are like lotuses. She used to be protected by Raghava and Lakshmana. At the foot of the tree, she is now being guarded by rakshasis with malformed eyes. She is like a lotus whose beauty has been destroyed by ice. One after another, she has suffered from hardships. She is like a female chakravaka, separated from her companion. Janaka's daughter has faced this calamity and is miserable. The ashoka trees are bending down under the burden of flowers on the tips of their branches and are generating sorrow in her. The winter is over and the one with thousands of cool beams[111] has arisen.' The ape looked at all this, considered and made up his mind that this was indeed Sita. The spirited one, strong among the apes and the bears, was seated on that tree.

Chapter 5(15)

The sparkling moon arose in the sparkling sky, with a complexion like that of a clump of lotuses, as if a swan was entering the blue water. The radiance of the one whose radiance is sparkling seemed to help him. The cool rays of the moon seemed to sprinkle the son of the wind god. He saw Sita, with a face resembling the full moon. She was immersed in a burden of sorrow, like a heavily laden boat submerged in water. Hanumat, the son of the wind god, wished to

[111] The moon.

see Vaidehi. Not very far from her, he noticed rakshasis who were terrible to behold. There were those with one eye, many ears, with ears covering the body, without ears, with ears like cones and with high noses that stretched up to the head. There were those whose heads were gigantic, others whose necks were long and thin. There were those with dishevelled hair, without hair and hair that was like blankets. There were those with elongated ears and foreheads and with breasts that hung down. There were those with long lips and with lips that began at the chin. There were those whose faces hung down and those whose knees hung down. They were short, tall, hunchbacked, malformed and dwarfs. The teeth jutted out and the mouths were malformed. There were those with green eyes and disfigured faces. They were malformed and dark in complexion. They were black, angry and quarrelsome. They wielded giant spears, spikes and clubs made out of black iron. There were those with faces like wild boar, deer, tigers, buffaloes and jackals. There were those with feet like elephants, camels and horses and others with heads that were drawn in. There were those with a single hand or foot and those whose ears were like those of donkeys and horses. Some others possessed ears like cows, elephants and monkeys. Some had no nose, others had large noses. Some had horizontal noses, others were with malformed noses. Some had noses like elephants. For others, the nose was affixed to the forehead. Some had feet like elephants, others possessed gigantic feet. Some possessed feet like cows, others had hair on their feet. Some possessed large heads and necks, others large breasts and stomachs. Some possessed large mouths and eyes, others long tongues and nails. There were those with faces like goats, elephants, cows and pigs. There were those with faces like horses, camels and donkeys. The rakshasis, terrible to behold, wielded spears and clubs in their hands. They were angry and quarrelsome. Their teeth jutted out and their hair was the colour of smoke. The rakshasis possessed malformed faces. They were always drinking. They always loved flesh and drink. Their limbs were smeared with flesh and blood. They subsisted on flesh and blood. The best among apes saw them. Their sight was such that it made the body hair stand up.

They were seated around a large tree with a large trunk. The prosperous Hanumat noticed the unblemished queen and princess, Janaka's daughter, seated under the tree. She was tormented by grief and her radiance had faded. Her hair was covered in filth. She was like a star that had fallen down on the ground after its merit had been exhausted. The greatness of her character made her prosperous, but she was unable to see her husband and was in the midst of a calamity. She was without her excellent ornament, the ornament of her husband's love. Seized by the lord of the rakshasas, she was without her relatives. She was like the wife of an elephant, separated from her herd and captured by a lion. She was like the marks of the moon at the end of the monsoon, when it is covered by autumn clouds. Her form was suffering, like that of a veena that is not touched. She should be with her husband, but was separated from him and was under the subjugation of the rakshasas. In the midst of Ashokavana, she was immersed in an ocean of grief. She was surrounded by them, like Rohini by the planets. The queen was like a creeper without flowers and Hanumat saw her there. Her limbs were smeared in filth and her body was devoid of ornaments. She was like a lotus in mud. She shone, but did not shine. The beautiful one was attired in a wrinkled and dirty garment. The ape Hanumat saw the one with eyes like those of a fawn. There were marks of distress on the queen's face. Without her husband's energy, she was faded. Sita, the dark-eyed one, protected herself through her own good conduct. Hanumat saw Sita, with eyes like those of a fawn. As terrified as a fawn, she glanced around in different directions. The trees, bearing shoots, seemed to be burnt down by her sighs. She was in a tide of sorrow, with a fresh wave of sorrow rising up. The son of the wind god obtained unsurpassed delight on seeing Maithilee. She was radiant even without her ornaments. Her well-proportioned limbs were full of forgiveness. On seeing the one with the maddening eyes, delight was generated in him. However, having bowed to Raghava, Hanumat also shed tears. The valiant one bowed down to Rama and Lakshmana. Delighted at having seen Sita, Hanumat composed himself.

Chapter 5(16)

While he was searching for Vaidehi in that grove full of trees in blossom, a little bit of the night was still left. Towards the end of the night, he heard chants of the brahman being uttered by the *brahmarakshasas*[112] who were excellent as officiating priests at sacrifices, knowledgeable in the six Vedangas.[113] The mighty-armed and immensely strong Dashagriva was woken up by the auspicious sounds of musical instruments that were pleasant to hear. The powerful Indra among the rakshasas was woken up at the right time. With his garlands and garments dishevelled, he thought of Vaidehi. Intoxicated by desire, he was severely afflicted by his desire for her. The rakshasa was not capable of suppressing this desire in himself. He adorned himself in all kinds of excellent ornaments and went to the spot where there were many trees filled with all kinds of flowers and fruits. It was surrounded by lakes and adorned with many kinds of flowers. It was supremely extraordinary and was always full of colourful and maddened birds. He saw the avenues, with gates made out of gold and gems. It was pleasant to the eye and was full of many kinds of deer.[114] There were many kinds of deer and fruit that had fallen down. Ashokavana was always full of trees and he entered it. As he proceeded, only one hundred women followed Pulastya's descendant, like the women of the gods and the gandharvas following the great Indra. Some of those women held lamps made out of gold. Others held whisks and fans made out of hair and palm leaves in their hands. Some walked ahead, with golden vessels filled with water. Others proceeded at the rear, holding round cushions. To the right walked a beautiful woman with a golden and bejewelled plate full of drink in her right hand. Another one proceeded at the rear, holding a

---

[112] A brahmarakshasa is a brahmana who has become a rakshasa.

[113] The six Vedangas are *shiksha* (articulation and pronunciation), *chhanda* (prosody), *vyakarana* (grammar), *nirukta* (etymology), *jyotisha* (astronomy) and *kalpa* (rituals).

[114] The text uses the word of *ihamriga*, so this is something other than ordinary deer (*mriga*). The word ihamriga means wolf. Interpretations take this word to mean artificial deer.

golden staff with an umbrella that was like a swan and as radiant as the full moon. The eyes of Ravana's excellent women were still full of sleep. But they followed their brave husband, like lightning follows a cloud. The ape who was the son of the wind god heard the sound from the girdles and anklets of these excellent women.

The ape Hanumat saw the one who was unthinkable in his strength and manliness, the performer of unmatched deeds, approach the area around the entrance. All the directions were illuminated by the many lamps that were carried. These were being carried ahead of him and were wet with fragrant oil. He was full of desire and insolence and his large eyes were slanted. He was like Kandarpa,[115] without a bow being carried. His excellent upper garment dazzled with the froth from crushed amrita.[116] When it got attached to his armlet, he playfully freed it. He[117] was hidden in the thick mass of leaves, surrounded by flowers. It was as if he[118] was approaching him. The elephant among apes looked everywhere and saw Ravana's excellent women, full of youth and beauty. The extremely handsome and extremely illustrious king was surrounded by them. With these women, he entered the grove that was full of the sounds of animals and birds. The immensely strong one was intoxicated. His ears were like cones and his ornaments were colourful. He saw Vishravasa's son, the lord of the rakshasas. He was surrounded by those excellent women, like the moon by the stars. The great and spirited ape saw the immensely energetic one. The ape thought, 'This is the mighty-armed Ravana.' The immensely energetic Hanumat, the son of the wind god, leapt down. Though he was fierce in his energy, he was surpassed by the other one's energy.[119] Hanumat hid himself behind the leaves.[120] Ravana desired to see the one whose limbs were fair, with excellent hips and well-formed breasts, with hair that was dark at the tips.

[115] Madana or Kama, the god of love.
[116] Amrita is being used here as a term for liquor.
[117] Hanumat.
[118] Ravana.
[119] Ravana's energy was greater than that of Hanumat.
[120] Despite having jumped down from the tree.

Chapter 5(17)

At that time, the unblemished princess, Vaidehi, saw Ravana, the lord of the rakshasas. He was full of youth and beauty and was adorned with excellent ornaments. The beautiful one trembled, like a plantain tree in a storm. The large-eyed one, beautiful in complexion, covered her stomach, thighs and breasts with her hands. She sat down and wept. Dashagriva saw Vaidehi, protected by a large number of rakshasis. She was miserable and afflicted by grief, like a boat submerged in the ocean. Firm in her vows, she was seated on the bare ground. She was like the branch of a tree, severed and fallen down on the ground. Her beautiful limbs were adorned with filth. Though she deserved to be ornamented, there were no ornaments on her. In her wishes and with horses that were her own resolution, she seemed to be going towards Rama, the lion among kings who knew about his soul. Full of her thoughts and sorrow, she was weeping alone, as if dried up. Devoted to Rama, the beautiful one did not see an end to her miseries. Seated there, she seemed to writhe like the wife of an Indra among the serpents. She was like Rohini, invaded by the smoke of the planet that is like a comet.[121] She possessed good conduct and was born in a noble lineage. Her conduct was in conformity with dharma. In addition, she was full of good conduct. However, she seemed to have been born in a wicked lineage.[122] She was like great deeds that were now suffering, like respect suffering from dishonour. She was like wisdom that had decayed and hopes that had been dashed. She was like expectations that had been belied, like commands that had been countered. She was like a direction that blazes at the time of destruction, like worship that has been taken away. She was like a devastated lotus, like an army with the brave warriors killed. She was like the radiance of austerities when it has been destroyed, like

[121] The text uses the word *dhumaketu*, which means something that has smoke as its standard. The word usually means a comet or a meteor. However, the image is of Rohini being attacked by the evil planet Ketu. Therefore, dhumaketu can simply mean the smoking Ketu.

[122] Because of her present state.

a river that has withered away. She was like a sacrificial altar that has been greatly desecrated, like the flame of a fire that has been pacified. She was like the night of a full moon when the lunar disc has been devoured by Rahu. She was like a lotus pond when it has suffered severely from an elephant's trunk, with the petals of the lotuses destroyed and with the birds frightened away. Afflicted by sorrow on account of her husband, she was like a river where the flow of water has dried up. She seemed to be devoid of good cleansing, like a night in krishna paksha. She was extremely delicate. She was born with excellent limbs. She deserved a house that was full of stores of jewels. But like the stalk of a lotus that has just been uprooted, she was being scorched by the heat. She was like the wife of a king among elephants, separated from the herd, seized and tied to a pillar, sighing in her great grief. She wore a single long braid in her hair. But though she took no care, she was still radiant. She was like the earth covered with a wealth of trees, blue at the end of the rainy season. Because of fasting, sorrow, thoughts and fear, she was emaciated and lean. The store of austerities ate little and was miserable. Miserable with grief, she joined her hands in salutation, as if before a god, and sought Dashagriva's defeat at the hands of the foremost among the Raghu lineage. He[123] saw that the unblemished one, with white eyes with excellent lashes that were coppery red at the ends, was weeping, for the sake of his death. Maithilee was extremely devoted to Rama. Ravana tempted her.

Chapter 5(18)

The joyless and miserable ascetic lady was surrounded by them.[124] On seeing this, Ravana addressed her in sweet words that were full of meaning. 'O one with thighs like the trunk of an elephant! On seeing me, you have hidden your breasts and stomach. Because

[123] Ravana.
[124] The rakshasis.

of your fear, you desire that you might yourself disappear. O large-eyed one! I desire you. O beloved one! Show me great respect. You possess qualities in all your limbs. All the worlds find you to be pleasant. O Sita! No men, or rakshasas who can assume any form at will, can harm you. Dispel the fear that has arisen on account of me. O timid one! There is no doubt that when rakshasas use force to abduct and have intercourse with the wives of others, in every way, this is their own dharma.[125] O Maithilee! There is desire in my body and with that desire coursing through, I desire you. But despite this, if you do not desire it, I will not touch you. O queen! O beloved one! Trust me. You have nothing to fear on this account. I truly love you. You should not become addicted to this sorrow. Your hair is in a single braid. You are sleeping on the ground. You are thinking and your garment is faded. You are fasting at the wrong times. These will bring no benefit to you. O Maithilee! When you get me, you will obtain wonderful garlands, sandalwood, aloe, many kinds of garments, divine and other ornaments, extremely expensive drinks, beds and seats, songs, dances and musical instruments. You are a jewel among women. Do not behave in this way. Have ornaments on your body. O one who is excellent in form! On obtaining me, how can you not become beautiful to behold? This birth is beautiful and your youth is ebbing away. It is like the swift flow of water. Once it has passed, it does not return again. O one who is auspicious to behold! I think that after creating you, the one who has created all forms, the creator of the universe,[126] did not create any other form like you. O Vaidehi! You possess beauty and youth. On approaching you, which man, even if it is the grandfather himself,[127] is capable of withdrawing? O one whose face is like the one with the cool beams! O wide-hipped one! Whichever part of your body I look at, my eyes become affixed to that. O Maithilee! Give up this confusion and become my wife. Among the many excellent women here, become my chief queen. O timid one! All the jewels that have been forcibly seized from the worlds, this kingdom and I myself belong

---

[125] This is sanctioned for rakshasas.
[126] Brahma.
[127] Brahma.

to you. O beautiful one! For your sake, I will conquer the entire earth with its garland of many cities and give it to Janaka. I do not see anyone else on earth who can counter me in strength. Behold my great energy in a battle, when I engage in a duel. The armies of adversaries, gods and asuras, were incapable of withstanding me. They were unsuccessful in encounters and were scattered by me. Their standards were routed. Desire me today and I will perform an excellent good deed for you in return. Let your limbs be extremely radiant with ornaments. I will do this good deed for you and behold your excellent form. O one with the beautiful face! In return for my generosity, do a good deed for me. As you desire, enjoy these objects of pleasure. O timid one! Drink and sport. Give away all the riches on earth, as you wish. You can confidently do whatever you want. You can command without any fear. Because of my favours, you can sport and your relatives can also sport. O fortunate one! Behold my prosperity. That prosperity and fame will become yours. O extremely fortunate one! Rama's garments consist of tattered rags. What will you do with him? Rama will be defeated. Bereft of prosperity, he will roam around in the forest. He will resort to the vow of sleeping on the bare ground. There will be a doubt about whether he will remain alive or not. O Vaidehi! Even if he so wishes, Rama will not be able to see you. You will be like the moonlight when it is covered by dark clouds with flocks of cranes in the front. From my hands, Raghava does not deserve to get you. That would be like Hiranyakashipu's deeds passing into Indra's hands. O one with the beautiful smiles! O one with the beautiful teeth! O one with the beautiful eyes! O charming one! O timid one! Like Suparna takes away a serpent, you are stealing my mind. Your silken garments have faded. You are lean and without ornaments. On seeing you, I am no longer interested in desiring my own wives. All my other women who are in the inner quarters possess all the qualities. O Janakee! Rule over all of them. O one whose hair is black at the tips! These women are supreme in the three worlds. They will serve you, like the apsaras serve Shri. O one with the excellent eyebrows! O one with the beautiful hips! As it pleases you, enjoy me and all the riches and wealth in the worlds, those that belong to Vaishravana.[128] O queen! Rama is not my equal in austerities, strength, valour, riches, energy or fame. Drink. Sport. Pleasure. Enjoy the objects of the senses. There are stores of riches from the directions. There is the entire earth. O one who should play! As you wish, sport with me. Let your relatives meet you and sport too. O timid one! Along the shores of the ocean, there are always nets of flowering trees. Sport with me in those groves. Adorn your limbs with golden and sparkling necklaces.'

Chapter 5(19)

Sita heard the words of the terrible rakshasa. Her tone was miserable and afflicted. She replied slowly, in a miserable voice. Sita was afflicted by grief and weeping. The ascetic lady was trembling. The beautiful one, devoted in vows to her husband, thought about her husband. The one with the beautiful smiles placed a blade of grass between them and replied.[129] 'Withdraw your crazy mind from me. Turn your mind towards those who are your own. You should not crave me, like those who are the performers of wicked deeds should not aspire for success. My duty is to have a single husband. I will not perform the reprehensible task of deviating from this. I have been born in a great and auspicious lineage and have also got a noble lineage.'[130] Having said this, the illustrious Vaidehi turned her back towards Ravana. Then she again spoke these words. 'I am the wife of another person and it is inappropriate that I should be your wife. It is virtuous to have an eye towards dharma. O virtuous one! Follow the vows of the virtuous. O one who roams around in the night! The wives of others should be protected, just as you protect your own ones. Treat others like your own self and find pleasure in your own

---

[128] Kubera.

[129] When one was speaking to an unworthy person, there was a custom of placing a blade of grass in between.

[130] The one she married into.

wives. A person who is not satisfied with his own wives is fickle.
His senses are fickle. For someone whose wisdom is inferior in this
way, the wives of others will convey him to his defeat. Are there no
virtuous people here? Or do you not follow those virtuous ones!
That is the reason your words and mind have turned towards
what is false and do not accept the medication prescribed by the
discriminating. After having obtained a king who is not cleansed
in soul and is addicted to bad policy, prosperous kingdoms and
cities are destroyed. In that way, Lanka, full of heaps of jewels,
has obtained you. Because of the crimes of a single person, it will
soon be destroyed. O Ravana! O one who lacks foresight! The
creatures will rejoice at the destruction of a perpetrator of wicked
deeds who has brought about his destruction because of what he
himself has done. People who have been slighted by your wicked
deeds will be delighted and will say, "It is good fortune that this
terrible one has faced this calamity." I am incapable of being
tempted through prosperity or wealth. Like radiance cannot be
separated from the sun, I cannot be separated from Raghava. He is
the greatly revered protector of the worlds. After having used his
arm as a pillow, how can I use the arm of another one as a pillow?
I am an appropriate wife for that lord of the earth. I am his, like
learning and bathing at the end of a vow belong to a brahmana
who knows about his soul. O Ravana! I am miserable and it is
best that you should take me to Rama, like a female elephant that
lives in the forest meets with a lord of elephants. It is appropriate
that you should wish to have Rama, bull among men, as your
friend. That is unless you desire a terrible death for yourself. The
wielder of the vajra may let you go. The Destroyer may let you go
for a long time. However, when he is enraged, Raghava, the lord
of the worlds, will not let someone like you escape. You will hear
a great roar from the sound of Rama's bow. It is like the thunder
of the vajra, when released by Shatakratu. Marked with the signs
of Rama and Lakshmana, those well-jointed and swift arrows,
shafted with the feathers of herons, will soon descend here,
like flaming serpents. They will slay the rakshasas and envelop
everything everywhere, without leaving any space anywhere. Like

Vinata's son[131] plucking out a serpent with force, Rama will be the great Garuda and the Indra among the rakshasas will be a great serpent. My husband is the destroyer of enemies and will quickly take me away from you. Like Vishnu with the three strides, he will take away the blazing prosperity from the asuras. Because of the wicked deeds you performed, the army of the rakshasas was slain in Janasthana and it became a killing field. You were incapable of protecting them. You entered the lonely hermitage when the two lions among men weren't there. O inferior one! You abducted me when the two brothers had gone out. Like a dog smells out the scent and is incapable of remaining in a spot when there is a tiger present, you smelt out Rama and Lakshmana. In a conflict with them, you will be unable to withstand both of them together, just as in the conflict, one of Vritra's arms was incapacitated by Indra's arms. Swiftly, with Soumitri, the protector Rama will take away your life with his arrows, just as the sun dries up a little bit of water. Whether you go to Kubera's mountain or his residence, or whether you go to King Varuna's assembly hall, there is no doubt that Dasharatha's son will free you,[132] just like a great tree is uprooted by a bolt of thunder that is its destiny.'

Chapter 5(20)

The lord of the rakshasas heard Sita's harsh words. He replied to Sita in words that were disagreeable, though they seemed to be agreeable. 'In whatever form women are sought to be assured, that is exactly the way a person becomes subservient. A person who speaks pleasantly is rebuffed in exactly the same way.[133] Because my desire for you has been awakened, I have controlled my rage. This is like an excellent charioteer controlling the horses, even when they

---

[131] Garuda.

[132] Of your life.

[133] If a man is conciliatory, he has to yield to women. If he speaks sweetly, he is rebuffed.

are striding along a smooth road. Among men, desire is undesirable, since it binds them down. Among people, compassion indeed leads to affection. O one with the beautiful face! That is the reason I have not killed you. Since you are addicted to someone who is on a false exile,[134] you should be slain and should not be shown respect. O Maithilee! Because of the harsh and terrible words you have spoken to me, you deserve to be killed.' Ravana, the lord of the rakshasas, spoke to Vaidehi in this way. Thereafter, full of rage and fury, he again spoke to Sita. 'I will protect you for two months. After that, you will be killed by me. O one who is beautiful in complexion! By then, you must climb on to my bed. After those two months, if you do not desire me as your husband, you will be cooked in the great kitchen as my breakfast.' On seeing that the Indra among the rakshasas was thus censuring Janakee, the large-eyed maidens of the gods and the gandharvas grieved. When she was censured by the rakshasa, some used their lips and others used their faces and eyes to somehow comfort her.

Reassured by them, Sita, encased in the pride and strength of her good conduct, spoke these beneficial words to Ravana, the lord of the rakshasas. 'Your deeds are reprehensible and it is certain that there is no one who is able to restrain you from adhering to something that is not beneficial. Like Shachi is to Shachi's lord, I am the wife of the one with dharma in his soul. In the three worlds, who other than you will desire me in his mind? O worst among rakshasas! I am the wife of the infinitely energetic Rama. Having spoken these wicked words, who will free you from your destination? This is like a proud elephant and a hare who are together in the forest. Rama is said to be the elephant and you are said to be the inferior hare. You have abused the protector of the Ikshvaku lineage and are not ashamed. You will not be able to approach his dominion, not even with your eyes. O ignoble one! These eyes of yours are cruel, malformed and black and tawny. Since you have looked at me with these, why have they not fallen down on the ground? I am the wife of the one with dharma in his soul and Dasharatha's

---

[134] Meaning Rama.

daughter-in-law. Since you spoke about me, why has your tongue not shrivelled away? You ought not to speak about the austerities Rama has observed. O Dashagriva! You deserve to be burnt down. Yet, I am not burning you down with my energy. I belong to the intelligent Rama and you are incapable of abducting me. There is no doubt that this has been ordained by destiny for the sake of you being killed. You used your bravery against your brother, the lord of riches,[135] who possessed strength. However, for Rama, why did you resort to stealing his wife?'[136]

Ravana, the lord of the rakshasas, heard Sita's words. He dilated his cruel eyes and looked towards Janakee. He was like a blue cloud. His arms and head were huge. His stride possessed the spirit of a lion. He was handsome and the tips of his tongue and eyes blazed. He was attired in red garlands and garments. The ornaments on his body were made out of molten gold. With colourful garlands and pastes, he looked like a mountain covered with dust that was moving. A long dark blue *shronisutra*[137] extended around his body. It looked like the serpent around Mandara, at the time of extracting amrita.[138] He was adorned with earrings that had the complexion of the rising sun. He was like a mountain with ashoka trees that were full of red blossoms and shoots. His eyes red with rage, he looked at Vaidehi. Like a serpent that was sighing, Ravana spoke to Sita. 'You are pointlessly following someone who follows bad policy.[139] I will destroy you today, like the sun destroys sandhya with its energy.'[140]

Having told Maithilee this, King Ravana, who made his enemies scream, commanded all the rakshasis, who were terrible to behold. Some had a single eye, others had a single ear. For some, the ear covered the body. There were those with ears like cows and

---

    [136] Without using your strength.
    [137] Usually, a string tied around the loins. But sometimes, also used for the belt to which a sword was tied.
    [138] When amrita was produced by churning the ocean, Mandara was the base and Vasuki was the rope used for churning.
    [139] Meaning Rama.
    [140] The morning sandhya, dispelled by the light of the rising sun.

elephants, others with long ears or no ears. There were those with feet like elephants, horses or cows, others with hair on the feet. There were those with a single eye, or a single foot. There were those with thick feet, or no feet. Some possessed gigantic heads and necks, others possessed gigantic breasts and stomachs. There were those with gigantic faces and eyes, long tongues, or no tongues. There were those without noses. There were those with mouths like those of lions, cows or pigs. 'O rakshasis! All of you collectively act so that Sita Janakee swiftly comes under my subjugation. Act favourably and unfavourably, use sama, dana and bheda. Raise the prospect of danda and make Vaidehi comply.' The Indra among the rakshasas repeatedly instructed his rakshasis. Overcome by desire and anger, he censured Janakee.

A rakshasi named Dhanyamalini quickly approached Dashagriva. She embraced him and spoke these words. 'O great king! Sport with me. What use will this Sita be to you? As a vehicle for desire, if someone uses a person who is not interested in desire, that only torments his body. A greater pleasure is obtained from a person who wishes to use herself as a vehicle of desire.' Thus addressed, the powerful one flung that rakshasi away. With a complexion like that of the blazing sun, he entered his residence. The maidens of the gods, the gandharvas and the nagas were all around him, surrounding Dashagriva as he entered that excellent house. Maithilee based herself on supreme dharma and trembled because of her fear for Ravana. Confounded by desire, he abandoned Sita and entered his own radiant residence.

Chapter 5(21)

King Ravana, who made his enemies scream, spoke to Maithilee in this way. Having instructed all the rakshasis, he departed. The Indra among the rakshasas left and went to his inner quarters again. The rakshasis, terrible in form, rushed towards Sita. The rakshasis, senseless with rage, reached Sita. They addressed Vaidehi in these extremely harsh words. 'The great-souled Ravana is the excellent descendant of Pulastya. O Sita! However, you are showing great disrespect to the idea of being Dashagriva's wife.'

After this, a rakshasi named Ekajata spoke these words to Sita, addressing her as one whose waist could be clasped in the hands.[141] Her eyes were coppery red in anger. 'Among the six Prajapatis, the fourth Prajapati is a son born through Brahma's mental powers.[142] He is renowned as Pulastya. Through his mental powers, the energetic maharshi Pulastya had a son. His name was Vishravasa and he was like Prajapati in his radiance. O large-eyed one! His son is Ravana, the one who makes his enemies scream. You should become the wife of that Indra among rakshasas. O one who is beautiful in her limbs! Why are you not showing due respect to the words I have spoken?' At this, a rakshasi named Harijata spoke these words. Her eyes were like those of a cat and she widened them in her anger. 'The thirty-three gods[143] and the king of the gods have been vanquished by him. You should become the wife of that Indra among rakshasas. He is immersed in valour. He is brave. He does not retreat from the field of battle. He is strong and brave. Why don't you wish to become his wife? The immensely strong king will give up his wives, the ones he respects the most. Ignoring all those immensely fortunate ones, Ravana will serve you. In the prosperous inner quarters, full of many kinds of jewels, there are one thousand women. Abandoning all of them, Ravana will serve you. In battles, he has disarmed the gods, the serpents, the gandharvas and the danavas. The one who has defeated them in battles has come to your side. The great-souled Ravana possesses all the riches. O wicked one! Why don't you want to become the wife of that Indra among rakshasas? The sun does not scorch him. The wind god is terrified of him and does not blow. O long-eyed one! Why aren't you by his side? Scared of him, the trees shower down flowers. O

---

[141] The waist was slender enough to be cupped by the two hands. But a slender waist was not a sign of beauty among the rakshasas.

[142] The number of Prajapatis varies from text to text and eleven or fourteen is a more common number. Therefore, it is difficult to determine which six are meant.

[143] Eight Vasus, eleven Rudras, twelve Adityas and two Ashvins.

one with the excellent eyebrows! The mountains and clouds yield
the water that he desires. O beautiful one! He is king of kings in the
kingdom of the nairittas. Why don't your thoughts turn towards
becoming Ravana's wife? O queen! O beautiful one! This is the
truth and I have spoken beneficial words to you. O one with the
beautiful smiles! Accept them. Otherwise, you will no longer exist.'

Chapter 5(22)

The rakshasi women, with disfigured faces, approached Sita.
Harshly, those women addressed her in these disagreeable
and harsh words. 'O Sita! The inner quarters are pleasing to all
creatures. It is full of expensive couches. Why don't you show
due respect to the idea of residing there? You are a human and
you should not show a great deal of respect to the idea of being a
human's wife. Withdraw your mind from Rama. Otherwise, you
will no longer exist. O unblemished one! He has been dislodged
from his kingdom. He has failed in his objective. He is impotent.'

Sita, whose eyes were like lotuses, heard the words of the
rakshasis. Her eyes overflowing with tears, she spoke these words.
'All of you have come together and have spoken words that are
condemned by the worlds. In your minds, why aren't these words
regarded as sin? A human lady should not become the wife of a
rakshasa. If you want, all of you can eat me. But I will not act in
accordance with your words. He may be distressed and he may have
been separated from his kingdom. But he is my husband and my
preceptor.'

Hearing Sita's words, the rakshasis became senseless with rage.
Goaded by Ravana, they censured her in harsh words. Hanumat
was silent, hidden in the shimshapa tree. The ape heard the rakshasis
censure Sita. As she trembled, they angrily surrounded her from
all directions. They licked their blazing lips in a horrible way and
bit their elongated teeth. Extremely angry, they quickly grabbed
their battleaxes and said, 'This one does not deserve to be the wife

of Ravana, the lord of the rakshasas.' The one with the beautiful
face was censured in this terrible way by the rakshasis. Shedding
tears, she approached the shimshapa tree. Near the shimshapa tree,
Sita was surrounded by the rakshasis. The large-eyed one reached
the spot and was overwhelmed by sorrow. She was wan and her
face was distressed. The garment that she wore was faded. In every
direction, those terrible rakshasis censured her.

There was a rakshasi named Vinata and she was terrible to
behold. Her teeth and stomach jutted out. Assuming an angry form,
she said, 'O Sita! You have displayed enough affection towards your
husband. O fortunate one! In everything, it is thought that anything
in excess leads to hardship. O fortunate one! I am satisfied with
you. You have followed the norms created by humans. O Maithilee!
However, I speak words to you that are in the nature of medication.
Act accordingly. Serve Ravana as your husband. He is the lord of all
the rakshasas. He is brave and handsome. He is like Vasava, the lord
of the gods. He is accomplished and is ready to renounce. He speaks
pleasantly to everyone. Rama is a miserable human. Abandon him
and seek refuge with Ravana. O Vaidehi! You will have celestial
unguents on your limbs. You will be adorned in celestial ornaments.
From today, become the mistress of all the worlds. O queen! O
beautiful one! Be like Svaha[144] to Agni, or Shachi to Indra. O Vaidehi!
Rama is miserable and has lost his lifespan. What do you have to do
with him? If you do not act in accordance with these words, in this
very instant, all of us will eat you up.'

There was another one and her name was Vikata. Her breasts
hung down. She roared, raised her fists and angrily spoke to Sita.
'O extremely evil-minded one! You have uttered many words that
are disagreeable in form. O Maithilee! Because of our mildness
and our compassion towards you, we have tolerated them. But
you are not acting according to our beneficial words, which are
appropriate for the time. You have been brought to this shore of
the ocean, which is extremely difficult to reach. O Maithilee! You
have entered Ravana's terrible inner quarters. You are imprisoned

[144] Agni's wife.

in Ravana's house and are protected exceedingly well by us. Even Purandara himself will find it impossible to save you. O Maithilee! Act in accordance with my beneficial words. There has been enough of shedding tears. Cast aside this futile grief. Serve affection and delight. Abandon this incessant misery. O Sita! As you wish, sport happily with the king of the rakshasas. O timid one! You know that the youth of women is not permanent. Until it is over, enjoy the happiness. O one with the maddening eyes! With the king of the rakshasas, roam in the beautiful gardens, mountains and groves. O beautiful one! Seven thousand women will remain under your control. Serve Ravana as your husband. He is the lord of all the rakshasas. O Maithilee! If you do not act in accordance with the words I have spoken, I will pluck out your heart and eat it.'

There was a rakshasi named Chandodari and she was cruel to behold. She twirled around a giant spear and spoke these words. 'The eyes of this one are as agitated as that of a deer. Because of her fear, her breasts are trembling. On seeing her, abducted by Ravana, a great desire arises in me. It is my view that I will eat her liver, spleen, the flesh above the heart, the heart and its muscles, the entrails and the head.'

At this, a rakshasi named Praghasa spoke these words. 'Let us crush this cruel one's neck. Why are we delaying? Let us then inform the king that the woman has died. There is no doubt that he will then tell us to eat her up.'

At this, a rakshasi named Ajamukhi spoke these words. 'Let us kill her, chop her up into equal pieces and divide those amongst us. We will divide her among ourselves. I do not like quarrels. Let drinks be brought quickly and many kinds of garlands.'

At this, a rakshasi named Shurpanakha spoke these words. 'I like what Ajamukhi has said. Liquor destroys all kinds of sorrow. Let it be brought quickly. After we have tasted human flesh, we will dance in Nikumbhila.'[145]

Sita, who was like the daughter of a god, was censured in this fashion by the extremely terrible rakshasis. She let go of her fortitude and wept.

---

[145] In front of the goddess named Nikumbhila.

Chapter 5(23)

The cruel rakshasis uttered many harsh and terrible words. Janaka's daughter wept. She was greatly terrified and her voice was indistinct because of her tears. Thus addressed, the spirited Vaidehi told the rakshasis, 'A woman should not become the wife of a rakshasa. I will not act in accordance with your words. If all of you so wish, you can eat me up.' Sita was like the daughter of a god and was in the midst of the rakshasis. She had been censured by Ravana. Afflicted by grief, she could not find any peace. She trembled a lot and seemed to sink into her own body. She was like a doe in the forest, separated from her herd and oppressed by wolves. Because of her great sorrow, she clung on to a blossoming branch. Grieving and with her mind shattered, she thought about her husband. Her large breasts became wet from the tears that were flowing from her eyes. She reflected, but could not see an end to her miseries. She trembled and fell down, like a plantain tree in a storm. Because she was frightened and scared of the rakshasis, her face turned pale. Sita's long braid of hair was also seen to tremble, as if it was a wriggling snake. She sighed, afflicted by grief. The sorrow robbed her of her senses. Afflicted, Maithilee shed tears and lamented. Afflicted by grief, she exclaimed, 'Alas, Rama!' The beautiful one again said, 'Alas, Lakshmana! Alas, my mother-in-law Kousalya! Alas, Sumitra! The aphorism that learned people cite is indeed true. "If it is the wrong time, for a woman or a man, it is extremely difficult to come by death." I am being oppressed by these cruel rakshasis. I am miserable and without Rama. But even then, I am alive, for more than an instant. I am miserable and have a limited store of merit. I will perish, like one without a protector. I am like a laden boat tossed around in the ocean, struck by the force of the wind. I am unable to see my husband and am under the control of the rakshasis. I am indeed suffering because of my sorrow, like a bank deluged by the water. His eyes are like lotus petals and his brave stride is like that of a lion. He is grateful and pleasant in speech. Those who are able to see my lord are fortunate. Rama knows about his soul and I have been separated from him in every way. It is as if I have tasted a fierce poison. It is extremely rare that I should still be alive. Earlier, what kind of great sin have I committed in a different life? That is the reason I have obtained this extremely terrible and dreadful misery. Surrounded by this great sorrow, I wish to give up my life. When I am protected by these rakshasis, I cannot reach Rama. Indeed, shame on being a human. Shame on being under someone else's control. I am incapable of giving up this uneasy life.'

Chapter 5(24)

Her lowered face was overflowing with tears. The child, Janaka's daughter, lamented and started to speak. She seemed to be mad and crazy. She grieved and her senses were in a whirl. Like a young mare, she writhed and rolled around on the ground. 'When Raghava was distracted, the rakshasa Ravana, who can assume any form at will, crushed me and brought me here by force, though I was crying. I am under the control of the rakshasis and I am being censured in an extremely terrible way. Suffering from great grief, I am thinking. I am not interested in remaining alive. There is no point to my remaining alive. There is no point to ornaments. Without maharatha Rama, I am residing amidst these rakshasis. Since I have been separated from him, shame on an ignoble person like me. Since I am able to sustain my life for more than an instant, my life must be a wicked one. Without the beloved one, what respect do I have for life? What is the point to happiness? He is the lord of the earth, up to the frontier of the ocean. He is pleasant in speech. I will cast aside my body. Let it be sliced up and eaten. Abandoned by my beloved, I cannot withstand this sorrow for a long time. I will not touch Ravana, the roamer in the night, with my left foot. Where is the question of doing something reprehensible, like desiring him? He does not know a refusal. He does not know me. He does not know my lineage. His nature is cruel and he wishes to obtain me. I will be cut, sliced, divided and burnt in a blazing fire, but I will not serve Ravana. What is the point behind this long prattling? Raghava is famous, wise, grateful and compassionate. He is good in conduct. I suspect that because of my misfortune, I may suffer and he may turn hard-hearted. He single-handedly disabled fourteen thousand rakshasas in Janasthana. Why should he not be able to reach me? I have been imprisoned by the rakshasa Ravana, who is limited in valour. Indeed, my husband is capable of slaying Ravana in a battle. In a battle in Dandakaranya, Rama slew Viradha, bull among rakshasas. Why should he not be able to reach me? Lanka is in the middle of the ocean and is extremely difficult to assail. However, should he so desire, there will be no obstruction in the path of Raghava's arrows. His beloved wife has been abducted by a rakshasa. What is the reason why Rama, firm in his valour, has still not reached her? I suspect that Lakshmana's elder brother does not know that I am here. Had he known it, the spirited one would have shown his intolerance towards the oppressor. The king of the eagles would have gone to Raghava and told him about the abduction. But he was brought down by Ravana in an encounter. Though he was aged, Jatayu performed a great deed in protecting me. In a duel, he stood before Ravana. If Raghava knows that I am here now, he will use his arrows and angrily remove rakshasas from all the worlds. He will blow away the city of Lanka. He will dry up the great ocean. He will destroy Ravana's name and his inferior deeds. The protectors of the rakshasis will be slain in house after house and they will weep, just as I am now. There is no doubt about this. Rama and Lakshmana will search out the Lanka of the rakshasas. When the two of them see an enemy, he will not be able to remain alive even for an instant. Lanka will soon become like a cremation ground, with the roads filled with the smoke from funeral pyres. There will be flocks of vultures everywhere. In a short while, my wish will be fructified. This evil course of action is telling me about the destruction that all of you will face. Inauspicious portents are being seen in Lanka. In a short while, it will be robbed of its lustre. There is no doubt that Ravana, worst among the rakshasas, will be slain and the invincible Lanka will be destroyed and dried up, like a woman who has become a widow. It is auspicious and prosperous now. But its lord and the rakshasas will be destroyed. The city of Lanka will become like a woman whose husband has been destroyed. There is no doubt that rakshasa maidens will weep in house after house. In a short while, I will hear the sounds of those who are afflicted by grief. It will be dark and the radiance will be destroyed. The bulls among the rakshasas will be killed. The city of Lanka will be burnt down by Rama's arrows. When the brave Rama knows that I am now in Ravana's residence, the ends of his eyes will turn red. The cruel and wicked Ravana has set a time period for me. But it is actually his time that is over. The nairittas perform wicked deeds and do not know what should not be done. Because of their adharma, a great catastrophe now presents itself. The rakshasas who eat flesh do not know about dharma. It is certain that the rakshasa is thinking of me as breakfast. What will I do without Rama? He is pleasant to behold. His eyes are red at the ends. Unable to see him, I am extremely miserable. If there is someone here who can give me some poison now, without my husband, I wish to quickly see the god Vaivasvata.[146] Rama, Lakshmana's elder brother, does not know that I am alive. Had they known this, they would have searched out my route above.[147] There is no doubt that on account of sorrow over me, Lakshmana's brave elder brother has gone to the world of the gods. He has given up his life on earth. The gods, the gandharvas, the siddhas and the supreme rishis are blessed. They are able to see Rama, my lotus-eyed protector. Perhaps the intelligent one is observing dharma and kama for their sake. I am the wife of the royal sage Rama. He is the *paramatman*.[148] There is affection towards someone who can be seen. There is no affection towards someone who cannot be seen.[149] But those who are ungrateful destroy affection and Rama will not destroy it. Do I not possess any qualities? Why am I suffering misfortune in this way? I am the beautiful Sita who deserves the best.

[146] Yama.

[147] Meaning, on earth and above it.

[148] The supreme soul.

[149] This shows some doubt about Rama no longer being affectionate towards her, because he cannot see her.

But I am without Rama. Without the great-souled one, it is better to be dead than alive. Rama is unblemished in his character. He is brave and is the destroyer of enemies. Or perhaps the two brothers, best among men, are roaming around, having taken to the forest. They may have cast aside their weapons and are surviving on roots and fruits in the forest. Perhaps the evil-souled Ravana, Indra among rakshasas, has deceitfully killed the two brave brothers, Rama and Lakshmana. I have come to a point in time where, in every possible way, I desire to die. But even when I face this hardship, death has not been ordained for me. The great-souled sages who revere truth are indeed blessed. Those immensely fortunate ones have conquered their souls. Therefore, they have no likes or dislikes. Misery results from likes. Affection leads to greater fear. Those great-souled ones have separated themselves from either. I bow down before them. I have been abandoned by my beloved Rama, who knows about his soul. Having come under the subjugation of the wicked Ravana, I will cast aside my life.'

Chapter 5(25)

When Sita said this, the terrible rakshasis became senseless with rage. Some of them went to the spirited Ravana to tell him about this. The rakshasis, terrible to behold, approached Sita. They again addressed her in harsh words, the purport of which was a single objective. 'O ignoble one! O Sita! O one who has made up his mind to be wicked! The rakshasis will happily devour your flesh now.' Sita was thus censured by those ignoble ones.

An aged rakshasi named Trijata was lying down. On seeing this, she spoke these words. 'O ignoble ones! Eat your own selves. Do not devour Sita. This is Janaka's beloved daughter. She is Dasharatha's daughter-in-law. Today, I have seen a terrible dream that makes the body hair stand up. This is about her husband's existence and the destruction of the rakshasas.' When Trijata said this, the rakshasis became senseless with rage. All of them were terrified and addressed

Trijata in these words. 'What kind of night was it and what dream
have you seen? Tell us.'

Hearing the words that emerged from the mouths of the
rakshasis, at that time, Trijata addressed them in words that
described what she had seen in the dream. 'There was a divine
palanquin made out of ivory and it was in the sky. It was yoked
to one thousand horses and Raghava was himself in it. In my
sleep, I saw Sita, attired in white garments. I can see her now, on
Mount Shveta, surrounded by the ocean. Sita joined Rama, like
the radiance attached to the sun.[150] I also saw Raghava astride a
gigantic elephant with four tusks. It was as large as a mountain
and with Lakshmana, he[151] wandered around on it. Those two
tigers among men blazed in their own energy. Wearing white
garlands and garments, they presented themselves before Janakee.
Janakee was on the summit of the mountain. Her husband grasped
her and placed her on the shoulder of the tusker in the sky. After
this, the lotus-eyed one arose from her husband's lap. I saw that
she used her hands to wipe the moon and the sun. Thereafter,
those two princes were on that excellent elephant. With the large-
eyed Sita, they stationed themselves above Lanka. Kakutstha came
here himself, with his wife, Sita. He was on a chariot that was
yoked to eight white bulls. Wearing white garments, Lakshmana
approached. He was with his brother, Lakshmana, and his wife,
Sita. From the Pushpaka vimana, Ravana fell down on the ground.
He was seen to be dragged along by a woman, with his head
shaven and attired in black garments. He was on a chariot that
was yoked to donkeys. His garlands and unguents were red. He
headed in the southern direction and entered a lake full of mud. A
woman dressed in red garments tied Dashagriva by the throat. She
was dark and her limbs were covered with mud. She dragged him
in the southern direction. Dashagriva rode a wild boar, Indrajit
rode a porpoise and Kumbhakarna rode a camel. They left for
the southern direction. I saw an assembly hall that was filled with

[150] Sita joined Rama on the palanquin.
[151] Rama.

the sounds of singing and the playing of musical instruments. Rakshasas attired in red garlands and red garments were drinking there. The beautiful city of Lanka, filled with horses, chariots and elephants, was seen to be plunged in the ocean, with its arches and gates shattered. In Lanka, all the rakshasa women were smeared with ashes. They were drinking oil and dancing, laughing in loud voices. All the bulls among rakshasas, Kumbhakarna and the others, grasped a red garment and entered a lake filled with cowdung. Go away.[152] You will be destroyed. Raghava will obtain Sita. With the rakshasas, he will kill you in his great rage. His beloved and extremely revered wife followed him on his exile to the forest. Raghava will not condone the act of her being terrified and censured. Therefore, enough of these cruel words. One must resort to reassurances. The idea of requesting Vaidehi appeals to me. In the midst of miseries, if a woman sees this kind of a dream, she will be freed from all her varied miseries and obtain supreme pleasure. O rakshasis! Why do you want to address her in words of censure? A terrible fear for the rakshasas has presented itself from Raghava. Bow down and please Maithilee, Janaka's daughter. She will certainly save the rakshasis from this great fear. The signs on this large-eyed one's limbs are such that nothing contrary, however subtle, can be seen. There is only the shadow of a bad quality, arising out of dread and misery.[153] She does not deserve unhappiness. This is the queen who presented herself in the sky. I can see that the prospect of Vaidehi accomplishing her objective has presented itself. Raghava will be victorious and the Indra among the rakshasas will be destroyed. I can see that her eyes, which are as large as lotus petals, are throbbing. There is a reason for this and hear from me about this great joy. Suddenly, one of Vaidehi's arms is trembling. The left arm of this accomplished one has become a trifle erect. Her excellent left thigh is like an elephant's trunk. It is trembling, indicating that Raghava will stand before her. A bird is entering its nest on a branch and

---

[152] This is Trijata speaking, after recounting the dream.
[153] The only discernible bad quality is the grief.

repeatedly uttering words of comfort, that happiness will arrive. It is calling repeatedly, as if cheerfully urging her.'

Chapter 5(26)

Sita heard the unpleasant words spoken by Ravana, Indra among the rakshasas. Afflicted by these disagreeable tidings, she was terrified, like the daughter of a king of elephants attacked by a lion along the extremities of a forest. The timid one was amidst the rakshasis and was severely censured by Ravana's words. Sita was like a young girl released in the middle of a desolate forest and lamented. 'In this world, the learned do speak the truth. Death does not come before the appointed time. With my merits exhausted, I am being threatened here and am able to sustain life for more than an instant. I am joyless and am filled with many kinds of misery. Since it has not been shattered into one thousand fragments, like the summit of a mountain struck by a bolt of thunder, my heart must indeed be extremely hard. However, not the slightest bit of sin can be attributed to me. The one who is disagreeable to behold[154] can kill me. I am not inclined to give myself to him, any more than a brahmana can give a mantra to someone who is not a brahmana. Before long, the ignoble Indra among the rakshasas will certainly use sharp weapons to sever my limbs, like a scalpel is used to slice a foetus, unless the lord of the worlds[155] comes here. For a miserable person like me, these two months of misery will seem to be like a long time. I will be like a thief who has committed a crime against the king, and at the end of the night, has been bound up before being killed. Alas, Rama! Alas, Lakshmana! Alas, Sumitra! Alas, Rama's mother and my mother! I am limited in fortune and face this calamity, like a boat in the great ocean, tossed around in a strong storm. Those two spirited sons of the king sought to capture

[154] Ravana.
[155] Rama.

the creature that was in the form of a deer. They will certainly be killed because of me, like two bulls among lions struck by a bolt of lightning. I am limited in fortune and it is certain that Destiny tempted me then, in the form of a deer. Thus, the son of a noble one abandoned a stupid person like me and Rama's younger brother abandoned Lakshmana's elder brother. Alas, Rama! O one who is truthful in his vows and long-armed! O one whose face is like the full moon! Alas! O one who loves to bring benefit to the world of the living! Alas! You do not know that I will be killed by the rakshasas. I have had no divinity other than you. My forgiveness, sleeping on the ground, control, dharma and vows towards my husband have proved to be futile, like an act done for men who are ungrateful. The dharma that I followed has been unsuccessful. The devotion towards a single husband is futile. Lean and pale, I am unable to see you. I am without you and have no hope of meeting you. You obeyed the rule of following your father's command. Having followed this vow, you will return from the forest. You will be without fear and will have accomplished your objective. I think that you will find pleasure with large-eyed women. O Rama! There is desire in me for you. I am tied to my affection for you. However, before long, I will be destroyed. My austerities and vows have been futile and I abandon them. I am limited in fortune. Shame on this life. Someone like me must quickly give up life, through poison or sharp weapons. But in this house of the rakshasa, there is no one here who will give me poison or a weapon.' Tormented by thought, she thought a lot. She seized her braid of hair and thought, 'I will hang myself with this braid and quickly go to Yama's abode.' In this way, Sita lamented a lot. She remembered Rama in all her soul. She trembled, with her mouth dry, and approached that excellent tree which was full of flowers. Delicate in all her limbs, she approached it and seized a branch of that tree. The one with the auspicious limbs thought of Rama, Rama's younger brother and her own lineage. Many kinds of portents presented themselves before her—many that did not indicate sorrow, indicating that perseverance ensures victory in this world. Those are portents that had earlier been seen, as signifying success.

Chapter 5(27)

The unblemished one was there, distressed. Her hair was beautiful. Her joy had vanished and her mind was suffering. But auspicious omens presented themselves before the auspicious one, like dependents cluster around a man who is prosperous. Her auspicious left eye had long eyelashes. It was bright, large and dark, set in a white disc. That single eye started to throb, like a red lotus when it is struck by a fish. Her beautiful left arm was round and thick. It deserved to be smeared with excellent aloe and sandalwood paste. For a long time, her beloved had used it as an excellent pillow. That started to quickly quiver. She had been born with two excellent thighs. They were close together and plump, like the trunk of an Indra among elephants. The left one started to tremble, as if indicating that Rama was standing in front of her. Her excellent complexion was like that of gold, but was slightly soiled because of dust. Her eyes sparkled. Her limbs were excellent and the tips of her teeth were sharp. Her garment was slightly dislodged.[156] Her eyebrows were excellent. These and other signs seemed to speak and tell her that her objective would be successful, just as a seed is devastated and destroyed by the wind and the sun, but is rejuvenated with delight when it rains. Her lips were like the bimba fruit. Her eyes, eyebrows and the tips of her hair were excellent. Her eyelashes were curved. Beautiful white teeth could be seen inside her mouth. She was like the moon, freed from Rahu's mouth. Her sorrow was dispelled. Her exhaustion vanished. Her fever was quietened. She was like a creature who wakes up in delight. The noble one's fair face was radiant. It was as if the one with the cool beams has arisen in the night.

Chapter 5(28)

The brave Hanumat heard the truth about everything—Sita, Trijata and the censure of the rakshasis. He looked at the

---

[156] Another good omen.

queen, who was like a god in Nandana. After this, the ape had many different kinds of thought. 'Many thousands and tens of thousands of apes have searched for her route in all the directions and I have found her. I am a well-appointed spy who is capable of remaining unnoticed by the enemy. I have wandered around in secret and have not been detected by them. In particular, I have examined this city of the rakshasas and the power of Ravana, the lord of the rakshasas. I should comfort the wife of the one who is immeasurable and is compassionate towards all beings. She desires to see her husband. I will comfort the one whose face is like the full moon. She confronts a hardship that she has not faced earlier and sees no signs of it coming to an end. The senses of this queen are overcome by grief. If I return without reassuring her, a taint will be attached to that act of departure. If I leave, this illustrious princess will be unaware about her salvation. Janakee will give up her life. The mighty-armed one's face is like the full moon and he is eager to see Sita. He deserves to be comforted by me. However, in the presence of the ones who roam around in the night, I am incapable of speaking to her. Indeed, how should I set about my task? That is the reason I face a difficulty. If I do not comfort her during whatever is left of the night, there is no doubt that, in every way, she will give up her life. If I do not speak to this slender-waisted one, when Rama asks me what words did Sita utter about him, what will I say in reply? If I quickly leave this place, without Sita's message, with his angry and fierce eyes, Kakutstha will burn me down. For Rama's sake, even if I urge my master[157] to come here, his arrival with his soldiers will be unsuccessful. I will remain among the rakshasis who are here and watch out for an opportunity. She is in a great deal of torment and I will slowly comfort her. I am extremely small in stature. In particular, I am an ape. I can speak the language of humans, such as Sanskrit.[158] But if I speak the language of humans, such as Sanskrit, Sita will think that I am Ravana and will be frightened. I must certainly speak in the language of humans, in words that are

[157] Sugriva.

[158] The word used is *samskrita*, which means cultured and polished. Instead of Sanskrit as we know it today, this may simply mean the polished language of humans.

full of meaning. Without that, this unblemished one is incapable
of being comforted by me. Because of the rakshasas, she is already
scared. If she sees my form and I speak to Janakee, she will again
be overcome by terror. When that fear is engendered, this spirited
one will make a sound. The large-eyed one knows that Ravana can
assume any form at will. When Sita suddenly makes a sound, the
large number of rakshasis, who are like the Destroyer, will wield
many kinds of terrible weapons and assemble. The ones with the
disfigured faces will then surround me from all sides. They will use
their strength to try and kill me and capture me. They will see me
run around on the branches, the trunks and twigs of these excellent
trees. Consequently, they will be filled with fear and suspicion.
They will see my giant form wandering around in the grove. The
rakshasis with the disfigured faces will be filled with dread and
fear. The rakshasis will summon the rakshasas whom the Indra
among rakshasas has appointed in the residence of the Indra among
rakshasas. Causing anxiety, they will descend here with force to
crush me, wielding many weapons like spears, arrows and swords
in their hands. They will angrily surround me. Even if I destroy that
army of rakshasas, I will not be able to reach the other shore of the
great ocean. Many swift-acting ones will envelop me and capture
me. This one[159] will not know whether I have been captured or have
not been captured. Wishing to harm, these violent ones may cause
injury to Janaka's daughter. Rama and Sugriva's task will face a
danger. She is surrounded by rakshasas and signs of her trail have
vanished. Janakee resides here, surrounded and protected by the
ocean. If I am killed or captured by the rakshasas in the encounter,
I do not see anyone else who can help in accomplishing Rama's
task. When I am killed, even when I think about it, I do not see any
other ape who can leap one hundred yojanas across this large and
extensive ocean. If I so wish, I am capable of killing thousands of
rakshasas. But then, I will not be able to reach the other shore of
the great ocean. The outcome of a battle is uncertain and in doubt.
The idea does not appeal to me. Which wise person will embark on

[159] Sita.

an uncertain act, when he is himself unsure? There is a great sin in my speaking to Sita. However, if I do not speak to her, Vaidehi will give up her life. Accomplished objectives are lost if one acts against the time and the place, like darkness is dispelled at the rising of the sun, especially if the messenger is confused. Even if the intelligence has distinguished what must be done from what must not be done, if the messenger prides himself on being learned, the task may be destroyed and is not successful. How can the task not be destroyed? How can I avoid confusion? How can my leaping across the ocean not be rendered unsuccessful? How can she hear my words and not be agitated?' Intelligent among intelligent ones, Hanumat thought in this way. 'Rama is unblemished in his deeds and is my friend. If I think about him in my mind and recount those exploits, there will be no agitation. Rama is supreme among the Ikshvaku lineage and knows about his soul. I will offer words about him, auspicious words that are in conformity with dharma. I will make her hear all those sweet words that I speak. I will make everything intelligible, so that she trusts me.' Hidden among the branches of the tree and glancing towards the lady, the greatly fortunate one spoke many sweet words about the lord of the world.

Chapter 5(29)

The great ape reflected thus, in many kinds of ways. He spoke sweet words and made Vaidehi hear those. 'There was a king named Dasharatha and he possessed chariots, elephants and horses. He was auspicious in conduct and performed great deeds. He was upright and immensely illustrious. He was born in a lineage of emperors and was like Purandara in his strength. He was devoted to non-violence. He was not inferior. He was compassionate and truth was his valour. He was foremost among those of the Ikshvaku lineage. He was prosperous and extended his prosperity. He possessed all the qualities of a king. He was extensive in prosperity and was a bull among kings. He was famous in the four corners of earth. He was happy and conferred happiness. He loved his eldest son, whose face was like the lord of the stars. His name was Rama and he was especially best among all archers. He protected his own conduct and protected his people. He protected the world of the living. Dharma represented supreme austerities for him. The brave one did not waver from the truth. Following his aged father's command, with his wife and his brother, he went on an exile to the forest. In the great forest there, while on hunts, he killed Khara and Dushana. On hearing that they had been slain in Janasthana, Ravana was angry and abducted Janakee. I have heard about her from Raghava and have found her, with the beauty, complexion and prosperous signs that were described.' After saying this, the bull among apes stopped for a while. Hearing this, Janakee was filled with great wonder. Her excellent hair curved at the tips. The timid one's face was covered with her hair. But she raised it and looked at the shimshapa tree. Not knowing what to think, she looked diagonally, up and down. She then saw the adviser of the lord of the apes. The son of the wind god resembled the rising sun.

Chapter 5(30)

Her mind awhirl, she saw the ape, humble and pleasant in speech, hidden inside the branches. Seeing the best among apes present himself humbly, the beautiful Maithilee thought that this was a dream. Seeing him, she was struck severely and lost her senses, as if she had lost her life. In a short while, the large-eyed one regained her senses and started to think. 'Today, I have seen a malformed ape in my dream and this is prohibited by the sacred texts. I hope that Rama, Lakshmana and my father, King Janaka, are well. This is not a dream. Afflicted by sorrow and grief, there is no sleep for me. Since I am without the one whose face is like the full moon, there is no happiness for me. In all my sentiments, I am tormented by his thoughts. I have felt my desire for him today. Since I am always thinking about him and seeing him, I must have heard this. Perhaps I have been thinking about my wishes and debating them with my intelligence. What is the reason why he possesses this kind of form? The form is clearly manifest and it is speaking to me. I bow down before the lord of speech, the wielder of the vajra, Svayambhu and the fire god. This resident of the forest is in front of me. Let what he has spoken come true and let there be no violation of this.'

Chapter 5(31)

The immensely energetic Hanumat, the son of the wind god, joined his hands in salutation, holding them above his head. He addressed Sita in sweet words. 'Your eyes are like lotus petals. You are attired in a silken garment that is faded. Who are you? O unblemished one! You are standing, holding on to a branch of the tree for support. Why are tears of sorrow flowing from your eyes? This looks like water that is spreading along the petals of two lotus flowers. O beautiful one! Who are you? Have you been born among the gods, the asuras, the serpents, the gandharvas, the rakshasas, the yakshas or the kinnaras? O one with the beautiful face. Who are you? Have you been born among the Rudras, the Maruts, or the Vasus? O beautiful one! To me, you seem to be a divinity. Are you Rohini, best among stellar bodies and best among those who possess all the qualities? Abandoned by the moon, have you fallen down from the abode of the gods? O dark-eyed one! Are you the fortunate Arundhati and have you angered your husband, Vasishtha, through some confusion?[160] O extremely slender-waisted one! Are you grieving because your son, father, brother or husband has left this world and gone to that world?[161] Marks can be discerned on your body and it is my view that you must be the queen of a king or a princess. If it pleases you, tell me what I am

---

[160] Thus leading to a curse.
[161] The world hereafter.

asking. Are you the Sita who has been forcibly abducted by Ravana from Janasthana?'

Vaidehi spoke these words to Hanumat, who was still in his refuge on the tree. 'I am the daughter of the great-souled Janaka of Videha. My name is Sita and I am the intelligent Rama's wife. I spent twelve years in Raghava's residence, a place that can satisfy all the objects of desire. I enjoyed all human objects of pleasure. In the thirteenth year, the king and his preceptor prepared to instate the descendant of the Ikshvaku lineage in the kingdom. When arrangements were being made for Raghava's consecration, the queen named Kaikeyee spoke these words to her husband. "From today, I will not consume the daily drink and eat the daily food. If Rama is consecrated, that will be an end to my life. O supreme among kings! You had gladly given me your word earlier. If that is not going to be rendered false, let Raghava go to the forest." The king was truthful in speech. Hearing Kaikeyee's cruel and disagreeable words, he was confused. He remembered the boon he had granted to the queen. The aged king was established in the dharma of truth. Weeping, he sought the kingdom from his illustrious eldest son. In his mind, the handsome one thought that his father's words were dearer than the consecration. He accepted those words. He does not receive without giving. He never speaks anything disagreeable. Rama has truth as his valour and he does these even at the expense of his life. The immensely illustrious one cast aside his immensely expensive upper garment. He mentally gave up the kingdom and entrusted me with his mother. Without him, the thought of residing in heaven does not appeal to me. I was quickly ready to leave for the forest, ahead of him. The immensely fortunate Soumitri, the delight of his friends, was ahead of us. Adorning himself in the bark of trees, he followed his elder brother. We were firm in our vows and showed a great deal of respect to the command of our lord.[162] We had not seen the forest, severe to behold, earlier. But we entered it. The infinitely energetic one resided in Dandakaranya and I, his wife, was abducted by the rakshasa, the evil-souled Ravana. He has

[162] Dasharatha.

shown me the favour of letting me live for two months. When that period of two months is exceeded, I will give up my life.'

Chapter 5(32)

Hearing her words, Hanumat, the leader of the apes, transited from one kind of sorrow to another kind of sorrow. Comforting her, he replied, 'O queen! I am Rama's messenger and have come to you with his message. O Vaidehi! Rama is well and has asked about your welfare. He knows about the *brahmastra* weapon.[163] He is supreme among those who know the learning of the Vedas. O queen! He is Rama, Dasharatha's son, and he has asked about your welfare. The immensely energetic Lakshmana is loved by him and follows his master. He is tormented by grief and greets you, with his head bowed down.'

The queen heard about the welfare of those two lions among men. Delight and joy pervaded through all her limbs and she told Hanumat, 'This is a fortunate account and seems to me like a common aphorism. "Even if it is one hundred years, as long as a man is alive, joy comes to him."' Meeting each other, they were greatly affectionate towards each other. They confidently started to converse with each other. Sita was miserable with grief. Hearing her words, Hanumat, the leader of the apes, attempted to approach her. But as soon as Hanumat sought to inch closer to her, Sita suspected that he might be Ravana. 'Alas! Shame. Shame on what I have done. Why have I told him this? Having assumed a different form, it is Ravana who has come to me.' Afflicted by grief, she let go of the branch of the ashoka tree. The one with the unblemished limbs sat down on the ground. The mighty-armed one spoke to Janaka's daughter. However, scared and terrified, she did not look at him again.

Sita, with a face like the moon, saw that he was worshipping her. With a long sigh, she addressed the ape in a sweet tone. 'O

[163] Brahma's weapon.

one who uses maya! Even if you are Ravana himself and have immersed yourself in maya, you have again given rise to torment in me. This is not right. You are indeed the Ravana who abandoned his own form and assumed the form of a mendicant. I have seen that in Janasthana. O roamer in the night! O one who can assume any form at will! I am miserable and emaciated because of fasting. You are again giving rise to torment in me. This is not right. If you have indeed come here as Rama's messenger, may you be fortunate. O best among the apes! I love accounts about Rama and I am asking you about them. O ape! Tell me about Rama's qualities. I love them. O amiable one! Steel my mind, just as water erodes the bank of a river. I was abducted a long time ago. O resident of the forest! Sleeping happily, I am seeing this dream where Raghava has sent someone. Even if I see the brave Raghava and Lakshmana in a dream now, I will not suffer. But even the dream is censuring me. I do not think that I have seen this ape in my dream, because prosperity is incapable of arising from that.[164] I am now in the midst of prosperity. How have my senses been confused in this way? Is this because of the movement of the wind?[165] Has this perverse condition arisen from madness? Is this a mirage? Perhaps I am mad and confused and this is a sign of madness. I must ascertain the nature of my own self and about this resident of the forest.' Thus, in many kinds of ways, Sita debated the pros and the cons. Since rakshasas can assume any form at will, she then thought that this must be the lord of the rakshasas. Having decided this, the slender-waisted Sita, Janaka's daughter, did not reply to the ape.

Hanumat, the son of the wind god, understood what Sita was thinking. He spoke words that were pleasant to the ear and delighted her. 'He is as energetic as the sun. Like the moon, he is loved by the world. Like the god Vaishravana, he is the king of all the worlds. He is full of valour, like the immensely illustrious Vishnu. He is

---

[164] A dream.

[165] In Ayurveda, wind (*vata*), bile (*pitta*) and phlegm (*kapha*) are the three *dosha*s or humours in the body and they are always striving against each other. This is a reference to vata.

truthful and pleasant in speech, like the god Vachaspati.[166] He is
handsome, extremely fortunate and beautiful, like the embodied
form of Kandarpa. He is angry and strikes at the right place. He
is the best maharatha in the world. The world rests on the arms
of the great-souled one. The form of a deer drew Raghava away
from the hermitage and you were abducted from that deserted spot.
You will witness the consequences of that. Before a long period of
time, the valiant one will slay Ravana in a battle. He will angrily
release arrows that blaze like the fire. I am a messenger sent by him
and I have come here before you. Because he has been separated
from you, he is afflicted by grief and has asked about your welfare.
The immensely energetic Lakshmana is one who extends Sumitra's
delight. The mighty-armed one has greeted you and has asked about
your welfare. O queen! The ape named Sugriva is Rama's friend. He
is the king of the foremost among the apes and he has asked about
your welfare. Rama, Sugriva and Lakshmana always remember
you. O Vaidehi! Despite being under the control of the rakshasis,
it is good fortune that you are still alive. You will soon see Rama,
maharatha Lakshmana and the infinitely energetic Sugriva, amidst
crores of apes. I am Sugriva's adviser and I am an ape named
Hanumat. Leaping across the great ocean, I entered the city to come
here to see you. O queen! I am not the one you take me to be.[167]
Abandon your suspicion. Trust my words.'

Chapter 5(33)

Vaidehi heard that account of Rama from the bull among the
apes. She replied in words that were gentle and sweet. 'How
did you come into contact with Rama? How did you get to know
Lakshmana? How did this meeting between apes and men take
place? O ape! What are the signs on Rama and Lakshmana? If you

[166] The lord of speech, Brihaspati.
[167] That is, Ravana.

again tell me these, I will not be immersed in sorrow. Where was he? What is Rama's form like? How were his thighs? How were his arms? Tell me about Lakshmana.'

Hanumat, the son of the wind god, was addressed by Vaidehi in this way. At this, he started to recount the truth about Rama. 'O Vaidehi! O lotus-eyed one! You know this. But it is good fortune that you are asking me about your husband's appearance and that of Lakshmana. O large-eyed one! I will tell you about the marks and signs Rama and Lakshmana possess. Listen. Rama's eyes are like the petals of a lotus. All creatures find him to be pleasant. O Janaka's daughter! He was born with beauty and accomplishments. He is like the sun in energy, like the earth in forgiveness, like Brihaspati in his intelligence and like Vasava in his fame. He protects the world of the living. He protects his own people. The scorcher of enemies protects his own conduct and dharma. O beautiful one! In the world, Rama is the protector of the four varnas. He is the one who ensures that ordinances are observed in this world. He is radiant. He is worshipped. He is exceedingly devoted to the vow of brahmacharya. He does good deeds for the virtuous. He knows how to implement tasks. He knows about royal skills. He is humble. He is revered by the brahmanas. He is learned and possesses good conduct. The scorcher of enemies is modest. He knows about the Yajur Veda. He is humble. He knows the rites of the Vedas. He is greatly worshipped. He is knowledgeable about *dhanurveda*, the Vedas and the Vedangas. The mighty-armed one possesses broad shoulders. His neck is like a conch shell and his face is auspicious. His collarbone is hidden. His eyes are coppery red. O queen! Rama is famous among people. His voice is like the sound of a kettledrum. The powerful one's complexion is soothing. His limbs are symmetric and well proportioned. His complexion is dark. He is firm in three places.[168] He is long in three places.[169] He is even in three places.[170] He is tall in three places.[171] He has three

[168] Breast, wrist and feet.
[169] Eyebrows, arms and soles.
[170] Hair, testicles and knees.
[171] Breast, navel and lower abdomen.

lines.[172] There are three spots that are depressed.[173] There are four parts that aren't too long.[174] There are three twirls in his hair. He has four lines.[175] He has four lines.[176] He is four cubits tall.[177] He is symmetric in four parts.[178] There are fourteen parts that are symmetric.[179] He possesses four teeth.[180] He possesses four kinds of gait.[181] His lips, cheekbones and nose are large. He is smooth in five parts.[182] He has excellent joints in eight places.[183] He has ten lotuses.[184] Ten parts are large.[185] He is extensive in three ways.[186] He is pure in two ways.[187] Six parts of the body are high. He is fine in nine places.[188] Raghava obtains three things.[189] He is devoted to the dharma of truth. He is prosperous. He accumulates and dispenses favours. He knows about the time and the place. He speaks pleasantly to everyone. His stepbrother, Soumitri, cannot be defeated. He is like him in affection, form and qualities. Those two roamed around the earth, searching for your trail. They saw the lord of the animals,[190] who had been dislodged by his elder

[172] On the belly and in the neck.

[173] The middle of the soles, the lines on the soles and the nipples.

[174] The neck, the penis, the back and the shanks.

[175] At the root of the thumb, indicating knowledge of the four Vedas.

[176] On the forehead, indicating longevity.

[177] The word used is *kishku*. Kishku is the length of a forearm, that is, one cubit. If a cubit is taken as 18 inches, this gives a height of 72 inches, or 6 feet.

[178] Cheeks, arms, shanks and knees.

[179] Eyebrows, nostrils, eyes, ears, lips, nipples, elbows, wrists, knees, testicles, loins, hands, feet, thighs.

[180] This is not to be taken literally. All it means is that the four teeth, at the ends of the upper and lower jaws, were large.

[181] Lion, tiger, elephant and bull.

[182] Hair, eyes, teeth, skin and soles.

[183] Arms, fingers, toes, eyes, ears, thighs, calves and knees.

[184] Ten parts of the body that are like lotuses—face, mouth, eyes, tongue, lips, palate, breasts, nails, hands and feet.

[185] Chest, head, forehead, neck, arms, heart, mouth, feet, back and ears.

[186] Radiance, fame and deeds.

[187] The father's side and the mother's side.

[188] Hair, moustache, beard, nails, body hair, skin, joints in the fingers, penis and perception.

[189] Dharma, artha and kama.

[190] Meaning Sugriva.

brother. He was on the slope of Rishyamuka, in a region that was full of many trees. Sugriva, pleasant to behold, was seated there, terrified of his brother. We are the ones who serve Sugriva, the king of the apes who is devoted to the truth. His elder brother had dislodged him from the kingdom. Those two, supreme among those who wield bows and attired in bark, came to the beautiful region in Mount Rishyamuka. The bull among apes saw the two tigers among men, wielding bows. His fear confused him and he leapt down from the summit of the mountain. Stationed on the summit, the Indra among the apes soon sent me to those two. Because of the command of the lord Sugriva, I went to those two tigers among men, who possess beauty and the signs. I joined my hands in salutation and stood there. Ascertaining the nature of the truth, those two were delighted with me. Taking those two tigers among men on my back, I went to that spot.[191] I told the great-souled Sugriva the truth. They spoke to each other and a great affection resulted. Those two lords among men, accomplished in their deeds, and the lord of the apes comforted each other and recounted what had happened earlier. At this, Lakshmana's elder brother assured Sugriva, who had been restrained by his brother, Vali, fierce in his energy, because of a woman. Lakshmana told Sugriva, the Indra among the apes, about the sorrow that Rama, the performer of unblemished deeds, was suffering from, because of your disappearance. Hearing the words that Lakshmana had spoken, the Indra among the apes sat down. He lost his radiance, like the sun when it has been grasped by a planet.[192] There were ornaments that had adorned your body. When you were being abducted by the rakshasa, the mass of ornaments had fallen down on the ground. The leaders of the apes brought all those to Rama. Cheerfully, they showed him these. But they had no idea about your route. I gave Rama the jingling ornaments that I had collected and he lost his consciousness. He was like a god. He displayed those ornaments on his lap and lamented like a god. He looked at

---

[191] Where Sugriva was.
[192] An eclipse, the planet being Rahu.

them and wept repeatedly. They ignited a fire of grief in Dasharatha's son. Afflicted by grief, the great-souled one lay down for a long time. Using many kinds of words, with a great deal of difficulty, I made him get up again. With Soumitri, Raghava repeatedly looked at those extremely expensive ornaments and then showed them to Sugriva. O noble one! Because he could not see you, Raghava was tormented. He was incessantly consumed by a fire, like the fire that rages inside a mountain.[193] Because of you, Raghava suffered from lack of sleep, grief and worries. They tormented the great-souled one, like a fire to a house in flames. Because of the sorrow at not being able to see you, Raghava trembled. It was like a large pile of boulders trembling because of a huge earthquake. O daughter of a king! Though he roamed around in extremely beautiful groves, rivers and waterfalls, because he could not see you, he found no pleasure in these. O Janaka's daughter! Raghava, tiger among men, will soon kill Ravana, with his friends and relatives, and get you back. Rama and Sugriva contracted an agreement with each other, about the slaying of Vali and about searching you out. The spirited Rama killed Vali in an encounter. In an assembly of all the bears and the apes, he made Sugriva their lord. O queen! The unity between Rama and Sugriva was generated in this way. Know me as Hanumat and I have come here as their messenger. When he got his kingdom back, Sugriva summoned the great apes. For your sake, he despatched those extremely strong ones in the ten directions. They were commanded by Sugriva, the extremely energetic Indra among the apes. Resembling the king of the mountains, they left towards different parts of the earth. The prosperous and extremely strong Angada is Vali's son. Surrounded by one-third of the forces, this tiger among apes left. We lost our way in Vindhya, supreme among mountains. We were overcome by great grief and many days and nights passed. The designated time passed and we lost all hope of accomplishing our task. Terrified of the king of the apes, we were ready to give up our lives. O queen! We searched forests, impenetrable areas in the mountains and mountainous waterfalls.

[193] A volcano.

But we could not find you and were ready to give up our lives. O
Vaidehi! We were immersed in a severe ocean of grief and lamented
with Angada about your loss, Vali's death, our engaging in praya
and Jatayu's death. We had not been able to follow the command
of our master. We had lost hope and were about to die. As if to
accomplish the task, a large and valiant bird arrived there. This
was the brother of the king of the eagles.[194] His name was Sampati
and he was a king of the eagles. Hearing about his brother's death,
he angrily spoke these words. "Why has my younger brother been
killed? Who has destroyed him? O supreme among the apes! I wish
to hear this from you." Angada told him the exact truth about the
great destruction in Janasthana, wrought by the rakshasa who was
terrible in form. Hearing about Jatayu's death, Aruna's son was
saddened. O beautiful one! He informed us about your residing in
Ravana's abode. We heard Sampati's words, which enhanced our
delight. With Angada at the forefront, all of us left that spot. The
bulls among the apes were content and happy. They were anxious
to see you. When the army of the apes saw the ocean, they were
depressed. However, I dispelled their terrible fear and leapt across
the one hundred yojanas. I entered Lanka, filled with rakshasas, in
the night. I saw Ravana, and you suffering from grief. O
unblemished one! I have told you everything, just as it occurred. O
queen! I am the messenger of Dasharatha's son. Speak to me. Rama
made the effort because of you and I have come here because of
you. O queen! Know me to be the son of the wind god, Sugriva's
adviser. Kakutstha, supreme among those who wield all kinds of
weapons, is well. Lakshmana, who possesses all the excellent signs,
is engaged in serving his senior. O queen! I am engaged in ensuring
the welfare of your valiant husband. Following Sugriva's words, I
am the only one who has come here. I have come without any help.
I can roam around, assuming any form at will. Desiring to search
out your trail, I have crossed over the southern direction. I will
dispel the grief of the army of the apes. I will remove their torment.
I will tell them that, through good fortune, I have been able to meet

[194] Jatayu.

you. O queen! It is through good fortune that my leaping across the ocean has not been futile. It is through good fortune that I have come here. Catching sight of you will bring me fame. The immensely valorous Raghava will soon kill Ravana, the lord of the rakshasas, with his friends and relatives, and get you back. O Vaidehi! There is an excellent mountain named Kouraja.[195] From there, the ape Kesari went to Gokarna. My father, the great ape, was commanded by the gods and the rishis. At the sacred tirtha that was near the lord of the rivers, he killed Shambasadana.[196] O Maithilee! Hence, I was born in the ape's field, through the wind god. Because of my own deeds, I am famous in the worlds as Hanumat. O Vaidehi! So that you trust me, I have recounted your husband's qualities.'

Sita was afflicted because of her grief. However, because of the indications he had given, she trusted him and accepted him as a messenger. Janakee obtained great joy and delight. From her eyes, with those curved eyelashes, tears of joy started to flow. Her face was beautiful and her large eyes were coppery red and white. The large-eyed one became as radiant as the lord of the stars, when it is freed from Rahu. She thought it obvious that Hanumat was an ape and nothing else. After this, Hanumat spoke to the one who was beautiful to behold. 'Urged by the maharshis, the foremost among the apes killed the asura Shambasadana in a battle. O Maithilee! I have been born from Vayu and in my power, I am the equal of that ape.'[197]

Chapter 5(34)

To inspire confidence in Sita, the immensely energetic Hanumat, the son of the wind god, again spoke these words of assurance. 'O immensely fortunate one! I am an ape who is the intelligent

[195] Across different versions of the text, the name of this mountain varies widely. The Critical Edition uses Kouraja.

[196] The demon named Shambasadana and the tirtha named Gokarna were on the shores of the ocean. Kesari was thereafter granted the boon of a son.

[197] Kesari.

Rama's messenger. O queen! Look at this ring. It bears the mark of Rama's name. O fortunate one! Because of this, your grief should be diminished. Take it and look at it. It used to be an ornament on your husband's hand. O Janakee! I got it from your husband. You should be delighted.'

Her face was beautiful. Her large eyes were coppery red and white. She was filled with great joy, like the lord of the stars when freed from Rahu. The young one was delighted at news of her husband and also felt shy. Content at news about her beloved, she praised the great ape. 'O supreme ape. You are valiant. You are capable. You are wise. Single-handedly, you have penetrated this spot, full of rakshasas. The ocean extends for one hundred yojanas and is the abode of makaras. Using your praiseworthy valour, you have crossed it, as if it was a puddle.[198] O bull among the apes! I do not think that you are an ordinary ape. You have no fear and respect for Ravana. O best among the apes! If you have been sent by Rama, who knows about his soul, you are worthy of being addressed by me. The invincible Rama sent you without testing you, in particular, to me. He did not know about your valour. It is good fortune that the accomplished Rama has dharma in his soul and is devoted to dharma, just as the immensely energetic Lakshmana, the extender of Sumitra's delight, is. If Kakutstha is well, why is he not igniting his great rage, like the fire that arises at the end of a yuga, and burning up the girdle of the ocean? Those two are capable of restraining even the gods. But I think I must suffer this misery and calamity. Is Rama not distressed? Is he not tormented? Is Purushottama engaged in the task that must be undertaken next? Is he miserable and scared? Is the task confusing him? Is the son of the king engaged in the tasks that a man must undertake? Is he resorting to the two or three modes?[199] Has the scorcher of enemies won over well-wishers and friends? Has he obtained friends and have friends approached him? Does he have

---

[198] The text uses the word *goshpada*. This literally means the mark of a cow's foot in the soil and the small puddle of water that fills up such a mark, that is, a trifle.

[199] This refers to sama, dana, danda and bheda. Dana does not fit the context. Therefore, two modes probably refers to danda and bheda, while three modes refers to sama, danda and bheda.

good friends? Do the friends show him respect? Does the son of
the king hope for the favours of the gods? Will he obtain manliness
and good fortune? With me away, I hope Raghava has not lost his
affection for me. O ape! Will he free me from this hardship? He
always deserves happiness. He does not deserve unhappiness. Having
faced this great misery, I hope that Rama is not despondent. How
are Kousalya and Sumitra? Have you heard anything about whether
Bharata is well? Raghava deserves respect. Is he grieving because
of me? Is Rama distracted because of something else? Will he save
me? Bharata is devoted to his brother. For my sake, will he send a
terrible *akshouhini*,[200] protected by standards and ministers? For my
sake, will the handsome Sugriva, the lord of the apes, give him brave
apes who use teeth and nails as weapons? Will the brave Lakshmana
who knows about weapons, the extender of Sumitra's delight, use
his net of arrows to devastate the rakshasas? In a short while, will
I see Ravana and his well-wishers destroyed in a battle by Rama,
using his terrible weapons? His face has the complexion of gold. His
face is as fragrant as a lotus. Without me, has it dried up and become
sorrowful and miserable, like a lotus bereft of water and scorched by
the sun? He gave up his kingdom because of his devotion to dharma
and took me to the forest on foot. He was not distressed, nor scared.
He did not grieve. Does he still bear that kind of fortitude in his
heart? In his affection, he does not differentiate between his mother,
his father, or anyone else. I am as equal as anyone else. O messenger!
I wish to remain alive only as long as I am inclined to hear about my
beloved.' The queen spoke these words, full of deep meaning and full
of sweet meaning, to the Indra among the apes. The beautiful one
ceased, wishing to hear those beautiful words, full of Rama, again.

Hearing Sita's words, the son of the wind god, terrible in valour,
joined his hands in salutation above his head. He again spoke these
words in reply. 'O lotus-eyed one! Rama does not know that you are
here. Hearing my words, Raghava will swiftly arrive here. He will
bring a large army consisting of large numbers of apes and bears. He

---

[200] An akshouhini is an army consisting of 21,870 chariots, 21,870 elephants, 65,610
horse riders and 109,350 foot soldiers.

will stupefy and agitate Varuna's abode with his torrent of arrows. Kakutstha will pacify the rakshasas in the city of Lanka. If the goddess of death is stationed in his path, with gods and asuras, Rama will kill them too. Because he cannot see you, the noble one is overcome by sorrow. Like an elephant afflicted by a lion, Rama cannot find any peace. O queen! I swear to you on the mountains Dardara,[201] Malaya, Vindhya, Meru, Mandara and roots and fruits. You will see Rama's handsome face, with excellent eyes, lips like the bimba fruit and with beautiful earrings, like the full moon when it rises. O Vaidehi! You will soon see Rama seated on the top of Mount Prasravana, like Shatakratu in the vault of heaven. Raghava does not consume any flesh. He does not partake of any liquor. He does not eat the well-prepared forest fare every day, but only on every fifth day. His inner soul is completely immersed in you. Therefore, Raghava does not drive away the gnats, mosquitoes, insects and reptiles from his body. Rama is always thinking. Rama is always overcome by sorrow. He is overcome by desire for you and does not think of anyone else. In general, Rama does not sleep. Even if that excellent man sleeps, he speaks the sweet words, "This is Sita", and awakens. If he sees a fruit or a flower or anything else that pleases the mind of a woman, he sighs several times and addresses you, "Alas, beloved!" O queen! He is ever tormented. He addresses you, "O, Sita!" The great-souled son of the king is firm in his vows. He is making efforts to get you back.'

She was grieving just as much as Rama was grieving. On hearing this account of Rama, her sorrow was dispelled. Videha's daughter was like the moon on a night at the beginning of autumn, when the clouds have gone away.

Chapter 5(35)

Sita, with a face like the full moon, heard his words. She spoke these words, which were full of dharma and artha, to Hanumat.

---

[201] This mountain is also called Dardura.

'O ape! Rama's mind is not on anyone else and he is overcome by sorrow—the words uttered by you are like amrita mixed with poison. Death[202] seems to tie up a man with a noose and drag him towards prosperity or extremely pervasive and extremely terrible adversity. O supreme among apes! Indeed, living creatures cannot resist destiny. Look at Soumitri, Rama and me being confused by this adversity. How will Raghava reach the other shore of this ocean of grief? He is like an exhausted person swimming in the ocean when the boat has been destroyed. Having destroyed the rakshasas, slain Ravana and uprooted Lanka, when will my husband see me? He should be told to hurry, before this year is over. I will only remain alive till the end of this year. O ape! This is the tenth month of the year and two months remain. That is the time the cruel Ravana has earmarked for me. Even when his brother, Vibhishana, has entreated with him not to oppress me, his mind is not inclined to do so. The idea of returning me does not appeal to Ravana. Ravana has come under the subjugation of destiny and death stands in his path. O ape! Vibhishana's eldest daughter is a maiden named Anala. Her mother sent her to me and she is the one who herself told me about this. There is an intelligent bull among the rakshasas named Avindhya. He is patient, good in conduct, aged and extremely revered by Ravana. For the sake of being saved from Rama, he also told the rakshasa this. But the evil-souled one did not listen to his beneficial words.[203] O best among the apes! I hope that my husband will soon get me back. After all, my inner soul is pure and he possesses many qualities. O ape! Enterprise, manliness, spirit, non-violence, gratitude, valour and power exist in Raghava. Without his brother, he slew fourteen thousand rakshasas in Janasthana. Which enemy will not be terrified of him? Hardship is incapable of disturbing that bull among men. I know about him, just as Puloma's daughter[204] knows about Shakra. O ape! The brave Rama's net of arrows is like the rays of the sun. The rakshasa's enemies are like water and will be dried up, just as the water is dried

---

[202] In the sense of destiny.
[203] This bit about Anala and Avindhya doesn't quite belong.
[204] Shachi.

up.' Afflicted by grief, she conversed about Rama in this fashion. Her face was full of tears.

The ape Hanumat told her, 'Hearing my words, Raghava will swiftly arrive here. He will bring a large army with him, full of large numbers of apes and bears. O unblemished one! Alternatively, I can free you from the rakshasas right now and from the misery here. Climb on to my back. With you on my back, I will cross the ocean. I even bear the strength to carry Lanka, with Ravana. O Maithilee! I will establish you on Prasravana now, with Raghava, like oblations offered to Shakra through the fire. O Vaidehi! With Lakshmana, you will see Raghava today, while he is engaged in his task, like Vishnu for the death of the daityas. The immensely strong one is in his hermitage. On seeing you, he will be energized. He will be like Purandara seated on the head of the king of the elephants.[205] O queen! O beautiful one! Do not hesitate. Ascend my back. Like Rohini with the moon, wish to be united with Rama. Ascend my back and swim across the sky that is like the great ocean, conversing with the wonderfully rayed moon and the sun. O beautiful one! When I take you away from here, none of the residents of Lanka possesses the strength to follow in my path. There is no doubt that I will leave just as I came here, leaping through the sky. O Vaidehi! Behold my enterprise.'

Maithilee heard the extraordinary words spoken by the best among the apes. She was astonished and all her limbs were filled with delight. She told Hanumat, 'O Hanumat! How can you wish to carry me over such a long distance? O leader of the apes! I think this is nothing more than the nature of an ape. You possess a small body. O bull among the apes! Yet, you wish to take me away from here, to the presence of my husband, who is an Indra among men.'

Hearing Sita's words, Hanumat, the handsome son of the wind god, thought that this was a new kind of insult directed towards him. 'This dark-eyed one does not know about my spirit and my power. Therefore, let Vaidehi see that I can assume any form at will.' Hanumat, supreme among apes, thought this. The destroyer

[205] Airavata.

of enemies showed Vaidehi his own form. The intelligent bull among the apes leapt down from the tree. To instil confidence in Sita, he started to increase his size. He became as large as Mount Mandara and blazed like the lord who was the fire god. The bull among the apes stood in front of Sita. The extremely strong ape was like a mountain and his face was coppery red. His terrible teeth and nails were like the vajra. He told Vaidehi, 'I possess the strength to carry Lanka from here, with its mountains, forest regions, palaces, turrets, gates and its lord.[206] O queen! That being the case, remove all hesitation from your mind. O Vaidehi! Dispel all the grief in Raghava, together with Lakshmana.'

Seeing him, standing like a mountain, Janaka's daughter, with large eyes like lotus petals, replied to the son of the wind god, 'O great ape! I know about your spirit and your strength. Your extraordinary speed is like Vayu and your energy is like Agni. O bull among the apes! How can any ordinary person come to this place, reaching the other shore of the immeasurable ocean? I know that you possess the strength to go and carry me too. We must certainly turn our minds to the best means of quickly achieving success in the objective. O best among the apes! But it is not desirable that I should go with you. Your great speed is like Vayu's speed and that speed may confound me. I will be in the sky, progressively crossing over the ocean. As you proceed, because of fear and the force, I will fall down from your back. I will fall down in the ocean, full of whales, crocodiles and fish. I will be disabled by my fear and will quickly become excellent food for them. O destroyer of enemies! There is no doubt that it is not possible for me to go with you. I am doubtful because you will also have my burden to bear. The rakshasas, terrible in their valour, will see that I am being carried away. The evil-souled Ravana will command them to follow. Those brave ones will surround you, with spears and clubs in their hands. O brave one! Because of me being a burden, you will face a danger. You are without a weapon and many rakshasas with weapons will attack you from the sky. With me to protect, how will you possess

[206] Ravana.

the strength to engage with them? You will have to fight with the rakshasas, who are cruel in their deeds. O supreme among apes! Afflicted by fear, I will fall down from your back. The rakshasas are terrible and possess great strength. O excellent ape! How will you counter them? They may triumph over you. If you ignore me and fight, I may fall down. When I fall down, the wicked rakshasas will seize me and take me away. They may take me away from your hands and even kill me. In any battle, victory and defeat are seen to be uncertain. Censured by the rakshasas, I may face a calamity. O best among the apes! All your efforts will then be rendered futile. If you wish, you are sufficient to kill all the rakshasas. However, if you kill the rakshasas, Raghava's fame will be diminished. Alternatively, the rakshasas may seize and hide me in a place that the apes and Raghava do not know about. Then every effort that you have made on my account will be futile. That is the reason there is great merit in Rama coming here with you. O mighty-armed one! The great-souled Raghava, his brother, you and the lineage of your own king are dependent on my remaining alive. If those two[207] lose hope and are tormented by grief, all the bears and apes will give up their lives. O ape! O supreme among apes! Since my devotion to my husband is of utmost importance, I cannot touch another person's body and ascend your back. I do not wish to. I did have to touch Ravana's body, but that was because he used force against me. I was helpless and disabled, without a protector. What could I have done? It is appropriate that Rama kills Dashagriva, with the rakshasas, and takes me away from here. I have seen and heard about the great-souled one's valour. He can crush in battles. The gods, the gandharvas, the serpents, the rakshasas—no one is Rama's equal in a battle. The extremely strong one is like Vasava in valour. On witnessing the work of his wonderful bow, who will be able to stand before Raghava, with Lakshmana? He blazes like the fire, when that fire is fanned by the wind. With Lakshmana, Raghava is a destroyer in a battle. He is like a maddened dishagaja. Aided in a battle by the best among the apes, he will be like the sun

---

[207] Rama and Lakshmana.

at the end of a yuga, with his arrows like its rays. O best among the apes! Quickly bring my husband here, with Lakshmana and the other leaders. I have suffered from grieving about Rama for a long time. O foremost among the apes! Act so that you can give me delight.'

Chapter 5(36)

The tiger among apes was delighted at hearing these words from Sita. The one who was eloquent in the use of words replied, 'O queen! O one who is auspicious to behold! The words that you have spoken are worthy of you. This is in conformity with the nature of virtuous women who are humble. The large ocean extends for one hundred yojanas. It is not appropriate for a woman to ascend my back and cross it. O humble one! O Janakee! You have spoken about a second reason—no one other than Rama should touch you. O queen! This is worthy of the great-souled one's wife. O queen! Other than you, who else is capable of uttering such words? O queen! I will tell Kakutstha everything accurately, all that you have said in my presence. O queen! I said what I did because of many reasons. I wished to ensure pleasure to Rama. My mind was full of affection towards him. Lanka is difficult to penetrate and the great ocean is extremely difficult to cross. I possess the strength. That is the reason I mentioned it. I wish to take you right now, because of my friendship for Raghu. I am filled with affection and devotion for my senior. There was no other reason for my mentioning it. O unblemished one! If you are not interested in going with me, give me a sign that Raghava can recognize.' Hanumat spoke to her in this way.

Sita, who was like the daughter of a god, gently spoke the following words, with the syllables punctuated by tears. 'As the best sign, tell my beloved the following. "There is a spot at the foot of Mount Chitrakuta, towards the north-east. Ascetics reside in hermitages there. There is plenty of roots, fruits and water.

Mandakinee is not very far from that sacred hermitage. The clumps of groves there are full of many kinds of fragrant flowers. While we were strolling, we became wet and I lay down on your lap. After some time, Bharata's elder brother lay down on my lap.[208] A crow desired flesh and pecked me with its beak. At this, I picked up a stone and restrained the crow. But the crow hid itself and continued to peck at me. The crow did not refrain from its desire to obtain flesh. When I was angry at the bird, my garment was dislodged and I sought to tighten the string. You saw me in that state. You laughed at me and I was both angry and ashamed. Suffering from the crow that was seeking food, I sought refuge with you. Exhausted, I sat down and again clung to you. I was both angry and happy and was comforted by you. My face and eyes were full of tears and you gently wiped them away. O lord! Enraged by the crow, I was then seen by you. Sighing like a virulent serpent, he spoke these words.[209] 'O one with thighs like an elephant's trunk! Who has pierced you between the breasts? Who has shown this anger towards a five-hooded serpent and played in this way?' He looked around and saw the crow. Its sharp talons bore traces of blood and it was stationed there, facing my direction. 'Is this crow, supreme among birds, Shakra's son? It is roaming around on earth and seems to possess a speed like that of the wind.' After this, the mighty-armed one's eyes whirled around in rage. The supreme among intelligent ones made up his mind about the cruel crow. He picked up a blade of grass and invoked it with brahmastra. It blazed like the fire of destruction and he hurled the flaming blade in the bird's direction. He hurled the blazing blade of grass towards the crow. Followed by it, the crow adopted many different modes of flight. Wishing to save itself, it roamed around all the worlds. It was abandoned by its father[210] and by all the gods and the maharshis. Having circled the worlds, it came and sought refuge with you. It fell down on the ground and sought refuge with the one who grants refuge.

[208] Sita sometimes addresses Rama directly and sometimes indirectly.

[209] There is a break in continuity because the Critical Edition excises some shlokas. The crow had pecked at Sita between her breasts and hurt her.

[210] Indra.

Though it deserved to be killed, Kakutstha protected it because of his compassion. Having not been able to find peace anywhere in the worlds, it had come to you as refuge. It had returned, tired and distressed. He told it, 'It is impossible for brahmastra to fail. What should be done?' It replied, 'Let it destroy my right eye.' It bowed down before Rama and King Dasharatha. Having been released by the brave one, it returned to its own abode. O lord of the earth! For my sake, you released a brahmastra at a crow. How can you pardon someone who has abducted me? O bull among men! Therefore, out of compassion towards me, undertake great efforts. I have heard that non-violence is supreme dharma. I also know about your great valour, great enterprise and great strength. You cannot be agitated. You are like the deep ocean that cannot be crossed to the other shore. You are like Vasava and are the lord of the earth, right up to the ocean. You are supreme among those who know about weapons. You are spirited and strong. O Raghava! What is the reason that you are not releasing your weapons towards the rakshasas? The serpents, the gandharvas, the asuras and large numbers of Maruts are incapable of withstanding Rama's force in a battle. If the valiant one has any respect for me, why does he not use his sharp arrows to destroy the rakshasas and take me away? Why does Lakshmana, the scorcher of enemies, not follow his brother's command? Why does the brave and extremely strong one not save me? Those two tigers among men are like Vayu and Indra in their energy. Even the gods find them to be unassailable. Why are they ignoring me? There is no doubt that I have committed a great crime. Though they are capable, those two scorchers of enemies are ignoring me." For my sake, bow down your head and greet the lord of the world.[211] The spirited Kousalya gave birth to this excellent son. Ask about his welfare. Ask about the excellent one Sumitra gave birth to, the one who followed Rama. He gave up all the garlands and jewels, beloved and beautiful women and the great riches from the world that are extremely difficult to obtain. He did this to honour and please his father and his mother. Because he was devoted, the one

---

[211] Sita is now speaking to Hanumat.

with dharma in his soul gave up supreme happiness. He followed his brother Kakutstha and protected him in the forest. The mighty-armed one has shoulders like a lion. He is spirited and is pleasant to behold. His behaviour towards Rama is like that towards a father and towards me like that towards a mother. The brave Lakshmana did not know that I was being abducted. The handsome one serves his seniors. He is capable and does not speak much. For my father-in-law, this prince was most loved and the best. I have always loved Lakshmana more than his brother, Rama. The valiant one carries whatever burden is imposed on him. On seeing him, Raghava no longer remembers the aged and noble one.[212] For my sake, convey these words to him[213] and ask about his welfare. Lakshmana is loved by Rama. He is always mild, pure and accomplished. Repeatedly, tell my brave lord, Rama, this. "O Dasharatha's son! I will only sustain my life for a month. If it is more than a month, I will no longer remain alive. I am stating this truthfully. You must save me from Ravana. The evil-acting one has defiled me. O brave one! Like Koushiki, you must save me, even from patala."'[214]

After this, Sita removed the auspicious and divine *chudamani*[215] and tied it up in her garment. She gave it to Hanumat, so that it could be given to Raghava. The brave one received the excellent jewel. His arm could not pass through it, so he fixed it to his finger.[216] The supreme among apes accepted the excellent jewel and greeted her. He circumambulated Sita, bowed down and stood by her side. At having been able to see Sita, he was filled with great delight. Though his body was still there, his mind went out to Rama. He accepted that extremely expensive and supreme jewel.

[212] Dasharatha.

[213] Lakshmana.

[214] This is interpreted in two ways. When Indra killed Vritra, Lakshmi entered the earth and Vishnu saved her and returned her to Indra. According to this interpretation, Koushiki means Lakshmi, since Koushika is one of Indra's names. Alternatively, Koushiki is the sage Utathya's wife. Varuna carried her away to patala, but Utathya saved her.

[215] Jewel worn on the top of the head.

[216] There was a small hole (bore) in the chudamani for a thread or strand of hair to pass through it. Hanumat's size was greatly reduced. Even then, his arm could not pass through that bore. His finger did.

It was powerful and had been worn by Janaka's daughter. He was like an excellent mountain that had been freed from a storm. With a delighted mind, he readied himself for his return.

Chapter 5(37)

After having given Hanumat the jewel, Sita told him, 'From this token, Rama will ascertain the truth. Seeing this, the brave Rama will remember three things—me, my mother and King Dasharatha. O supreme among apes! Urge your enterprise again and think about what needs to be done next to accomplish the objective. O supreme among apes! You are worthy of setting about this task. Think about making efforts so that misery comes to an end.' The son of the wind god, terrible in his valour, pledged to do what she had said. He bowed his head down before Vaidehi and prepared to leave. The queen got to know that the ape who was the son of the wind god was ready to go. With her voice choking with tears, Maithilee addressed him in these words. 'O Hanumat! Ask about the welfare of both Rama and Lakshmana and about that of all the aged apes, Sugriva and his advisers. You must think of a means whereby the mighty-armed Raghava can help me to cross this ocean of grief. The illustrious Rama must accomplish this while I am still alive. O Hanumat! Speak such words to him and you will accomplish dharma. On constantly hearing the words of encouragement that I have spoken, the manliness of Dasharatha's son will be enhanced and he will get me back. Hearing the message and the words that I have spoken, the brave one will properly resort to his valour and accomplish the objective.'

Hearing Sita's words, Hanumat, the son of the wind god, joined his hands in salutation above his head. He spoke these words in reply. 'Kakutstha will swiftly arrive, surrounded by apes and bears. He will vanquish the enemies in the battle and dispel your grief. I do not see any mortals, immortals or asuras who are interested in standing before him when he volleys out his arrows. The sun god,

Parjanya and Vaivasvata Yama are not capable of standing before him in a battle, especially when you are the reason. He is worthy of ruling over the entire world, right up to the frontiers of the ocean. O Janaka's daughter! Rama's victory will be for your sake.' His words were spoken well, appropriate and were full of the truth. Hearing them, Janakee showed him a lot of respect and spoke to him. As he was leaving, Sita glanced at him repeatedly.

Filled with affection towards her husband, she entreated him in friendly words. 'O brave one! O scorcher of enemies! If you so think, reside here for one day. Hide yourself in some place. Rest and then leave tomorrow. Someone like me is unfortunate. O brave one! However, your presence will save me from this great sorrow for at least a short while. O tiger among apes! After you leave, until you return, there is no doubt that were will be an uncertainty about my remaining alive. The sorrow about not being able to see you will also torment me. O ape! It will be like another kind of sorrow igniting the present sorrow and increasing it. O brave one! O lord of the apes! There is still a great doubt before me and that concerns your companions, the apes and the bears. This great ocean is extremely difficult to cross. How will they be able to manage it? How will the soldiers, the apes and the bears, and the two best of men manage that? There are only three creatures who possess the strength to cross this ocean—Vinata's son,[217] you and the wind god. O brave one! This is extremely difficult to cross and that is the task you must devote yourself to. O one who is supreme in accomplishing tasks! Do you see any solution to this? If you wish, you alone are capable of accomplishing this objective. O slayer of enemy heroes! You possess sufficient fame and can generate strength. With all his soldiers, if Rama vanquishes Ravana in the battle and with me, returns in victory to his own city, this will enhance his fame. If Kakutstha, the destroyer of enemy forces fills Lanka with his arrows and takes me away, that will be worthy of him. You are like the great-souled one in your valour. Act so that he can exhibit his valour in the battle.'

[217] Garuda.

Those words were full of meaning and were full of reasons. Hearing them, Hanumat spoke his final words in reply. 'O queen! Sugriva, the lord of the apes and the leader of the soldiers of the apes and the bears, is full of spirit. For your sake, he has made up his mind. He is surrounded by thousands and crores of apes. O Vaidehi! To destroy the rakshasas, he will come here swiftly. The apes are there. They are full of valour. They are spirited and extremely strong. They have made up their minds and follow his command. They are great and infinitely energetic. They do not weaken in their tasks. Nothing can bar their progress, above, below and diagonally. Using their great enterprise, they have circumambulated the earth, with its oceans and mountains, several times, following the path resorted to by the wind. There are many residents of the forest who are my equal and superior to me. There is no one in Sugriva's presence who is inferior to me. If I can reach this place, why can't those extremely strong ones? The best ones are sent. The ordinary ones are not sent. O queen! Therefore enough of this lamentation. Set aside your sorrow. The leaders of the apes will arrive here in a single leap. Those two extremely spirited ones, lions among men, will arrive here before you on my back, like the rising moon and the sun. Those two brave ones, Rama and Lakshmana, supreme among men, will come to the city of Lanka and destroy it with their arrows. Raghava, the descendant of the Raghu lineage, will kill Ravana and his companions. O beautiful one! Having obtained you, he will return to his own city. O fortunate one! Therefore, comfort yourself. Wait for the time and you will see Rama, blazing like the fire. The Indra among the rakshasas will be slain, with his sons, advisers and relatives. You will be united with Rama, like Rohini with the moon. O queen! O Maithilee! You will quickly reach the other shore of this ocean of grief. You will soon see Ravana being killed by Rama.' Having comforted Vaidehi in this way, Hanumat, the son of the wind god, made up his mind to leave. He spoke to Vaidehi again. 'You will soon see Raghava. He has made up his mind to slay your enemies. With a bow in his hand, Lakshmana will present himself at the gate of Lanka. You will soon see the apes assemble, with complexions like Indras among elephants. They are brave. They are like lions and tigers in their valour and use nails and teeth as weapons. O noble one! There will be many leaders of foremost apes dancing around in Lanka, on the summit of Malaya. They will be like mountains and clouds. Rama cannot obtain peace. He is like an elephant afflicted by a lion. His inner organs are oppressed by the terrible arrows of Manmatha. O queen! Do not weep and grieve. Do not have anything disagreeable in your mind. You have a husband and a protector who is like Shakra, Shachi's husband. Does anyone exist who is superior to Rama? Is there anyone who is Soumitri's equal? Those two brothers, who are like the fire god and the wind god, are your support. O queen! You will not reside in this place for a long time, inhabited by the extremely terrible hordes of rakshasas. Your beloved will arrive in a short while. Permit me. It will be only a short while before we meet again.'

Chapter 5(38)

On hearing the words of Vayu's great-souled son, Sita, who was like the daughter of a god, spoke words that were beneficial for her own self. 'O ape! On seeing you and hearing these pleasant words, I am delighted. I am like seeds that have half-sprouted, when the earth obtains rain. My limbs are afflicted by grief and I wish to touch the body of that tiger among men. Therefore, act compassionately towards me. O one who is supreme among all the apes! Give this sign to Rama. Tell him how he angrily flung the blade of grass towards the crow and destroyed one of its eyes.[218] You should remember. "The *tilaka* mark on my forehead had once got effaced and you had drawn a tilaka mark on the side of my cheek. How can the valiant one, who is the equal of the great Indra and Varuna, condone this abduction of Sita? She is residing amidst the rakshasas. I have protected this divine chudamani extremely well.

---

[218] The word now used is *ishika*. This means blade of grass, but also means arrow. Since we have earlier been told that Rama invoked a blade of grass with brahmastra, we will continue to stick to blade of grass.

O unblemished one! On seeing it, I have rejoiced in my hardship, as if I had seen you. This beautiful piece was produced from the water. Immersed in sorrow, I will not be able to survive after this. I am bearing this intolerable misery for your sake. The extremely terrible rakshasis censure me in words that shatter the heart. O destroyer of enemies! I will only sustain my life for one month. O son of a king! If it is more than a month, without you, I will not remain alive. The king of the rakshasas is terrible and the sight of him does not bring me happiness. If I hear that you are not coming, I will not remain alive even for an instant."'

Hearing Vaidehi's piteous words, Hanumat, the extremely energetic son of the wind god, spoke to her in a voice that was choking with tears. 'O queen! I am truthfully swearing before you. Because he grieves over you, Rama has withdrawn from everything. Since Rama is overwhelmed with sorrow, Lakshmana is tormented. Tolerate this in some way. This is not the time to grieve. O beautiful one! In a short while, you will see an end to your sorrows. For the sake of seeing you, those two unblemished princes will undertake efforts to burn down Lanka. O large-eyed one! Having slain the cruel Ravana and his relatives in the battle, the two Raghavas will get you and their own city back. O unblemished one! Give me another sign so that Rama knows. To generate delight in him, you should again give me something else.'

Thus addressed, she said, 'This is an excellent token. Rama will see this, the ornament from my hair. O Hanumat! O brave one! This is sufficient for him to trust your words.' The supreme among apes accepted that beautiful and excellent gem. He bowed his head down before the queen and prepared to leave. Making up his mind to leap and exert himself, the bull among the apes used his great force to increase his size. On seeing this, the face of Janaka's daughter filled with tears. Distressed and in a voice choking with tears, she said, 'O Hanumat! The two brothers, Rama and Lakshmana, are like lions. Ask about their welfare and about that of Sugriva and all his advisers. You must think of a means whereby the mighty-armed Raghava can save me from this ocean of grief. This force of sorrow is fierce. I am also censured by the guards. When you reach Rama, tell him about this. O supreme among apes! May your journey be auspicious.' The princess spoke these meaningful words. Having accomplished his objective, the ape was delighted in his mind. He could see that only a little bit of the task remained to be accomplished. He made up his mind to leave for the northern direction.

Chapter 5(39)

He was ready to leave and she honoured and praised him with her words. Having left that spot, the ape started to think. 'I have seen the dark-eyed one and only a little bit of the task remains to be accomplished. I will ignore the three modes and check out the fourth.[219] For rakshasas, the quality of sama has not been thought of. Nor does dana work for those who possess plenty of riches. For people who are insolent about their strength, bheda will not be successful. Therefore, the idea of valour appeals to me. With the exception of valour, nothing can accomplish the objective. It is determined that nothing else will achieve the purpose. If the best of their heroes are killed in an encounter now, subsequently the rakshasas may behave in a milder way. After having accomplished the indicated task, if a person accomplishes many other tasks without having contravened the primary task, he is the one who has truly accomplished the objective. Even if a task is light, there is more than one means to accomplish it. He who knows that there are many means of achieving it is a person who truly knows and is capable of accomplishing the objective. If I leave this place and go to the residence of the lord of the apes after having ascertained the truth about the superiority and inferiority of them versus us, I will then have indeed followed my master's command. Indeed, how can I now be at ease and withstand the rakshasas in a battle? Indeed,

[219] Ignore sama, dana and bheda and test danda. The intention is to test Ravana's strength.

how can I use the essence of my own strength? How will Dashanana
show respect to me in a battle? I will face Dashanana in a battle.
This grove belongs to the cruel one and is like Nandana. It is full
of many kinds of trees and creepers and is pleasing to the eye and
the mind. I will destroy it, like a fire in a forest that is dry. When
this is devastated, Ravana will show his anger towards me. At this,
the lord of the rakshasas will summon a large army that consists of
horses, maharathas and elephants. They will use tridents made out
black iron and spears as weapons and a great battle will follow.
Using my invincible valour, I will engage with those who are terrible
in their valour. I will slay the soldiers who have been urged on by
Ravana. After that, I will happily go to the residence of the lord of
the apes.'

After this, the son of the wind god, terrible in his valour, used
the great force of his thighs to uproot and fling away the trees. The
brave Hanumat shattered the grove meant for pleasure and the many
trees and creepers that were full of maddened birds. The grove was
crushed. The trees were shattered and so were the waterbodies. The
summits of the mountains were crushed and became disagreeable to
see. Chambers made of creepers and chambers filled with pictures
were destroyed. Giant serpents, predatory beasts and deer were
whirled around. Chambers made out of stone were devastated and so
were other residences. That great grove assumed a devastated form.
The great-souled and great ape thus generated great displeasure and
accomplished his objective. The ape wished to fight single-handedly
against many extremely strong ones. He assumed a blazing form
and remained at one of the gates.

Chapter 5(40)

All the residents of Lanka were scared and terrified at the sounds
of the birds shrieking and noise of the trees being shattered.
Afraid and terrified, the animals and the birds screamed and fled.
Cruel portents presented themselves before the rakshasas. The

rakshasas, with disfigured faces, woke up from their sleep. They saw that the grove had been destroyed and saw the brave and great ape. The mighty-armed, greatly spirited and immensely strong one saw the rakshasis. To instil fear in them, he assumed an extremely gigantic form. The immensely strong one was gigantic in size and was like a mountain. On seeing the ape, the rakshasis asked Janaka's daughter, 'Who is he? Whom does he belong to? Where has he come from? Why has he come here? Why did he have a conversation with you? O large-eyed one! Tell us. O immensely fortunate one! Do not be afraid. O dark-eyed one! What did he talk to you about?' At this, the virtuous Sita, beautiful in all her limbs, said, 'How can I know about rakshasas who can assume any form at will? You are the ones who know about who he is and what he is doing. There is no doubt that only a snake knows about the trail of another snake. I am also scared of him. I do not know who he is. I only know him as a rakshasa who has come here, assuming any form at will.' Hearing Vaidehi's words, the rakshasis fled swiftly. Some remained, while others left, to inform Ravana about this.

The rakshasis, with disfigured faces, went to Ravana. They started to tell him about the malformed and terrible ape. 'O king! There is an ape with a terrible form in the middle of Ashokavana. Having conversed with Sita, the infinitely valorous one remains there. We have asked Sita Janakee, with eyes like a deer, about the ape. But though we have asked several times, she does not wish to tell us. He may be Vasava's messenger, or he may be Vaishravana's messenger. Or Rama, desiring to search out Sita, may have sent him. He possesses a terrible form. Your pleasure grove is full of many kinds of diverse animals and is beautiful. He has destroyed it. There is nothing in that region which has not been destroyed. However, he has not destroyed the place where Sita Janakee was. It is not obvious whether this was to protect Janakee or whether he was exhausted. But how can he have exhaustion? She must have been protected by him. There is a well-grown shimshapa tree that Sita herself had resorted to. It has beautiful and thick branches and leaves. That has been spared by him. His form is terrible. You should command that terrible chastisement be wreaked on him. He is the one who has conversed with Sita and has destroyed the grove. O lord of large numbers of rakshasas! You have accepted her in your mind. Other than someone who wants to give up his life, who will dare to converse with Sita?'

Hearing the words of the rakshasis, Ravana, the lord of the rakshasas, blazed like a fire into which oblations had been offered. Because of his anger, his eyes whirled around. There were brave rakshasas who were exactly like him and they were named *kimkara*s.[220] The immensely energetic one commanded them to seize Hanumat. There were eighty thousand spirited kimkaras. They emerged from his residence, with iron clubs in their hands. They possessed huge stomachs and large teeth. They were immensely strong and terrible in form. All of them wished to fight and were eager to seize Hanumat. They approached the ape, who was stationed at the entrance. They attacked with great force, like insects towards a fire. They attacked the best among apes with colourful clubs, bludgeons that were decorated with gold plating and arrows that were like the sun. However, the spirited and handsome Hanumat was like a mountain. He lashed his tail on the ground and roared loudly. At the sound of that roar, they became uncertain and were filled with fear. They saw Hanumat, as tall as a cloud in the evening. But because of the command of their master, the rakshasas attacked the ape without hesitation. Here and there, they attacked him with colourful and terrible weapons. From every side, the immensely strong one was surrounded by those brave ones. He remained at the gate and seized a terrible iron club. Seizing that club, he slew the ones who roamed around in the night. Seizing that, the son of the wind god roamed around in the sky, like Vinata's son moving around, having seized a serpent. The brave son of the wind god killed the kimkara rakshasas. Desiring to fight again, he remained at the gate. There were some rakshasas who managed to escape from that great fear. They went and told Ravana that all the kimkaras had been killed. Hearing that the immensely strong rakshasas had been killed, the king rolled his eyes. He commanded

[220] The word means servant.

Prahasta's son,[221] who was unmatched in valour and extremely difficult to vanquish in a battle.

Chapter 5(41)

Having killed the kimkaras, Hanumat started to think. 'I have shattered the grove, but the palace in the sanctuary[222] has not been destroyed. Therefore, I must also destroy the palace.' Having thought this, Hanumat made up his mind to exhibit his strength. The palace in the chaitya was as tall as the summit of Meru. Hanumat, best among apes and the son of the wind god, took a leap and climbed up on it. The invincible one attacked the tall palace in the sanctuary. Hanumat blazed in his prosperity and was like Pariyatra mountain. Hanumat, the son of the wind god, assumed an extremely gigantic form. He slapped his arms and filled Lanka with that sound. That sound of slapping struck the ears with a great clap. As a result of that sound, the birds fell down from the sky. 'The extremely strong Rama and the immensely strong Lakshmana will be victorious. King Sugriva, protected by Raghava, will be victorious. I am the servant of Rama, the Indra of Kosala and the performer of unblemished deeds. I am Hanumat, the son of the wind god and I have killed the enemy soldiers. In a battle, thousands of Ravanas are not capable of standing before me. I will strike with thousands of boulders and trees. I will shatter the city of Lanka and pay my respects to Maithilee. While all the rakshasas look on, I will accomplish my objective and leave.' Stationed atop the palace in the sanctuary, the bull among apes roared in a terrible way and that roar generated fear among the rakshasas.

Attracted by the great sound, hundreds of guards of the sanctuary advanced. They seized many kinds of weapons—spikes, swords and battleaxes. Gigantic in size, they surrounded the son of

[221] Named Jambumali.
[222] The word used is chaitya.

the wind god and released these. Surrounded by large numbers of rakshasas, the best among apes was resplendent. He was like a large whirlpool in the extensive waters of the Ganga. Enraged, the son of the wind god assumed a terrible form. The palace possessed a large pillar that was embellished with gold and had one hundred sharp edges. Using force, Hanumat, the son of the wind god, uprooted this. The immensely strong one whirled this around. Like the wielder of the vajra against the asuras, he killed hundreds of rakshasas. Stationed in the sky, the handsome one spoke these words. 'There are thousands of great-souled and strong apes who are just like me. They follow the orders of Sugriva and have been sent by him. There are hundreds, tens of thousands, hundreds of thousands and crores. Sugriva and they will come and destroy all of you. This city of Lanka will no longer exist, nor you, nor Ravana. You are tied in a bond of enmity with the great-souled lord of Ikshvaku.'

Chapter 5(42)

The Indra among rakshasas commanded Prahasta's powerful son. This was Jambumali, who possessed large teeth. He left, wielding a bow. He was attired in red garlands and garments. He wore a wreath and beautiful earrings. His eyes were large and wide. He was fierce and impossible to vanquish in a battle. His excellent bow was like Shakra's bow and he had large and beautiful arrows. He extended it[223] with force and it made a sound like the vajra and a bolt of thunder. The loud roar of him twanging the bow filled the directions. It suddenly penetrated the sub-directions and the sky and filled them up. He arrived on a chariot that was yoked to donkeys. On seeing this, Hanumat, filled with force, roared in delight. Hanumat, the large ape, was standing on the arch of the gate. The mighty-armed Jambumali pierced him with sharp arrows. He struck him on the face with an arrow that was in the shape of a crescent and on the head

---

[223] The bow.

with an arrow with a single tuft. He pierced the lord of the apes in the arms with ten iron arrows. His coppery red face was struck by an arrow and looked resplendent. It looked like a blooming lotus in the autumn, pierced by the rays of the sun.

Struck by the rakshasa's arrow, the great ape was enraged. Next to him, he saw a large and extremely huge boulder. The powerful one used his strength to uproot it and hurled it with force. Angrily, the rakshasa struck him back with ten arrows. Hanumat, fierce in his valour, saw that his attempt had been futile. The valiant one uprooted a giant sala tree and whirled it around. The immensely strong ape was whirling around that sala tree. On seeing this, the extremely strong Jambumali shot many arrows at him. He severed the sala tree with four arrows and struck the ape's arms with five. He pierced him with one arrow in the chest and ten between the breasts. His body covered in arrows, he was filled with great rage. He seized a club and whirled it around with force. Endowed with immense strength, he whirled it around with great force and even greater force. He flung down the club on Jambumali's broad chest. He[224] no longer possessed a head, arms or thighs. His bow, chariot, horses and arrows could no longer be seen. Using force, he killed maharatha Jambumali. With his limbs and ornaments shattered, he was killed and fell down on the ground. Jambumali was killed and so were the extremely strong kimkaras. Hearing this, Ravana was angry and his eyes turned red with rage. His coppery red eyes rolled around in anger. Prahasta's immensely strong son had been killed. The lord of those who roam around in the night quickly commanded the extremely brave and valiant sons of his advisers.

Chapter 5(43)

At this, the Indra among rakshasas urged the sons of his ministers. Seven of them emerged from the residence, as radiant as the

[224] Jambumali.

one with the seven rays.[225] They were extremely strong and were surrounded by extremely strong archers. They were accomplished in the use of weapons. They were best among those who knew about weapons and in their rivalry, sought to outdo each other. Their large chariots were embellished with nets made out of gold and had pennants and flags. These were yoked to horses and thundered like clouds. The infinitely valorous ones had colourful bows that were plated with molten gold. They twanged them cheerfully, like lightning amidst the clouds. On knowing that the kimkaras had been killed, their mothers, relatives and well-wishers were filled with grief and scared. Rivalling each other, adorned in ornaments made out of molten gold, they[226] rushed to fight Hanumat, who was stationed near the gate. They released showers of arrows and their chariots thundered and roared. The bulls among the nairittas roamed around and showered down like clouds filled with rain. Hanumat was enveloped by that shower of arrows. His form became invisible, like that of a king of mountains because of the rain. Swift in his movements, the ape, roaming around in the sparkling sky, evaded those arrows and the speedy chariots of those brave ones. The brave one could be seen in the sky, toying with those archers. He was like the wind god in the sky and the archers were like clouds. He roared in a terrible voice and terrified that large army. Hanumat roamed around and attacked the valiant rakshasas with force. The scorcher of enemies killed some with slaps and some with his feet. He killed some with his fists and tore some others with his nails. The ape crushed some with his chest and some others with his thighs. Because of his roars, some others fell down on the ground. Some were killed. Others fell down on the ground. Seeing this, all the soldiers were afflicted by fear and fled in the ten directions. Elephants shrieked in broken voices. Horses fell down on the ground. The seats, standards and umbrellas fell down on the ground, which was strewn with shattered chariots. He killed those prosperous rakshasas. The ape was extremely strong and fierce in

---

[225] Meaning the sun.
[226] The sons of the ministers.

his valour. He again wished to fight against some other rakshasas.
Therefore, the brave one again went to the gate.

Chapter 5(44)

Having got to know that the sons of the ministers had been
killed by the great-souled ape, Ravana concealed his thoughts
and thought of an excellent means. There were five foremost leaders
of the soldiers—Virupaksha, Yupaksha, the rakshasa Durdhara,
Praghasa and Bhasakarna. These brave ones were skilled in good
policy and Dashagriva commanded them. He was eager to seize
Hanumat, who possessed Vayu's speed in battle. 'All of you advance
in front of the army. Take a large army with you, with horses,
chariots and elephants. Chastise the ape. When you approach the
one whose residence is in the forest, you must be attentive. The
action that you undertake must not be contrary to the time and the
place. Debating about his deeds, I do not think that he is an ape. He
possesses great strength. In every way, he must be a great creature.
Using the strength of his austerities, perhaps Indra has created him
for some objective of his. With all of you, I have vanquished the
serpents, the yakshas, the gandharvas, the gods, the asuras and the
maharshis. To invade us in some way, they must have created him.
There is no doubt about this and he must be seized. The ape is cruel
in his valour and you must not disrespect him. I have seen apes
earlier, who were quick and extensive in their valour—Vali, Sugriva,
the immensely strong Jambavat, the commander Nila and others
like Dvivida. But their terrible speed, energy, prowess, intelligence,
strength, enterprise and capacity to change form was not like his.
It is thus known that this is a great creature in the form of an ape.
Resort to great efforts and seek to capture him. You are sufficient in
the field of battle. If they so wish, the three worlds, with Indra, the
gods, the asuras and humans are incapable of standing before you.
Nevertheless, someone who desires victory in a battle must know
about good policy. Make efforts to protect yourselves. Success in a

battle is fickle.' All those greatly energetic ones accepted the words
spoken by their master.

Like the fire in their energy, they attacked with great force. There
were chariots, crazy elephants and extremely swift steeds. There
were many kinds of sharp weapons. All of them had every kind of
force. The giant ape saw those brave and radiant ones. Garlanded
by the rays of his own energy, he was like the rising sun. Near
the gate, he possessed great force, great spirit and great strength.
He was immensely intelligent, immense in his enterprise, gigantic
in size and immense in strength. Stationed in all the directions, all
of them looked at him. Here and there, they used terrible weapons
to strike at him. Durdhara used five sharp and sparkling arrows,
yellow at the tip and with the complexion of lotuses, to strike him
in the chest. The ape was pierced in the chest with those five arrows.
He leapt up into the sky and roared, the sound echoing in the ten
directions. On his chariot, the brave Durdhara readied his bow.
The immensely strong one showered him with many hundreds of
arrows. From the sky, the ape countered these showers of arrows,
like the wind dispels a cloud filled with rain at the end of the rainy
season. The son of the wind god was oppressed by Durdhara. The
powerful one roared loudly and again extended his size. From a
distance, the ape violently descended on Durdhara's chariot. He
descended with great force, like a mass of lightning on a mountain.
The eight horses were crushed. The chariot, the wheel and the
kubara[227] were shattered. Giving up his life, Durdhara fell down on
the ground. Virupaksha and Yupaksha saw that he had fallen down
on the ground. Filled with rage, those two invincible scorchers of
enemies leapt up. When they suddenly leapt up, stationed in the
sparkling sky, the mighty-armed ape struck them in the chests with
two clubs. The forceful and immensely strong one struck them with
force. He was like Suparna in his valour and they fell down on the
ground again. The ape uprooted a sala tree. Using this, the son of
the wind god slew those two brave rakshasas. Knowing that those
three had been killed by the spirited ape, Praghasa attacked with

---

[227] Kubara is the pole for attaching the yoke to the chariot.

great force and struck the ape powerfully. The valiant Bhasakarna
angrily seized a spear in his hand. The illustrious tiger among apes
was alone and there were two of them. Praghasa pierced him with
a spear that was sharp at the tip. The rakshasa Bhasakarna struck
that supreme ape with a javelin. Pierced by those two on the body,
his body hair became smeared with blood. Angry, the ape assumed
a radiance that was like that of the rising sun. He uprooted the
summit of a mountain, with the animals, serpents and the trees.
With that, Hanumat, elephant among apes, killed those two brave
rakshasas. When those five leaders had been killed, the soldiers were
disheartened and the ape destroyed what remained of the army.
Like the one with the thousand eyes against the asuras, the ape
struck horses with horses, elephants with elephants, warriors with
warriors and chariots with chariots, destroying them. Elephants
and horses were killed. Wheels and giant chariots were shattered.
Rakshasas were slain. Everywhere on the ground, the paths were
obstructed with these. In the battle, he killed the brave ones with
their soldiers, standards, leaders and mounts. After this, the brave
ape again stood by the gate. He was like Death, having made up his
mind about the destruction of the subjects.

Chapter 5(45)

Hanumat crushed the five commanders, with their followers
and their mounts. At this, the king[228] looked at Prince Aksha,
who was not wounded and was ready and eager to fight in the
battle. He urged him with his eyes and the powerful one[229] picked
up a colourful and golden bow and leapt up, like a sacrificial fire
when oblations have been offered into it by the best of brahmanas.
The valiant one ascended a gigantic chariot that was like the rising
sun in complexion and was armoured with a plate made out of

---

[228] Ravana.
[229] Aksha.

molten gold. The bull among the nairittas ventured forth against the large ape. It[230] was fashioned out of the store of austerities he had accumulated and won for himself. It was decorated with armour that was made out of molten gold. The flag and the standard were decorated with jewels. It was yoked properly to eight excellent horses that possessed the speed of thought. It moved without obstructions and gods and asuras could not assail it. With a complexion like that of the sun, it could be controlled and could move around in the sky. A quiver, eight swords and bells were fixed to it. In due order, spears and javelins were arranged in the designated places. He ascended the chariot, which was like the sun in complexion. Filled with all the required objects, it was resplendent. There were ropes that dazzled like the sun and the moon. He emerged, like an immortal in his valour. The noise of horses, elephants and large chariots filled the sky and the earth, with its mountains. With the army, he approached the gate. The capable ape was standing there, waiting.

Having reached the ape, Aksha, the one with the tawny eyes, saw him standing there, like the fire of destruction at the end of a yuga, ready to destroy subjects. He was astonished and was filled with respect. He looked at him, with a lot of respect in his eyes. The immensely strong son of the king[231] weighed the force and valour of the enemy, the great-souled ape, and his own strength and increased his own size, like the sun at the end of the winter. Having considered the valour, stability and invincibility of Hanumat, though he was filled with rage in the battle, he controlled himself and provoked him[232] with three sharp arrows. He saw that the ape was proud and had conquered his exhaustion, having defeated the enemy. Aksha looked at him with an agitated mind and picked up a bow and arrow in his hand. His necklace and armlets were made out of gold and his earrings were beautiful. Swift in his valour, he approached the ape. Their unmatched encounter generated respect even among the gods and the asuras. Witnessing the battle between the ape and

---

[230] The chariot.
[231] Aksha.
[232] Hanumat.

the prince, the earth shrieked. The sun did not radiate heat. The
wind did not blow and the mountain quaked. The sky screamed and
the ocean was agitated. The brave one who knew the truth about
affixing, aiming and releasing, struck the ape on the head with three
arrows that were excellent at the tips and with golden tufts. These
were like venomous serpents. When those arrows struck him on
the head, blood started to flow from the wounds and he dilated his
eyes. With the arrows like rays, he was like the sun when it has just
arisen. He was as radiant as the sun, with its garland of rays. In the
battle, the supreme adviser of the lord of the apes glanced at the
excellent and eager son of the king, with his wonderful weapon and
his wonderful bow. He was filled with delight and was keen to fight
in the battle. Filled with strength and energy, his rage increased, like
the one with the rays in front of Mandara. Using his eyesight, which
were like the flames of a fire, he burnt down Prince Aksha's soldiers
and mounts. The rakshasa's bow was like Shakra's bow.[233] In the
encounter, he showered down arrows like a cloud. The lord of the
apes was like a mountain and he swiftly showered down arrows on
him, like a cloud showering down on an excellent mountain. The
ape saw him in the battle, terrible in his valour and with increasing
energy, strength, valour and arrows. On seeing Prince Aksha in the
encounter, like a cloud in his valour, he roared in joy. Because of his
childish nature, he[234] was brave and insolent in the battle. His anger
increased, with his eyes like wounds. He approached the ape, who
was unmatched in fights, like an elephant approaches a giant pit
that is covered with grass. When those forceful arrows descended
on him, he roared like the thundering of a cloud. The son of the
wind god, terrible to behold, swiftly leapt up into the sky, extending
his arms and his thighs. The supreme and powerful one among the
rakshasas was supreme among all charioteers. When the powerful
one leapt up, he too leapt up and enveloped him with arrows, like
a cloud raining down hail on a mountain. The brave ape followed
Vayu's path and like the wind, sought out gaps in between the

---

[233] A rainbow.
[234] Aksha.

arrows that were released. Terrible in his valour, he moved around, with the speed of thought. Using his eyes, he glanced at Aksha with a great deal of respect. With the bow and arrows, he was eager in the battle and shrouded the sky with many kinds of excellent arrows. The son of the wind god thought. The arrows pierced the ape between the arms. Struck by the noble prince, the great-souled one roared. The mighty-armed one knew the truth about what should be done in specific situations.

He thought about his adversary's prowess in the encounter. 'He is not acting like a child and his radiance is like that of the young sun. The extremely strong one is accomplishing this great deed. He is one who displays deeds in all kinds of encounters. But the idea of killing him does not appeal to me. This great-souled one is great and brave. He is controlled and can withstand a lot in an encounter. Because of the deeds and qualities he has exhibited, there is no doubt that he is revered by the serpents, the yakshas and the sages. He is stationed in front of me and is looking at me, with enhanced valour, enterprise and will. The valour of the one who acts fast will make the minds of even the gods and asuras tremble. If he is ignored, he will certainly overpower me. In this encounter, his valour is increasing. The idea of killing him appeals to me, because if an expanding fire is ignored, that cannot be tolerated.' He thus debated the enemy's force. Accordingly, the valiant one determined his own course of action. The immensely strong one, the great ape, made up his mind to kill him. Using slaps from his palms, the brave ape who was the son of the wind god and was following Vayu's path, slew the eight extremely swift horses. The great chariot was struck by the palm of the minister of the lord of the apes and destroyed. The seat was shattered and the kubara broke. Slain, the eight horses fell down from the sky on to the ground. The maharatha abandoned his chariot. Wielding a bow and a sword, he leapt up from the ground into the sky. His body took to the air, like the wind in its own abode. The ape also wandered around in the sky, frequented by the king of the birds,[235]

[235] Garuda.

the wind and the siddhas. The son of the wind god, forceful and
valiant, used his austerities, like a brave and fierce rishi. He seized
him by the feet, slowly and firmly. The ape whirled him around
one thousand times, like the lord of the birds does to a large
serpent. Though he was like his father[236] in valour, the excellent
ape hurled him down on the ground with great force. His arms,
thighs, waist and head were shattered. Blood started to flow from
his wounds. His bones and eyes were crushed. His joints were
fragmented and his entrails strewn around. The rakshasa was slain
and Vayu's son felled him on the ground. The great ape crushed
him down on the ground and generated a great fear in the lord
of the rakshasas. On seeing that the prince had been killed by the
ape, the maharshis who are great in their vows and move around
unimpeded, the assembled creatures, the yakshas, the serpents and
the gods, with Indra, were filled with wonder. Prince Aksha, with
eyes like wounds, was as resplendent as the son of the wielder of
the vajra. Having killed him, the brave one[237] again went to the
gate. He was like Death, when the time arrives for the destruction
of subjects.

Chapter 5(46)

When Prince Aksha was killed by Hanumat, the great-souled
lord of the rakshasas was enraged. However, he controlled
himself and commanded Indrajit, who was like a god. 'You are
supreme among those who know about weapons and can cause
grief to gods and asuras. The gods, with Indra, have witnessed
your deeds. Having worshipped the grandfather,[238] you have
obtained weapons. When you resort to that strength of weapons,
the asuras, the large number of Maruts and all those in the three
worlds are unable to overcome their exhaustion against you in

[236] Ravana.
[237] Hanumat.
[238] Brahma.

a battle. You are protected by the valour in your arms. You are also protected by your austerities. You know about the time and the place. You are supreme among intelligent ones. In a battle, there is nothing that you cannot accomplish. If you make up your mind and think about it, there is no deed you cannot accomplish. There is no one in the three worlds who does not know about the strength of your weapons and about your own strength. Your austerities and strength and the valour and power of your weapons in a battle are like mine. There is no one who can withstand you in the field of battle. Having thought about this, I am certain that I need suffer no exhaustion in my mind. All the kimkaras and the rakshasa Jambumali have been killed. So have the five brave commanders who were the sons of the advisers. Your beloved brother, Prince Aksha, has been killed. O destroyer of enemies! They did not possess the essence that you and I have. O intelligent one! I have witnessed the great strength, power and valour of this ape. Therefore, look towards your own essence and powerfully do something that is worthy of your own strength. Act so that the affliction of our soldiers can end and so that they find peace, when the enemy has been quietened. Consider your own strength and that of the enemy. O supreme among those who know about weapons! Prepare. Sending someone like you will not be recommended by the best among intelligent ones. But it is my view that this is what a kshatriya should do and is also in accordance with the dharma of kings. O destroyer of enemies! You will know how to use many kinds of weapons in the encounter. You will certainly know how to bring about the desired victory in the battle.'

Having heard his father's words, the accomplished one, with a power like that of the son of a god, circumambulated his lord with an undistressed mind. The brave one made up his mind to fight. Indrajit was worshipped by his own people. Eager to fight, he enthusiastically prepared himself for the battle. The son of the lord of the rakshasas was handsome, with eyes like the petals of lotuses. The immensely energetic one emerged, like the ocean on the day of the full moon. Indrajit, who was like Indra, ascended a chariot whose speed could not be checked. It was yoked to four *vyalas*[239] who were like the king of the birds in their speed, with sharp and pointed teeth. The supreme among archers was on that chariot. He knew about weapons and was supreme among those who knew about weapons. On that chariot, he swiftly advanced towards the spot where Hanumat was.

There was the clatter of the chariot. There was the sound from the twanging of the bow. Hearing this, the brave ape was even more delighted. Accomplished in fighting, he[240] picked up his gigantic bow and sharp arrows that were like darts. He advanced towards Hanumat. Filled with delight, with the bow in his hand, he too advanced towards the encounter. All the directions paled. The animals howled in hideous tones. The serpents and the yakshas assembled, as did the maharshis and the siddhas. Large flocks of birds covered the sky and extremely happy, started to call. The ape saw that Indrajit's chariot was advancing. The forceful one roared loudly and extended his size. Indrajit was on that divine chariot, with his colourful bow. He twanged his bow and created a sound that was like the clap of thunder. Both of them were extremely forceful. Both of them were extremely strong and were not scared of fighting. The ape and the son of the lord of the rakshasas were bound in enmity, like the Indra of the gods against the Indra of the asuras. He[241] was immeasurable and moved around along the path followed by his father, extending his size. As the brave one advanced on his great chariot and released his torrent of arrows, he avoided them. The brave one, the destroyer of enemy heroes, shot arrows that were long and sharp, with excellent shafts and colourful tufts that were made out of gold. They were aimed well and as they descended, they possessed the force of the vajra. There was the clatter of the chariot. There was the sound of drums, tambourines and kettledrums. There was the sound from the twanging of the

---

[239] Vyalas in Indrajit's chariot are usually taken to be tigers. However, a vyala is any vicious beast and can be a tiger, a lion, a leopard, an elephant, or even some kind of reptile.

[240] Indrajit.

[241] Hanumat.

bow. Hearing this, he[242] leapt up again. The great ape quickly moved around in the space left by the arrows. Though he[243] was accomplished in striking the target, the ape rendered this aim futile. Hanumat, the son of the wind god, remained ahead of the arrows and again stretched out his arms. Both of them were full of speed. Both of them were accomplished in modes of fighting. An excellent encounter ensued, agreeable to the minds of all creatures. Hanumat did not know the rakshasa's weak spot. The son of the wind god did not know the great-souled one's weak spot. They were like gods in their valour. As they clashed, it was as if they rendered each other's poisons futile.

The great-souled one saw that he was missing his aim. His arrows were failing and were falling down. He had a great thought. Accomplished in his soul, he controlled himself. The son of the king of the rakshasas made up his mind about the brave and foremost ape. Having noticed that the ape could not be killed, he thought of capturing him. The brave one was supreme among those who knew about weapons. He affixed the grandfather's extremely energetic weapon and aimed it towards the supreme ape. The one who knew the truth about weapons knew that he could not be killed. Therefore, Indrajit captured the mighty-armed son of the wind god. The ape was bound by the rakshasa's weapon. He could not move and fell down on the ground. The foremost ape realized that his force was constrained and that he had been tied down by the power of the weapon of the powerful one.[244] He thought that this was a favour being shown to him by the grandfather. This was Svayambhu's mantra and the brahmastra had been invoked with that mantra. Hanumat thought that this was a boon bestowed by the grandfather. 'I do not possess the strength to free myself from the bondage of this weapon, because of the powers of the preceptor of the worlds. I have thus determined that I must remain in the bonds of this weapon. Therefore, I must follow whatever ensues.' The ape thought about the energy of the weapon and about the

[242] Hanumat.
[243] Indrajit.
[244] Meaning Brahma.

favour the grandfather had shown towards him. He thought about
his strength of freeing himself from it[245] and decided to follow the
grandfather. 'Though I have been bound by the weapon, there is
no fear in me. I am protected by the grandfather, Indra and the
wind god. Even if I am captured by the rakshasas, there is a great
quality associated with that. I will have a conversation with the
Indra among the rakshasas. Therefore, let the enemy capture me.'
The slayer of enemy heroes decided this. Having considered it, he
made no attempt to move. The enemy captured him. Having been
captured by them, he roared and censured them.

The rakshasas saw that the scorcher of enemies was motionless.
They tied him up with ropes made out of hemp and barks from
trees. The idea of being captured by the enemy appealed to him.
He tolerated being seized by those brave ones. He was certain
that the Indra among the rakshasas would be curious to see him.
Once he was bound in bark, the valiant one was freed from the
bondage of the weapon. When there is another kind of bondage,
the bondage of a weapon ceases to exist. When the supreme among
apes was tied up in bonds made out of bark from trees, the brave
Indrajit started to think. 'He has been freed from the weapon. Once
a person is tied up in some other way, there cannot be the bonds
from a weapon. Alas! My great deed has been rendered futile. The
rakshasas have ignored the rules of a mantra. Yet another mantra
cannot be used on a weapon. Therefore, all of us face a danger.'
Bound up, Hanumat was dragged along by the rakshasas. But he
had not yet realized that he had been freed from the bondage of
the weapon. The cruel rakshasas beat Hanumat with sticks and
their fists. They dragged the ape to the presence of the Indra among
the rakshasas. Indrajit saw that because of the bondage of ropes
and barks from trees, he had been freed from the bondage of the
weapon. He exhibited the immensely strong and foremost ape to
the king and all his companions.

The excellent ape was bound, like a crazy elephant. The
rakshasas conveyed him to Ravana, Indra among the rakshasas.

---

[245] Which would occur in due course.

'Who is this? Whom does he belong to? Where has he come from? What is his task? Where is his refuge?' The brave rakshasas conversed in this way. Other rakshasas present were angry and said, 'Kill him. Burn him. Eat him.' After passing through those paths, the great-souled one suddenly found himself in the presence of the king of the rakshasas. He saw him, adorned by expensive jewels and surrounded by companions who were seated at his feet. The immensely energetic Ravana saw that supreme ape. He was being dragged here and there by the rakshasas with disfigured forms. The supreme among apes also saw the lord among the rakshasas. He was full of energy and strength and seemed to scorch like the sun. Dashanana looked at the ape, his eyes rolling around in anger. The best among his ministers were there, skilled and aged and good in conduct. He commanded them to ask the ape, in due order, about the reason why he had come here and his intention. The lord of the apes said, 'I have come to you as a messenger.'

Chapter 5(47)

Terrible in his valour, Hanumat was astounded at his[246] deed. Eyes coppery red with anger, he looked at the lord of the rakshasas. He was radiant and resplendent, on an extremely expensive golden throne. His immensely radiant crown was adorned with a net of pearls. There were colourful golden ornaments, as if they had been fashioned with the mind. They were embedded with diamonds and embellished with extremely expensive jewels. There was a sacred thread that was made out of expensive silk and he was smeared with red sandalwood paste. He was smeared with many colourful unguents, with diverse auspicious marks. His large heads were a sight to behold. With red eyes, he was terrible in form. His large and sharp teeth blazed and his lips hung down. With ten heads, the brave and extremely expensive one was dazzling. He was like the

---

[246] Indrajit's.

summit of Mandara, surrounded by many predatory beasts. There
was a radiant necklace on his chest, resembling a mass of excellent
and black collyrium. His face had the complexion of the full moon
and he was like a cloud garlanded with cranes. There were armlets
on his arms, which were smeared with excellent sandalwood paste.
The armlets shone, the thick arms resembling five-hooded serpents.
He was seated on a large and excellent throne made out of crystal,
decorated with gems, and a superb spread was laid over this. There
were women on every side, ornamented exceedingly well. They
served him, standing close to him, with whisks made of hair in their
hands.

Four ministers, insolent because of their strength, were seated
there. These were the rakshasas Durdhara, Prahasta, the rakshasa
Mahaparshva and the minister, Nikumbha. These ministers were
skilled in all the techniques of counselling. They were like the
four oceans that surround the entire world. These ministers were
skilled in all the techniques of counselling and there were others
with auspicious intelligence. They were like the advisers of the gods,
comforting the lord of the gods.

Hanumat saw the infinitely energetic lord of the rakshasas. He
was seated, like a cloud full of water atop the summit of Meru. He[247]
had been oppressed by the rakshasas who were terrible in valour.
Filled with great wonder, he looked at the lord of the rakshasas.
Hanumat saw the radiant lord of the rakshasas. Confounded by
his energy, in his mind, he thought the following. 'What a form.
What patience. What spirit. What resplendence. Marked with all
the signs, the king of the rakshasas is wonderful. Had adharma not
become stronger, this lord of the rakshasas might have become the
protector of the world of the gods, and even of Shakra. All the
immortals and the danavas are indeed terrified of him. If he seeks to
become angry, he will reduce the entire world to a single ocean.'[248]
The intelligent ape thought this and many other things when he saw
the infinitely energetic power of the king of the rakshasas.

[247] Hanumat.
[248] This is what happens at the time of the universal destruction.

Chapter 5(48)

Ravana, who made the worlds shriek, was suffused with great rage. The mighty-armed one looked at the coppery eyed one who was standing in front of him. The king's eyes were coppery red with rage. He spoke words full of great meaning, appropriate at the time, to Prahasta, his excellent adviser. 'Ask the evil-souled one where he has come from. What is the reason why he has come here? Why did he destroy the grove and oppress the rakshasis?' Hearing Ravana's words, Prahasta spoke these words. 'O fortunate one! Be reassured. O ape! You have no reason to be terrified. Even if you have been sent by Indra to Ravana's residence, tell me the truth. O ape! Do not be scared. You will be released. You have assumed a beautiful form and have entered this city. Do you belong to Vaishravana, Yama or Varuna? Are you a messenger sent by Vishnu, who desires victory? Though you possess the form of an ape, your energy does not show you to be an ape. O ape! If you tell us the truth now, you will be released. If you do not speak the truth, it will be extremely difficult for you to remain alive. State the reason why you have entered Ravana's residence.'

The supreme ape was thus addressed by the lord of large numbers of rakshasas. He said, 'I do not belong to Shakra, Yama or Varuna. I have no friendship with the lord of riches[249] and Vishnu has not urged me. Since birth, I have been an ape and I have come here in that form. It is extremely difficult to see the Indra among the rakshasas and I have now seen him. I destroyed the grove of the king of the rakshasas so that I might be able to see him. At this, those strong rakshasas arrived, wishing to fight with me. Wishing to protect my own body, I fought against them in the battle. Even the gods and the asuras are incapable of tying me down in a bond made of weapons. I have that privilege because of a boon that was conferred on me by the grandfather. I surrendered to the weapon because I wished to desire the king. Though I have been freed from that weapon, I have been greatly oppressed by the rakshasas. Know

[249] Kubera.

that I am the messenger of the infinitely energetic Raghava. O lord!
Listen to my words. They are like medication.'

Chapter 5(49)

The supreme among apes was spirited. He saw the greatly
spirited Dashanana. Without any anxiety, he addressed him in
words that were full of meaning. 'I have come to your residence
because of Sugriva's command. O Indra among the rakshasas. Your
brother,[250] the lord of the apes, has asked about your welfare. Listen
to the instruction of the great-souled Sugriva, your brother. These
words are full of dharma and artha and will be beneficial in this
world and in the next. There was a king named Dasharatha and
he had chariots, elephants and horses. He was like a father and
friend to people and was like the lord of the gods in his radiance.
The lord, his mighty-armed eldest son, always did what brought his
father pleasure. Following his father's command, he left and entered
the forest of Dandaka. He was with his brother, Lakshmana, and
his wife, Sita. The immensely energetic one is named Rama and he
resorts to the path of dharma. His wife, devoted to her husband,
got lost in the forest. She is the daughter of the great-souled King
Janaka of Videha. With his younger brother, the prince searched
for the queen's trail. Having reached Rishyamuka, he met Sugriva,
who pledged that he would help search for Sita. Rama bestowed the
kingdom of the apes on Sugriva. Having slain Vali in an encounter,
the prince established Sugriva as the lord in the kingdom of large
numbers of apes and bears. Sugriva, devoted to the truth, was eager
to search for Sita's trail. The lord of the apes sent the apes in all
the directions. Hundreds, thousands and tens of thousands of apes
left to search in all the directions, above, below and in the sky.
Some of them are equal to Vinata's son.[251] Some of them are like

---

[250] The word brother is only meant to underline affection.
[251] Garuda.

the wind god. Those immensely strong and brave apes are swift
and nothing can obstruct their path. My name is Hanumat and
I am the biological son of the wind god. For Sita's sake, I have
quickly crossed one hundred yojanas. Wishing to see her, I crossed
the ocean and came here. You know about dharma and artha. You
have obtained the results of your austerities. O immensely wise one!
You should not confine someone else's wife. This is against dharma
and there are many kinds of dangers associated with such an act.
It destroys the foundation of someone who does it and intelligent
people like you should not do it. If Rama and Lakshmana resort to
their rage, who—not even the gods and the asuras—is capable of
standing before their arrows and escaping? O king! There is no one
in the three worlds who can cause harm to Raghava, and having
done that, enjoys happiness. Therefore, these beneficial words are
in conformity with dharma and artha in the three periods of time.[252]
Listen to them and return Janakee to the god among men. It is
extremely difficult to see the queen and it is through good fortune
that I accomplished that. The remaining and subsequent part of
the task will be undertaken by Raghava. I have noticed that Sita is
overcome by sorrow. You have seized her, without knowing that
she is like a five-hooded serpent. Her energy is such that she is like
swallowed food that is exceedingly mixed with poison. Even the
asuras and the immortals are incapable of digesting her. You have
obtained dharma and the fruits of your austerities. By seizing her,
you will destroy good policy, your own life and whatever you have
received. Because of your austerities, you see that you cannot be
killed by asuras and gods. Therefore, you consider yourself to be
great. Sugriva is not a god. Nor is he an asura, or human. He is not
a rakshasa, a gandharva, a yaksha or a serpent. O king! Raghava
is human and Sugriva is lord of the apes. O king! Therefore, how
will you be able to save your life? The fruits of dharma do not
coexist with the fruits of adharma. Since dharma destroys adharma,
search for that kind of fruit. There is no doubt that, so far, you
have obtained the fruits of dharma. You will soon reap the fruits

[252] Past, present and future.

of this adharma. Comprehend the slaying in Janasthana.[253] Also comprehend the slaying of Vali. For your own welfare, comprehend the friendship between Rama and Sugriva. If I so wish, I can single-handedly destroy Lanka, with its horses, chariots and elephants. But that is not what has been decided. In the presence of large numbers of apes and bears, Rama pledged that he would destroy the enemies who had oppressed Sita. Even if Purandara himself causes an injury to Rama, he cannot obtain happiness, not to speak of people like you. Know that the one who is under your subjugation, the one you know as Sita, is your night of destruction. She will destroy all of Lanka. In the form and image of Sita, this is a noose of destiny. You have yourself strung it around your neck. Think of how you can be safe. You will see this city, with its mansions and streets, burnt down, consumed by Sita's energy and suffering from Rama's rage.'

Without any distress and speaking skilfully, the unmatched ape made him hear these disagreeable words. Dashanana's eyes widened in anger. He commanded that the great ape should be killed.

Chapter 5(50)

Hearing the words of the great-souled ape, Ravana was senseless with anger and commanded that he should be killed. When the evil-souled Ravana ordered his death, Vibhishana suggested that this was not recommended for a messenger. Since the lord of the rakshasas was angry, he thought about the task that was at hand. Having determined what should be done, the victor over enemies pacified and worshipped his elder brother. The one who was excellent in the use of words spoke these exceedingly beneficial words. 'O king! This is contrary to dharma and is condemned as being against the conduct of the worlds. For someone brave like you, this is tantamount to murdering the ape. There is no doubt that this enemy is insolent and has done something disagreeable

[253] Of the rakshasas.

that can't be measured. However, the learned do not speak about
killing a messenger. There are many kinds of punishments indicated
for a messenger. Disfiguring the limbs, striking with a whip, shaving
the head and engraving marks on the body—these are said to be
the punishments for a messenger. But we have not heard about a
messenger being killed. Your intelligence is refined in dharma and
artha. You can certainly make up your mind about what is superior
and what is inferior. How can someone like you be immersed in
anger? Spirited people control their rage. You are supreme among
all the gods and the asuras. In what is said to be dharma, in the
conduct of people, in the sacred texts, in using one's intelligence
and for someone who is as brave as you, this should not be done.
I do not see any qualities associated with the killing of this ape.
That kind of punishment should be inflicted on those who have
sent this ape. Whether he is virtuous or wicked, others have sent
him here. He is dependent on others and has spoken the words of
others. One should not kill a messenger. O king! If he is killed, I do
not see anyone else who can travel through the sky and then return
here again, after crossing to the other shore of this great ocean. O
vanquisher of the cities of enemies! Therefore, do not make attempts
to kill him. You should not resort to attempts that facilitate the work
of the gods and Indra.[254] Those two sons of the king are insolent.
They love fighting. If he is killed, I do not see any other messenger
who can travel over this long distance unobstructed and goad those
two into battle. You are valiant, enterprising and spirited. The gods
and the asuras find you impossible to vanquish. You delight the
minds of the nairittas. When there is the prospect of a war, you
should not destroy that opportunity. There are brave and controlled
ones engaged in your welfare. They are born in noble lineages and
possess great qualities. They are spirited and supreme among those
who wield weapons. There are crores of well-armed warriors ahead
of you. You must make the enemy realize your power. Let someone
follow your command, take one part of your army and capture
those two foolish princes.'

[254] Who seek to eliminate Ravana.

Chapter 5(51)

The immensely strong Dashagriva heard the beneficial words spoken by his excellent brother, appropriate for the time and the place. He said, 'You have spoken well. The killing of a messenger is condemned. Certainly, it is someone else who should be killed. Let him be chastised. Indeed, the tail is the beloved ornament for apes. Let it be burnt swiftly and let him leave with a burnt tail. Let all his kin and well-wishers, friends and allies, see him in a distressed and afflicted state, with his limb disfigured.' The Indra among the rakshasas commanded the rakshasas to ignite his tail and carry him everywhere around the city, including the crossroads.

Harsh in their anger, the rakshasas heard his words. They bound up his tail in tattered cotton garments. As his tail was being bound, the great ape increased his size, like a fire in the forest when it has obtained some dry kindling. The rakshasas sprinkled his tail with oil and applied fire, igniting it. But his soul was filled with rage and intolerance and his face was like the rising sun. He flung them down. The cruel rakshasas assembled together and tied up the supreme among apes again. Having been tied up, the brave one made up his mind about what was appropriate at the time. 'Even if I am bound, these rakshasas are incapable of doing what they wish against me. I can again tear up the bonds, leap up and kill them. I am alone sufficient to fight against all the rakshasas in a battle. However, for the sake of pleasing Rama, I will tolerate this. I must again roam around Lanka. When I looked over Lanka during the night, I did not properly see the fortifications that have been laid out. Now that night is over, I must certainly examine these. If they wish, let them tie me up again and ignite my tail. Even if the rakshasas oppress me, I will not suffer from any mental exhaustion.' Therefore, the spirited and great ape reduced his size. Delighted, the rakshasas advanced and seized the elephant among the apes. With the sound of conch shells and drums, they announced their own deeds. The rakshasas, cruel in their deeds, roamed around the city with him. Hanumat wandered around the great city of the rakshasas. The great ape saw wonderful palaces. The grounds were laid out well and neatly divided by crossroads. The ape saw paths thick with houses, points at which roads met, crossroads, quadrangles and royal roads. Everywhere, the rakshasas announced that the ape was a spy.

When the tip of Hanumat's tail was being set on fire, the rakshasis, with malformed eyes, went and told the queen this disagreeable news. 'O Sita! The ape with a coppery red face had a conversation with you. His tail has been set on fire and he is being conveyed around.' She heard these words, which were as cruel as she herself being abducted. Vaidehi was tormented by grief and prayed to the fire god. She desired the welfare of the great ape. The large-eyed one controlled herself and worshipped the bearer of oblations. 'If I have served my husband, if I have observed austerities, if I have been devoted to a single husband, may you be cool to Hanumat. If the intelligent one[255] has any compassion towards me, if there is a little bit of good fortune left for me, may you be cool to Hanumat. If I possess good conduct, if the one with dharma in his soul[256] knows that I am eager to meet him, may you be cool to Hanumat. If the mighty-armed and noble Sugriva, devoted to the truth, can save me from this misery, may you be cool to Hanumat.' The one with eyes like those of a fawn circumambulated the flames of the fire, fierce in its rays. The fire flamed up, as if telling her that all would be well with the ape.

When the tail was on fire, the ape started to think. 'Why is this blazing fire not burning me down everywhere? It can be seen that the flames are large, but no pain is being caused to me. It is as if a ball of snow has been placed on the tip of my tail. When I leapt, I saw the extraordinary powers of Rama over the mountain[257] and the lord of the rivers. It is evident that this is something like that. For the intelligent Rama's sake, the ocean and Mainaka showed him respect. Why should the fire not act in a similar way? Because of Sita's non-violence, Raghava's energy and the friendship with

---

[255] An indirect reference to Rama.
[256] Rama.
[257] Mainaka.

my father,[258] the fire is not burning me.' The ape among elephants
again thought for an instant. The great ape leapt up with force and
roared. As tall as the summit of a mountain, the handsome one
went to the city's gate. The son of the wind god stood away from
the arrays of rakshasas. In an instant, he again became as large as
a mountain. Immediately, he assumed an extremely tiny form and
freed himself from the bonds. Having freed himself, the handsome
one again assumed the form of a mountain. He looked around and
found a club near the gate. It was polished with black iron and the
mighty-armed one seized it. Using this, the son of the wind god
killed all the guards. Valiant and terrible in battle, he slew them.
He then looked around Lanka again. His tail was on fire, with a
garland of flames. He was as radiant as the sun, with its garland
of rays.

Chapter 5(52)

Having accomplished his desire, the ape looked around Lanka.
His enthusiasm increased and he thought about the part of the
task that remained to be accomplished. 'What remains to be done?
What should I do now? How can the rakshasas be tormented again?
I have destroyed the grove. I have afflicted and slain the rakshasas. I
have destroyed part of the army. However, the fortification remains
to be destroyed. When the fortification is destroyed, the task will
easily be accomplished.[259] Even if a little bit of effort is made, the
effort will be successful. The bearer of oblations is blazing on my
tail. It is appropriate that I should offer these excellent houses to it as
kindling and satisfy it.' Thus, the great ape roamed around the tops
of the houses in Lanka. His tail was on fire, like a cloud tinged with
lightning. Hanumat released a fire that possessed flames like those
of the fire of destruction. United with the wind, it became extremely

[258] The wind god.
[259] Of invading Lanka.

strong and greatly powerful. The fire spread, blazing like the fire of destruction. Borne along by the wind, the ignited fire spread from one house to another one. There were nets made out of gold, pearls and jewels. The houses were full of extremely expensive gems and all these were destroyed. Like the abodes of the siddhas when they have exhausted their store of merit, those mansions were shattered and fell down on the ground. He saw colourful minerals oozing out from all the houses, mixed with diamonds, coral, lapis lazuli, pearls and silver. A fire is never satisfied with wood and grass that can be found here and there. Like that, Hanumat was not content with the destruction of the Indras among the rakshasas. Lanka seemed to have been struck by a curse. It was enveloped in blazing flames. It was like warriors retreating, when their foremost leaders have been killed. It was overcome by the strength of Hanumat's rage. The rakshasas were scared and distressed. They were terrified because of the blazing flames of the fire. The great-minded Hanumat saw Lanka in this state, as if it had been struck by Svayambhu's rage.[260] He had killed a large number of rakshasas. He had destroyed the grove and many trees. He had released the fire in the abodes of the rakshasas. In his mind, the great-souled one reached out to Rama. The great ape, supreme among apes, ignited all of Lanka with the fire from his tail and then put that out in the ocean.[261]

Chapter 5(53)

The city was on fire and destroyed. The large numbers of rakshasas were terrified. On seeing Lanka in this state, the ape Hanumat started to think. 'A great fear has arisen here, and there is a sense of self-loathing in me. Having performed the task of burning Lanka down, have I done something that should not have been done? The best among men who use their intelligence to restrain the

---

[260] This is probably an oblique reference to the destruction that comes at the end of one of Brahma's days.

[261] The fire on the tail.

anger that has arisen, like water is used to quench a fire, are blessed and great-souled. If the noble Janakee was consumed in the process of burning down Lanka, in my ignorance, I will have destroyed the task of my lord. The reason why this task was started will have become unsuccessful. By burning down Lanka, I have not been able to save Sita. There is no doubt that I have accomplished a desired task. However, having been overcome by rage, I have destroyed the foundation. It is evident that Janakee has been destroyed. Nothing that can be seen has not been burnt. Everything in the city of Lanka has been burnt and nothing remains. The task has been rendered futile because of a confusion in my intelligence. Therefore, the idea of giving up my life here appeals to me. Shall I leap into the fire now, or shall I use the fire with the mare's head?[262] Shall I offer my body up to the creatures who reside in the ocean? If I remain alive, how can I possibly see the lord of the apes? Having destroyed all aspects of the task, how can I meet those two tigers among men? Indeed, I have exhibited the taint that arises from anger. In the three worlds, apes are known for their fickleness. Shame on the sentiments of *rajas*.[263] That has led to this helplessness and instability. Though my lord had asked me to, because of my passion, I have not been able to protect Sita. When Sita is destroyed, both of them[264] will be destroyed. When they are destroyed, Sugriva and his relatives will also be destroyed. Bharata has dharma in his soul and is affectionate towards his brother. When he hears this, with Shatrughna, will he be able to remain alive? The lineage of the Ikshvakus is devoted to dharma. When it is destroyed, there is no doubt that all the subjects will be afflicted and tormented by grief. Therefore, I am unfortunate and have destroyed the accumulation of dharma and artha. With my soul overcome by the taint of anger, it is evident that I have destroyed the world.' While he was thinking this, some omens presented themselves before him. Having himself experienced these earlier, he started to think again. 'Perhaps the fortunate one who

---

[262] Vadavamukha, the subterranean fire in the ocean.

[263] There are three qualities (*guna*)—*sattva* (goodness), rajas (passion and energy) and *tamas* (inactivity and darkness). This refers to the quality of passion and energy.

[264] Rama and Lakshmana.

is beautiful in all her limbs has been protected by her own energy. A fire does not destroy another fire. She is the wife of the infinitely energetic one, with dharma in his soul. She is also protected by her own good conduct and the fire will not touch her. When I engaged in my task of burning everything down, because of Rama's powers and Vaidehi's good deeds, the fire will not have consumed her. He is like a god to his three brothers, Bharata and the others. Rama's mind is devoted to her. How could she have been destroyed? The unmanifest lord[265] is the one who spreads everywhere and burns. But it did not burn my tail. How could it have burnt the noble one? Because of her austerities, truthfulness in speech and single-minded devotion towards her husband, the fire cannot burn her. The fire has not consumed her.'

He was thinking there, about the queen's devotion to dharma. At that time, Hanumat heard the words of the great-souled charanas. 'Indeed, Hanumat has performed a task that is extremely difficult to withstand. He has unleashed a fire in the residence of the terrible rakshasa. He has burnt this city of Lanka, with its mansions, ramparts and gates. However, Janakee was not burnt and we are astounded at this extraordinary event.' On seeing the auspicious omens, which were full of great qualities, and also because he heard the words of the rishis, Hanumat was delighted in his mind. The ape accomplished the desire in his mind. He got to know that the princess was unharmed. He made up his mind that he would return only after he had seen her once again.

Chapter 5(54)

Janakee was at the foot of the shimshapa tree. He presented himself before her, greeted her and said, 'It is good fortune that I see you here, unharmed.' As he prepared to leave, Sita looked at him repeatedly. Filled with affection towards her husband, she

[265] The fire.

addressed Hanumat in these words. 'If you so wish, you can single-handedly accomplish this task. O destroyer of enemy heroes! You are sufficient. This increase in your strength is laudable. However, if Kakutstha attacks Lanka and takes me away, that will be worthy of him. Therefore, tell him the truth so that the great-souled one is urged to exhibit a valour in the battle that is worthy of him.' Hanumat heard these humble words, full of reason. He replied in these words. 'Surrounded by the brave ones among the apes and the bears, Kakutstha will swiftly come here. He will vanquish the enemy in the battle and dispel your grief.' Hanumat, the son of the wind god, assured Vaidehi in this way. Having made up his mind to leave, he worshipped Vaidehi.

The tiger among the apes was eager to see his lord. The crusher of enemies climbed up Arishta, supreme among mountains. There were herds of elephants on the summit. There were dark blue forests. It was surrounded by many sala, tala, ashvakarna trees and bamboos. It was ornamented with flowering creepers. It was full of many kinds of animals. It was decorated with streaks of minerals. There were many waterfalls. There were piles of boulders. It was frequented by maharshis, yakshas, gandharvas, kinnaras and serpents. There was a dense growth of creepers and trees. The caves were populated by lions. There were large numbers of tigers. The trees had succulent roots and fruits. The extremely strong one, supreme among apes, climbed that mountain. He was goaded by the joy of soon being able to see Rama. The beautiful peaks of the mountain were crushed by his steps. Making a loud noise, the boulders were shattered. Having ascended the Indra among mountains, the great ape increased his size. He wished to cross from the southern shore to the northern shore of the salty ocean. The brave son of the wind god climbed the mountain. He then saw the terrible ocean, frequented by fish and serpents. Like the wind, the son of the wind god took to the sky. From the southern direction, the tiger among apes headed for the northern direction. The ape pressed down on that excellent mountain and it entered the ground, with all the creatures inhabiting it shrieking. The peaks trembled and the trees fell down. The flowering trees were crushed by the force of his thighs. Destroyed, they fell down on the ground, as if they had been struck by Shakra's weapon. There were extremely energetic lions inhabiting the caverns and these were afflicted. They roared in terrible voices and the sound was like that of the sky being shattered. The vidyadhara women leapt up suddenly from the mountain, terrified, their garments dishevelled and their ornaments flung away. There were extremely large and powerful serpents, with flaming tongues and filled with great poison. When their hoods and necks were crushed, they writhed. The kinnaras, the gandharvas, the yakshas and the vidyadharas suffered. They abandoned that supreme mountain and took to the sky. The beautiful mountain was afflicted by that powerful one. With its trees and tall peaks, it entered rasatala. The mountain was ten yojanas wide and thirty yojanas tall. It became level with the earth.

Chapter 5(55)

Without any exhaustion, he leapt across the sky, which was like an ocean. The moon was like a beautiful water lily. The sun was like an auspicious karandava. The Tishya[266] and Shravana nakshatras were like swans. The clouds were like moss and lichen. The nakshatra Punarvasu was like a giant fish. The red-limbed one[267] was like a giant crocodile. Airavata was like a large island. Svati nakshatra was like a graceful swan. The wind was like turbulent waves. The beams of the moon were like cool water. The serpents, yakshas and gandharvas were like full-blown lotuses and lilies. As he traversed through the extensive sky, the abode of the wind, the handsome ape seemed to devour the sky and etch a painting on the lord of the stars.[268] It was as if he was about to steal the sky, with its nakshatras and the solar disc. As he proceeded, Hanumat seemed to fling away the nets of clouds. There were large and dense

[266] Also known as Pushya.
[267] Mars.
[268] The moon.

clouds in the sky, possessing many hues—white, red, blue, yellow, green and pink. He repeatedly entered these nets of clouds and emerged again. He seemed to be like the moon, sometimes hidden and sometimes visible. He roared loudly, in a tone like that of a large cloud. The immensely energetic one again proceeded through the middle of the ocean. The valiant one touched the Indra among mountains[269] that possessed an excellent nave. With great force, like an iron arrow released from a bowstring, he approached it. After some time, he saw the great mountain Mahendra. It was like a cloud and the bull among apes roared.

In every direction, the apes heard the sound of this roar. All of them were eager, desiring to see their well-wisher. Jambavat, supreme among apes, was delighted in his mind. He summoned all the apes and addressed them in these words. 'There is no doubt that, in every way, Hanumat has been successful in his objective. Had he not been successful, he would not have roared in this way.' The apes heard the force of his arms and thighs and the great-souled one's roar. They rejoiced. Here and there, they started to jump around. Delighted, they leapt around from the summit of one mountain to the summit of another mountain. They wished to see Hanumat. Rejoicing, they seized flowering branches from the tops of the trees. The apes waved these around, as if they were garments. The great ape descended, like a giant cloud. On seeing him, all the apes stood there, their hands joined in salutation. The summit of Mount Mahendra was dense with trees. With great force, the ape, who was like a mountain himself, descended there. All the bulls among apes were delighted in their minds. They surrounded the great-souled Hanumat. Filled with great delight, all of them surrounded him. Since he had returned safe, their faces were full of joy. They brought gifts, roots and fruits, and offered these to him. The apes honoured the best among apes, the son of the wind god. They were happy. Some started to cackle. Rejoicing, some other bulls among apes brought the branches of trees.

[269] Mainaka.

Hanumat, the great ape, worshipped the seniors and the aged, Jambavat and the others, and Prince Angada. He was worshipped by the two of them[270] and honoured by the other apes. The brave one briefly stated, 'I have seen the queen.' He grasped the hand of Vali's son and sat down in a beautiful spot in a spot on Mahendra. Happy, Hanumat told the bulls among the apes, 'I have seen Janaka's daughter in Ashokavana. The unblemished one is protected by extremely terrible rakshasis. Desiring to see Rama, the child has her hair in a single braid. She is tired because of her fasting. Her garments are soiled. Her hair is matted. She is emaciated.' Maruti spoke these words, which were full of great meaning and like amrita. On hearing this, all the apes were delighted. Some whooped. Others yelled. Other extremely strong ones roared. Some cackled, Others roared back in response. Delighted, some other elephants among apes lashed their tails. Some raised their long and curved tails and waved them around. There were other apes who were like elephants. In their joy, they leapt down from the summit of the mountain and touched Hanumat. In the midst of the brave ones among the apes, when Hanumat spoke those words, Angada spoke these excellent words. 'There is no ape who is your equal in spirit and valour. You have leapt across the extensive ocean and returned again. It is through good fortune that you have seen the illustrious queen who is Rama's wife. It is through good fortune that Kakutstha will now abandon the grief that has resulted from his separation with Sita.' Delighted, the apes sat down on large boulders and surrounded Angada, Hanumat and Jambavat. Those excellent apes wished to hear about the leaping across the ocean and the sight of Lanka, Sita and Ravana. All of them joined their hands in salutation and looked towards Hanumat's face. The handsome Angada was surrounded by many apes. He was worshipped by them, like the lord of the gods surrounded by the gods in heaven. There was the illustrious and famous Hanumat. There was Angada, with armlets on his arms. Filled with those delighted ones, the large and tall summit of the mountain blazed in its prosperity.

[270] Jambavat and Angada.

Chapter 5(56)

On the summit of Mount Mahendra, with Hanumat at the forefront, the supremely strong apes were filled with great delight. Jambavat, rejoicing, asked the delighted great ape, the son of the wind god, about the details of the task he had undertaken. 'How did you see the queen? What happened there? What is the conduct of Dashanana, cruel in his deeds, towards her? O great ape! I am asking you the truth about everything. After having heard, we will again decide about what course of action should be taken next. When we go to the one who has control over his soul[271] and speak to him, tell us what we can reveal to him and what must be kept a secret.'

Thus addressed, his body hair stood up. He bowed his head down in the direction of Queen Sita and replied, 'In your presence, I came to the summit of Mahendra and leapt up into the sky. I controlled myself, desiring to reach the southern shore of the ocean. While I proceeded, a terrible impediment presented itself before me. A saw an extremely charming, golden and divine mountain. It obstructed my path and I thought the mountain was an impediment. I approached that divine, golden and supreme mountain. I made up my mind that I would have to shatter it. I struck that great mountain with my tail. The summit was like the sun and it shattered into one thousand fragments. Knowing what was my intention, the great mountain addressed me as a "son" and those sweet words delighted my mind.[272] "Know me to be your father's brother. I am the friend of the wind god. I am famous as Mainaka and I reside in the great ocean. O son! All the supreme mountains used to possess wings earlier. They freely roamed around the earth, causing obstructions everywhere. Hearing about the conduct of the mountains, the illustrious and great Indra, the chastiser of Paka, used his vajra to shatter their wings into thousands of fragments. O child! I was saved because your great-souled father, the wind god, hurled me

---

[271] Rama.

[272] In different places, the sequence of meeting Mainaka, Surasa and Simhika varies.

into the great ocean. O scorcher of enemies! I must seek to help
Rama. Rama is supreme among those who uphold dharma and he
is like the great Indra in his valour." I heard this from the great-
souled Mainaka. I told the mountain about the task that was in my
mind. Then, the great-souled Mainaka granted me permission.
Resorting to excellent speed, I proceeded along the rest of the
journey. For a very long period of time, I speedily proceeded along
the path. I then saw the goddess Surasa, the mother of the serpents.
In the midst of the ocean, the goddess addressed me in these words.
"O supreme among apes! The immortals have indicated that I can
devour you. Therefore, I must eat you. You have come to me after
a long time." When Surasa told me this, I joined my hands in
salutation and stood before her. With my face pale, I addressed her
in these words. "The prosperous Rama, Dasharatha's son and the
scorcher of enemies, has entered the forest of Dandaka with his
brother, Lakshmana, and Sita. The evil-souled Ravana has abducted
his wife, Sita. Following Rama's command, I am going to him as a
messenger. O one who resides in his dominion! You should seek to
help Rama. Otherwise, after seeing Maithilee and Rama, unblemished
in his deeds, I will present myself before your mouth. I am truthfully
pledging this. Listen to me." Surasa can assume any form at will
and she was thus addressed by me. She said, "No one can transgress
the boon that I received." Surasa was ten yojanas wide and said
this. In an instant, I extended myself to a size of fifteen yojanas. She
extended her mouth to make it as large as my size. On seeing her
extended mouth, I reduced my form. In an instant, I again assumed
the size of a thumb. I quickly descended into her mouth and in an
instant, emerged again. Assuming her own form, the goddess Surasa
again spoke to me. "O supreme among apes! O amiable one! May
you accomplish your objective. Go happily. Bring Vaidehi back to
the great-souled Raghava. O mighty-armed one! O ape! May you
be happy. I am pleased with you." At this, all the creatures uttered
words of praise to me. After this, like Garuda, I leapt up into the
extensive sky. My shadow was seized, but I could not see anything.
Having lost my speed, I looked around in the ten directions. I could
not see anything that could have robbed me of my speed. I thought,

"Who has caused this obstruction in my path? This kind of impediment has arisen, but no form can be seen." While I was thinking, I cast my glance in a downward direction and I saw a terrible rakshasi lying down in the water. The terrible one laughed and roared loudly. Without the slightest bit of fear, the horrible one addressed me in these words. "O large one! Who are you and where are you going? I am hungry and you have been desired by me. Be my food and please my body. I have been without food for a long time." I agreed to her words. I increased my size so that it became larger than what her mouth could hold. Desiring to devour me, the terrible one also started to increase the size of her large mouth. She did not understand me, nor the changes I brought about in my form. In an instant, I reduced my large size. Having seized her heart, I leapt up into the sky again. I extracted her heart, which was like a mountain. Extending her arms, the terrible one fell down in the salty waters. I heard the siddhas and charanas who were in the sky. "The terrible rakshasi, Simhika, has been quickly slain by Hanumat." Having killed her, I again remembered what remained to be done. After having travelled a long distance, I saw the southern shore of the ocean, decorated by trees. The city of Lanka is there. I reached the city that was the abode of the rakshasas when the sun was about to set. Undetected by the guards, terrible in their valour, I entered. There, I searched throughout the night for Janaka's daughter. Though I went to Ravana's inner quarters, I did not see the slender-waisted one there. Finally, I saw Sita in Ravana's abode. She could not see how she would reach the other shore of her ocean of grief. I saw her grieving, in a spot surrounded by walls. There was an excellent grove and a house constructed out of gold. Leaping over the wall, I saw many trees. In the midst of Ashokavana, there was a large shimshapa tree. Ascending that, I saw a grove of golden plantain trees. I saw the supremely beautiful one, not very far from the shimshapa tree. She was young and her eyes were like the petals of lotuses. Because of fasting, her face was emaciated. She was surrounded by cruel and disfigured rakshasis, who devour flesh and blood, like a deer by tigresses. I saw the lady, Rama's unblemished wife. I saw her, near that shimshapa tree. Then I heard an uproar, mixed with the sounds of girdles and anklets, in Ravana's residence and it increased in volume. Extremely anxious, I reduced my own size. Like a bird, I hid myself in the dense growth of the shimshapa tree. After this, the immensely strong Ravana and Ravana's wives reached the spot where Sita was. The beautiful Sita saw the lord of large numbers of rakshasas. She compressed her thighs and her thick breasts and covered them with her arms. Sita was supremely miserable and Dashagriva spoke to her. She did not say anything. He bowed his head down and said, "Treat me with a great deal of respect. O proud one! O Sita! Because of your insolence, if you do not welcome me, after two months, I will drink your blood." She heard the words of the evil-souled Ravana. Extremely angry, Sita spoke these excellent words. "O worst among rakshasas! I am the wife of the infinitely energetic Rama. I am the daughter-in-law of Dasharatha, the protector of the lineage of the Ikshvakus. Having spoken something that should not have been said, how has your tongue not fallen down? O ignoble one! Where is your valour? You came to abduct me when my husband was not present. You committed that crime when you were not seen by the great-souled one. You are not Rama's equal, not in serving, nor in fighting. Raghava performs sacrifices. He is truthful in speech. He prides himself in fighting." When Janakee spoke these harsh words, Dashanana suddenly blazed with anger, like a fire on a funeral pyre. The cruel one dilated his eyes and raised his right fist. When he was about to kill Maithilee, the women present started to wail. From among those women, one of the evil-souled one's wives rose up.[273] This beautiful one was named Mandodari and she restrained him. He was afflicted by desire and she addressed him in sweet words. "What do you have to do with Sita? You are like the great Indra in your valour. O lord! Find pleasure with the daughters of the gods, the gandharvas and the yakshas. What will you do with Sita?" Together, the assembled women quickly raised the immensely strong roamer in the night and took his away to his own residence.

---

[273] Earlier, we were told that Dhanyamalini restrained Ravana, Mandodari not having been mentioned.

When Dashagriva left, the rakshasis, with disfigured faces, censured Sita in cruel and extremely terrible words. Janakee reckoned that their words were like blades of grass. Though they censured Sita, they were unsuccessful in their attempts. After a while, those rakshasis, the devourers of flesh, refrained from their futile censure and roaring. They went and informed Ravana about Sita's great resolution. All of them assembled together, having lost their hopes and enterprise. They surrounded her from all directions and came under the subjugation of sleep. When they fell asleep, Sita remained engaged in the welfare of her husband. She lamented in piteous and distressed tones and extremely miserable, grieved. I saw Sita in that extremely terrible state. Though I had rested, because I thought about it, my mind was not at peace. Thinking about a means to start a conversation with Janakee, I started to praise the lineage of the Ikshvakus, worshipped by large numbers of royal sages. Having heard the words I had spoken, the queen replied to me, her eyes overflowing with tears. "O bull among the apes! Who are you? Whom do you belong to? Why have you come here? Why are you affectionate towards Rama? You should tell me this." Hearing her words, I uttered the following words. "O queen! Your husband, Rama, has an aide who is terrible in his valour. The brave one's name is Sugriva and the immensely strong one is the Indra among the apes. Know that I am his servant. I am Hanumat and I have come here. Your husband, Rama, unblemished in his deeds, has sent me here. O illustrious one! The prosperous tiger among men, Dasharatha's son, himself gave me this ring to give you, as a sign. Therefore, I wish that you should command me. O queen! What should I do now? Shall I convey you to Rama and Lakshmana's side? What is your reply?" Sita, Janaka's daughter, heard my words and understood. She said, "Let Raghava destroy Ravana and take me back." I bowed my head down before the noble and unblemished queen. I sought a sign that would bring pleasure to Raghava's heart. Thus addressed, the beautiful one gave me an excellent and supreme jewel. Having given it to me, she was extremely anxious and also gave me a message to convey in words. I controlled myself and bowed down before the princess. I circumambulated her and made up my mind to return here. However, having made up her mind, she again replied. She said, "O Hanumat! You must tell Raghava about what is happening to me here. Hearing that, the brave Rama and Lakshmana, with Sugriva, must quickly come here. Act accordingly. If that does not happen, two months of my life are left. Kakutstha will not be able to see me. I will die like one without a protector." Hearing her piteous words, I was filled with rage. Thereafter, I thought about what remained to be accomplished of the task. I increased my size, so that it became like a mountain. Desiring to fight, I started to destroy that grove. The clumps in the grove were destroyed and the terrified animals and birds started to flee. Having woken up, the rakshasis, with disfigured faces, started to look around. Seeing me in that grove, they assembled from here and there. Having assembled, they quickly went and told Ravana about this. "O king! An evil-souled one has destroyed your impenetrable grove. O immensely strong one! The ape does not know about your valour. O Indra among kings! Because of his wicked intelligence, he has done this disagreeable act towards you. Quickly command that he should be killed, so that he can head towards his destruction." Hearing this, the Indra among the rakshasas unleashed rakshasas named kimkaras. They were extremely difficult to defeat and they followed Ravana's inclinations. There were eighty thousand of them, with spears and clubs in their hands. With a club, I killed them in that part of the grove. When these were killed, the remaining ones lost their valour. They went and told Ravana that I had killed his soldiers. I then thought of attacking the chaitya and mansion there. With a pillar, I again killed one hundred rakshasas who were there. This was like an ornament of Lanka and it was destroyed by me. He then commanded Prahasta, Jambumali's son. He was with many rakshasas. They were fearful and terrible in form. That rakshasa possessed strength and was accomplished in fighting. However, with an extremely terrible club, I killed him and his followers. Hearing this, the Indra among the rakshasas sent an extremely strong son of one of his ministers. Ravana sent him, with a large army of foot soldiers. With the club, I conveyed all of them to Yama's abode. Hearing that the son of the minister had been

killed, Ravana sent four brave commanders, who were dexterous in
exhibiting their valour in a battle. I killed all of them, with their
soldiers. Dashagriva again sent his extremely strong son, Aksha.
Ravana sent him to fight, with a large number of rakshasas. The
prince, who was Mandodari's son, was learned about fighting. He
suddenly leapt up into the sky, with a sword and a shield. However,
I seized him by the feet. Whirling him around one hundred times, I
flung him down and crushed him. Dashanana heard that Aksha had
been killed. Ravana's second son is named Indrajit. Extremely
angry, he commanded this powerful one, who is invincible in battle.
In the encounter, I destroyed the energy of all those soldiers and
that of the bull among rakshasas. Having done this, I was filled with
great delight. However, the mighty-armed and immensely strong
one made great and renewed efforts. He had been sent by Ravana
with other brave ones, who were crazy and intoxicated. The
extremely swift one bound me down with a brahmastra. The
rakshasas bound me with ropes. Having seized me, they dragged me
to Ravana's presence. On seeing me, the evil-souled Ravana asked,
"Why have you come to Lanka? Why have you killed the rakshasas?"
I told him, "I have done everything for Sita's sake. O lord! Desiring
to see her, I came to your residence. I am the biological son of the
wind god. I am the ape Hanumat. Know me to be the ape who is
Rama's messenger and Sugriva's adviser. I have come here before
you with Rama's message. Listen to the message that I am conveying
to you. It is full of dharma and artha. It is beneficial and is like
medication. 'While I dwelt in the mountain Rishyamuka, filled with
large trees, I contracted a friendship with Raghava, who is valiant
in battle.[274] O king! He told me that his wife had been abducted by
a rakshasa. I undertook a pledge that I would help him. The lord
Sugriva had been deprived of his kingdom by Vali.[275] With the fire
as a witness, Raghava and Lakshmana contracted a pledge of
friendship with him. In the encounter, using a single arrow, he
destroyed Vali. He made the lord of the apes the great king over all

[274] This message is being delivered by Sugriva, which is odd.

[275] Though this is Sugriva's message, Sugriva is being mentioned in the third person.

the apes. With all our souls, we must now endeavour to help him. That is the reason, following dharma, he[276] is being sent to your presence. Swiftly bring Sita and hand her over to Raghava. Otherwise, the brave apes will destroy your army. From earlier times, who does not know about the power of the apes? They are invited to go, even to the presence of the gods.' I have told you what the king of the apes told me to tell you." When I said this, he looked at me with anger in his eyes, as if he was going to burn me down. He commanded the rakshasas, terrible in their deeds, to kill me. He has a brother named Vibhishana, who is extremely intelligent. For my sake, he beseeched the king of the rakshasas. "O tiger among the rakshasas. This should not be done. Abandon this thought. O rakshasa! The texts on royal policy have said that a messenger must not be killed. Instead, those who speak beneficial words say that the true message must be extracted from a messenger. O one who is unmatched in valour! Even if a messenger commits a grave crime, he can be disfigured. The sacred texts say that he must not be killed." Having heard Vibhishasana's words, Ravana instructed the rakshasas who were present to immediately set my tail on fire. Hearing his words, from every side, they bound up my tail in straw, bark and cotton cloth. Terrible in their valour, the rakshasas roared like lions. They struck me with staffs and fists and set my tail on fire. Tied up by the rakshasas with many ropes, I was like a puppet. However, I did not suffer at all and looked at the city during the day. The brave rakshasas bound me up and applied fire to me. They announced this along the royal roads and arrived at the city's gate. After this, I assumed an extremely gigantic form and again contracted myself. I freed myself from those bonds and assumed my natural form. Seizing an iron club, I killed those rakshasas. After that, with great force, I leapt on to the city's gate. With my tail, I set fire to the city and its mansions and turrets. Without any fear, I burnt down everything, like the fire of destruction does to subjects. Having burnt Lanka down, I again had a doubt. Having burnt Lanka down, I was unsure whether I had burnt Sita down in the

---

[276] Hanumat.

process. Then I heard words spoken by the charanas, uttered in auspicious syllables. They said, "It is amazing that Janakee has not been burnt down." Hearing those extraordinary words, I again had another thought. I went and saw Vaidehi again and took leave from her yet again. It is because of Raghava's powers, your energy and to accomplish Sugriva's objective that I have done all this. I have done all this there, properly. Now let us do all that which remains to be done.'

Chapter 5(57)

Hanumat, the son of the wind god, told them everything. He then again started to speak these excellent words. 'Because of Raghava's enterprise, Sugriva's efforts and Sita's good conduct, I was able to perform that great leap. O bull among the apes! The noble Sita's conduct is worthy of her. Ravana can burn down the worlds because of his austerities. If he is angry, he can burn them down. The lord of the rakshasas is powerful in every way. Though he touched her body, he has not been destroyed because of his austerities. It is like touching a flame with one's hand. That is the reason she has not behaved like a flame of fire. If she is enraged, Janaka's daughter is capable of removing all sins. In the midst of the evil-souled Ravana's Ashokavana, the virtuous one is in that pitiable state, under the shimshapa tree. She is tormented by grief and is surrounded by the rakshasis. She is like the marks on the moon, losing all resplendence at having been surrounded by the marks of clouds. Vaidehi does not think of Ravana, who is insolent because of his strength. Though Janakee has been confined, the one with the excellent hips is devoted to her husband. In all her soul, the auspicious Vaidehi is devoted to Rama. She is single-mindedly devoted to Rama, like Puloma's daughter to Purandara. She is attired in a single piece of garment, though it is soiled and covered with dust. She is tormented by griefs. Her limbs are miserable. Sita is engaged in her husband's welfare. In the midst of the rakshasis, she is repeatedly censured. I saw her in that pleasure garden, amidst malformed rakshasis. She is distressed and wears her hair in a single braid. She is devoted to thinking about her husband. She lies down on the ground. Her limbs are faded, like a lotus at the onset of the winter. In her attempt to refuse Ravana, she has made up her mind to die. Somehow, I managed to instil confidence in the one with eyes like those of a fawn. Thereafter, I spoke to her and told her everything. Hearing about the friendship between Rama and Sugriva, she was filled with joy. She is controlled and full of good conduct. She is excellent in devotion to her husband. That is the reason she has not killed the great-souled Dashagriva Dashanana. Rama will only be the instrument in bringing about his death.[277] Full of grief, the immensely fortunate Sita is like this. Everything that must now be done should be undertaken.'

Chapter 5(58)

Hearing his words, Vali's son took the permission of all the great apes, with Jambavat at the forefront. 'In this situation, let me tell you what I think we should do. It is proper that we should see those two princes when we have Vaidehi with us. I am alone sufficient to go to the city that is full of large numbers of rakshasas. I will quickly destroy Lanka and the immensely strong Ravana and bring her back, not to speak of a situation where I have these brave and powerful ones, who have cleansed their souls, with me. The apes are accomplished in the use of weapons. They are capable of ensuring victory. In the battle, I will destroy Ravana, with his soldiers, his vanguard, his sons and his brothers. Shakrajit's[278] weapons may be impossible to countenance in a battle—they are Brahma, Aindra, Roudra, Vayavya and Varuna weapons.[279] But

---

[277] That is, the real cause is Sita.

[278] Indrajit's.

[279] Divine weapons respectively associated with Brahma, Indra, Rudra, Vayu and Varuna.

I will destroy them and kill the rakshasas. I seek your permission
to restrain them with my valour. I will incessantly shower down a
continuous downpour of boulders. I can kill even the gods in an
encounter, not to speak of the roamers in the night. The ocean may
cross the shoreline, Mandara may tremble, but the army of soldiers
cannot make Jambavat quake in a battle. The brave ape who is
Vayu's son is sufficient to destroy all the numerous rakshasas
and the rakshasas who are their ancestors. From the force of the
thighs of Panasa and that of the great-souled Nila, Mandara can
be shattered, not to speak of rakshasas in the battle. Among the
gods, the asuras, the yakshas, the gandharvas, the serpents and
the birds, tell me who can fight against Mainda and Dvivida.
These two supreme among apes are extremely forceful and are
the sons of the two Ashvins. These two are proud that they have
received excellent boons from the grandfather. They are supremely
haughty. In earlier times, to show respect to the two Ashvins,
the grandfather of all the worlds gave them the unmatched boon
that no one would be able to kill them. Haughty and intoxicated
because of the boon, these two brave apes crushed a large army of
the gods and drank amrita. All the other apes can stand and watch.
When they are enraged, these two brave apes are alone capable
of destroying Lanka, with its horses, chariots and elephants. Even
though the queen has been seen, it is not proper for the apes to
go to the great-souled Raghava's presence without her. It is not
appropriate for you,[280] famous for your valour, to report that you
have seen the queen, but have not brought her back. O supreme
among apes! Even in the world of the immortals and the daityas,
there is no one who is our equal in leaping and valour. Hanumat
has killed the brave ones among the rakshasas. What should we do
now? We should get Janakee?'

He had thus made up his mind. However, Jambavat, supreme
among apes and one who understood the objective, though extremely
delighted, spoke these words that were full of meaning. 'O prince!
It is as you perceive it. We are not incapable of doing what you

---

[280] This is directed at Hanumat.

have made up your mind about. But you must consider what Rama intends and then determine the best means of accomplishing the objective.'

Chapter 5(59)[281]

The residents of the forest, the brave ones with Angada at the forefront, and the great ape, Hanumat, accepted the words that Jambavat had spoken. With Vayu's son at the forefront, all of them were delighted. The bulls among the apes abandoned the summit of Mahendra and started to leap away. They were like Meru and Mandara and like maddened elephants. Those immensely strong ones, gigantic in size, shrouded the sky. Hanumat was in control of his soul and greatly strong. He was worshipped by all creatures. His force was great, as if he was being borne along by the power of sight. His purpose was to accomplish his lord, Raghava's, objective, and to obtain great fame. All the foremost ones wished to tell their loved ones what had happened. All of them were delighted at the prospect of war. All the spirited ones had made up their minds about ensuring Rama's revenge. Those residents of the forest leapt. They leapt up into the sky. They reached a forest that was like Nandana, filled with trees and creepers. There was a grove named Madhuvana there and it was protected by Sugriva. It could not be approached by any creature and it pleased the hearts of all beings. An immensely brave ape named Dadhimukha always protected it. This foremost among apes was the great-souled Sugriva's maternal uncle. Having approached the large and beautiful grove that belonged to the Indra among the apes, the apes became extremely ferocious. Delighted, the apes saw the gigantic Madhuvana. Tawny, with the complexion of honey,[282]

---

[281] This entire incident of Madhuvana is irrelevant to the main line of the story and may well have been inserted later.

[282] Madhu is honey, so *madhuvana* means a grove filled with honey. Madhu also means liquor and the apes clearly became intoxicated.

the apes asked the prince[283] for some honey. After taking the permission of the aged apes, with Jambavat at the forefront, the prince gave them permission to taste some honey. The residents of the forest were delighted at having obtained the permission. Filled with joy, they began to dance around, here and there. Some sang, others bowed down. Some danced, others laughed. Some fell down, others wandered around. Some leapt, others spoke incoherently. Some leaned against each other. Some spoke excessively to each other. Some leapt from one tree to another tree. Some leapt down from trees on to the ground. With great force, some sprang down from the tops of large trees on to the ground. Some sang, others laughed and approached others. Some laughed, others laughed at others. Some wept, others made others weep. Some roared, others made others roar. The soldiers in the army of the apes were excited. Having drunk the honey, they were haughty and intoxicated. There was no one there who was not drunk. There was no one there who was not satiated. The ape named Dadhivaktra[284] saw that the grove was being destroyed and the trees, full of leaves and flowers, were also being destroyed. He was filled with anger and tried to restrain the apes. While they raged, the aged ape, the protector of the grove, reprimanded them. The immensely fierce and energetic one thought of means to protect the grove from those apes. He addressed some in harsh words. He approached others and struck them with his palms. He approached others and made them quarrel with each other. He approached others and tried conciliation. However, they were intoxicated and forcibly countered him. He couldn't restrain them by force. They got together and fearlessly attacked him. They saw nothing wrong in dragging him along in this way. They struck him with their nails. They bit him with their teeth. All the assembled apes struck the ape with their palms and feet. In their intoxication, they robbed the great forest of all its possessions.[285]

---

[283] Angada.
[284] Dadhivaktra is the same as Dadhimukha.
[285] Flowers, fruits and trees.

Chapter 5(60)

Hanumat, best among apes and bull among the apes, told them, 'O apes! Without any anxiety in your minds, drink the honey.' Hearing Hanumat's words, the supreme one among the apes, Angada, was delighted in his mind and told the apes to drink the honey. 'I must certainly make Hanumat's words come true and do what he says, even if it is a task that should not be performed, not to speak of at a time like this.'[286] Hearing the words that emerged from Angada's mouth, the bulls among apes were delighted and praised him. The apes honoured him. All the apes worshipped Angada, bull among the apes. Like the flow of a swift river, they headed towards Madhuvana. Delighted, they used their valour to attack the grove's guards. Those accomplished ones saw that they had been granted permission and they had heard about Maithilee. Together, they leapt on all the hundreds of guards of the grove of Madhuvana who approached and struck them. They seized many *drona*s of honey.[287] They got together and struck.[288] Others devoured the honey, brown in complexion, some drank honey and flung away the vessels thereafter. Still holding the leftover honey, others got intoxicated and struck others. Some resorted to the roots of trees. Others clung to branches. Some were extremely drunk. They spread out leaves and lay down on these. Because of the honey, the apes became mad. Though intoxicated, they seemed to be cheerful. They playfully struck each other. Others addressed others in slurred voices. Some roared. Others cheerfully whistled. Some apes were intoxicated by the honey and slept on the ground.

Dadhimukha sent those who were meant to protect the honey. However, attacked by those terrible apes, they fled in different directions. They were dragged by their thighs and were seen to be flung up into the sky. Extremely anxious, they went and addressed Dadhimukha in these words. 'Because of the boon granted by

---

[286] An occasion for celebration at having found Sita.

[287] A drona is a wooden vessel, as well as an unit of measurement. The wooden vessel holds as much as a drona.

[288] The guards.

Hanumat, they are destroying Madhuvana with their force. We have been dragged by our thighs and are seen to have been flung up into the sky.' The ape Dadhimukha, the guardian of the grove, became angry. Hearing that Madhuvana had been destroyed, he comforted those apes. 'Come here. Let us go to those extremely insolent apes. We will use our strength to restrain those who are devouring the honey.' Hearing Dadhimukha's words, the brave bulls among apes assembled together and again went to Madhuvana. Having seized a giant tree, Dadhimukha was in their midst. All those apes attacked with force. The apes picked up boulders, trees and rocks. Having seized these, they angrily went to where those elephants among apes were. The brave ones had imbibed the words of their master in their hearts. With salas, talas and rocks as weapons, they attacked swiftly. Thousands of brave guards attacked the insolent and strong apes who were on trees or under the trees. The bulls among apes saw the angry Dadhimukha. With Hanumat at the forefront, they attacked with force. Angada angrily used his arms to strike the immensely strong and mighty-armed *aryaka*,[289] who was wielding a tree. Intoxicated and blind, he did not realize that this was his maternal uncle. Using force, he swiftly crushed him down on the ground. In an instant, the ape among elephants suddenly lost his senses. His arms were shattered. He was distracted and blood began to flow. He could no longer fight. Somehow, the bull among apes managed to extricate himself from those apes. He went to a solitary spot and told the assembled servants. 'Let the others remain here. Let us go to where the master of the apes, the thick-necked Sugriva, is with Rama. I will make the king hear all the sins Angada has committed. On hearing my words, he will become intolerant and will slay these apes. Madhuvana is desired by the great-souled Sugriva. It is divine and belonged to his fathers and grandfathers. Even the gods find it impossible to approach it. Greedy for honey, all these apes have lost their lifespans. Sugriva will chastise and kill them and their well-wishers. These evil-souled ones have disregarded the

---

[289] Aryaka means noble one. More specifically, it means maternal uncle. Here, it means Dadhimukha, Angada's maternal uncle.

command of the king and deserve to be killed. Our intolerance, power and anger will certainly be successful.' The immensely strong Dadhimukha said this to the guardians of the grove. Surrounded by all the guardians of the grove, he quickly got up. In a short while, he reached the residence in the forest where the intelligent ape, Sugriva, the son of the sun, was. On seeing Rama, Lakshmana and Sugriva, he descended from the sky on to the flat ground. Surrounded by all the guards, the immensely valiant one, Dadhimukha, the supreme lord of the guardians, descended. His face was distressed. He joined his hands in salutation above his head. He lowered his head at Sugriva's auspicious feet.

Chapter 5(61)

The ape fell down, with his head lowered. On seeing this, the bull among apes became anxious in his mind and addressed him in these words. 'Arise! Why have you fallen down at my feet? Arise! O brave one! Do not be scared. Tell me the truth about what has happened.' Thus assured by the great-souled Sugriva, the immensely wise Dadhimukha arose and spoke these words. O king! Riksharaja, you, or Vali had never allowed unrestricted access to the grove and those apes have consumed it. When they were restrained by the guards of the grove, they oppressed them. Without any heed, they devoured and drank the honey. While some are devouring, others are flinging away what is left of the honey. When they are restrained, they are showing their eyebrows.[290] When they[291] angrily restrained them, they were oppressed. Those enraged bulls among apes prevented them[292] from entering the grove. They have many brave apes, bulls among apes. Eyes red with rage, they have driven away those other apes.[293] Some have been struck with the hands.

---

[290] In anger.
[291] The guards.
[292] The guards.
[293] The guards.

Some have been struck with the thighs. As they wished, they have dragged some and flung them up into the sky. While you are here as their master, those brave apes have been struck. As they wish, they are devouring all of Madhuvana.'

While he was reporting this to Sugriva, bull among apes, the immensely wise Lakshmana, the destroyer of enemy heroes, asked, 'O king! This ape[294] resides in the grove. Why has he come here? He is addressing you in grieving words. What is he drawing your attention towards?' Hearing the words spoken by the great-souled Lakshmana, Sugriva, eloquent in the use of words, replied to Lakshmana. 'O noble Lakshmana! This brave ape, Dadhimukha, has told me that the brave apes, Angada and other foremost ones, have devoured the honey. They should not have acted in this way and done what should not have been done. When they have overpowered the grove, those apes must have accomplished their task. There is no doubt that Hanumat, and no one else, has seen the queen. No one other than Hanumat could have accomplished the task. Hanumat, bull among apes, possesses the intelligence to accomplish the objective. He is established in conduct, valour and learning. With Jambavat as the leader, Angada as the lord of the force and Hanumat as the supervisor of the work, there cannot have been any other outcome. Indeed, Angada and the other foremost ones have destroyed Madhuvana. Those bulls among apes have returned after searching the southern direction. They returned and entered Madhuvana. Having arrived there, those apes destroyed the entire grove. When they were restrained by the guards, they collectively struck them with their thighs. This is the reason he has come here, to tell us about it in sweet words. This ape is named Dadhimukha and he is famous for his valour. O mighty-armed one! O Soumitri! Behold the truth. Sita has been seen. That is the reason all those apes have come and are drinking the honey. O bull among men! This famous grove has been bestowed as a divine boon. Had they not seen Vaidehi, those residents of the forest would not have destroyed it.'

[294] Dadhimukha.

At this, with Raghava, Lakshmana, with dharma in his soul, was delighted. They heard the words, pleasant to hear, that emerged from Sugriva's mouth. The immensely illustrious Rama and Lakshmana were extremely delighted. Hearing what Dadhimukha had said, Sugriva also rejoiced. Sugriva again addressed the guardian of the grove[295] in these words. 'O amiable one! Since they have accomplished their task, I am glad that they have devoured the grove. Since they were successful in their task, they can be pardoned and I forgive them. Since those apes, as insolent as the lord of animals,[296] with Hanumat as the foremost, have been successful in their task, with the two Raghavas, I wish to quickly see them and hear about the efforts they made to reach Sita.'

Chapter 5(62)

Hearing the words spoken by Sugriva, the ape Dadhimukha was delighted. He paid his respects to Raghava, Lakshmana and Sugriva. He bowed down before Sugriva and the two immensely strong Raghavas. With the other brave apes, he leapt up into the sky. As was the case earlier, he left with great speed. He descended from the sky on to the ground and entered that grove. He entered Madhuvana and saw those leaders of the apes. Having passed out the honey as water, all of them were still excited, but sober and chastened now. The brave one joined his hands in salutation and approached them. Delighted, he gently spoke these words to Angada. 'O amiable one! You should not be angry that the guards were enraged and tried to restrain and obstruct you. They did it in their ignorance. O immensely strong one! You are the prince and the lord of this grove. We have earlier committed a crime because of our folly. Therefore, you should pardon us. O supreme among apes! You are just like your father, the former lord of the

[295] Dadhimukha.
[296] A lion.

apes, and just like Sugriva. It is not otherwise. O unblemished one! I went to your paternal uncle and told him about all the residents of the forest arriving here. Hearing that you have come here, with all the leaders of the apes, he is not angry, but rejoiced, even on hearing that this grove has been destroyed. Sugriva, your paternal uncle and the lord of the apes, rejoiced. The king said, "Quickly send those apes here."' Hearing the words spoken gently by Dadhimukha, Angada, eloquent in the use of words, addressed the best among apes in these words. 'O leaders of the apes! I suspect that Rama has heard the account about our arriving here. O scorchers of enemies! Therefore, having accomplished our objective, it is not proper that we should remain here. As they wished, those who roam in the forest have drunk honey. They have rested. What is left to be done, except go to the place where Sugriva, my senior, is? I will do whatever the assembled leaders of the apes tell me. I am obedient to whatever task all of you indicate. Though I am the prince, I am not a lord who ought to command you. You have been successful in your objective and it is inappropriate for me to instruct you.' Angada said this and hearing these undecaying words, the residents of the forest were delighted in their minds and replied in these words. 'O king! O lord of the apes! Who but a lord can speak in this way? Every person who is prosperous is intoxicated and intolerant and thinks of himself as "I". These words are extremely worthy of you and no one else could have spoken them. This humility is telling us about your future good fortune. All of us have come here and are waiting for the right time to go where Sugriva, the undecaying lord of the brave apes, is. O best among the apes! Without you saying so, the apes are not able to step forward anywhere. We are telling you this, truthfully.'

When they said this, Angada replied, 'Fine. Let us go.' Having said this, he leapt up from the ground. All the leaders of the apes followed him and leapt up. They rose up into the sky and didn't leave any empty spaces, like the fire that arises from a sacrifice. Those apes rose up into the sky, powerfully and suddenly. They roared in loud voices, like clouds urged along by the wind.

Even before Angada reached, Sugriva, lord of the apes, spoke to the lotus-eyed Rama, who was senseless with grief. 'O fortunate one! Be comforted. There is no doubt that the queen has been seen. Otherwise, after the time indicated by us was over, they would not have come here. The mighty-armed Prince Angada, supreme among the apes, would not have come into my presence had the objective not been accomplished. Had he not been successful, he would not have made such an attempt. His face would have been distressed. He would have been distracted and his mind would have been cheerless. Had the lord of the apes been miserable, he would not have destroyed Madhuvana, protected formerly by his fathers and grandfathers. O Rama! O excellent offspring of Kousalya! O one who is good in his vows! Be comforted. There is no doubt that the queen has been seen and by no one other than Hanumat. There is no one else who could have accomplished the task. He has been the instrument. O supreme among intelligent ones! Hanumat certainly possesses intelligence, enterprise, valour and the energy of the sun—required for success. When Jambavat is the leader, Angada is the leader of the army and Hanumat is the supervisor, it cannot but be otherwise. O infinitely valiant one! You should no longer be overcome by thoughts.'

A cackling sound was then heard to approach from the direction of the sky. The residents of the forest were proudly roaring about Hanumat's deeds. As they approached Kishkindha, they seemed to be conversing about that success. The supreme among apes[297] heard the sound of the apes roaring. Cheerful in his mind, he stretched and curled up his tail. Desiring to see Rama, with Angada and the ape Hanumat at the forefront, the apes approached. With Angada and other foremost ones, those brave ones were filled with joy. They descended near the king of the apes and Raghava. The mighty-armed Hanumat bowed his head down. He told Raghava that the queen was unharmed and in control of herself. Having ascertained what was being said, Lakshmana was delighted and looked at Sugriva and the son of the wind god with affection and a great deal

[297] Sugriva.

of respect. Raghava, the destroyer of enemy heroes, was delighted and happy. He looked at Hanumat with a great deal of respect.

Chapter 5(63)

They went to Mount Prasravana, with its colourful groves. They bowed their heads down before Rama and the immensely strong Lakshmana. With the prince at the forefront, they greeted Sugriva. They then started to recount about Sita. In Rama's presence, all the apes told them everything about her being imprisoned in Ravana's inner quarters, the censuring by the rakshasis, her affection towards Rama and the time that had been given.[298] Hearing that Vaidehi was unharmed, Rama replied, 'How is Queen Sita? What is her attitude towards me? O apes! Tell me everything about Vaidehi.' Hearing Rama's words, in Rama's presence, the apes urged Hanumat, who was skilled in telling, to recount everything about Sita.

Hearing their words, Hanumat, the son of the wind god and eloquent in the use of words, spoke about how Sita had been seen in the following words. 'The ocean stretches for one hundred yojanas and I leapt across it. Having reached, I searched around for Janakee Sita's trail. The evil-souled Ravana's city, Lanka, is there. It is located on the southern shore of the ocean. I saw Sita there, in Ravana's inner quarters. O Rama! The beautiful one, your heart's desire, is sustaining her life in you. I saw her in the midst of the rakshasis, being censured repeatedly. In that pleasure garden, she is guarded by rakshasis with disfigured forms. Though she deserves to be happy with you, the queen faces this misery. She is confined to Ravana's inner quarters, guarded well by the rakshasis. She wears her hair in a single braid. She is distressed and is thinking about you. She lies down on the ground and her limbs are faded, like a lotus at the onset of the winter. Having refused Ravana, she has made up her mind to die. O Kakutstha! With her mind following you, the queen is

---

[298] The period of two months set by Ravana.

sustaining herself somehow. O unblemished one! I slowly mentioned the fame of the Ikshvaku lineage. O tiger among men! That instilled her confidence in me.[299] After this, I told the queen everything about why I had gone there. Hearing about the friendship between Rama and Sugriva, she was filled with joy. She is controlled and full of good conduct, faithful to you. Thus I saw Janaka's immensely fortunate daughter. O bull among men! She is fierce in her austerities and devoted to you. O immensely wise one! O Raghava! As a sign, she told me about what had occurred in secret, about the incident of the crow in Chitrakuta. Janakee told me, "O Vayu's son! Tell Rama, tiger among men, about everything that you have seen here. When you speak to him and Sugriva is listening, give him what I have protected with great care. This is the beautiful chudamani and I have protected it carefully. You should remember the tilaka you drew with a piece of stone. I am sending you this beautiful piece,[300] produced from the water. O unblemished one! Looking at this, I used to find joy in my hardship, as if I was looking at you. O Dasharatha's son! I will sustain my life for one more month. Having come under the subjugation of the rakshasa, I cannot sustain my life for more than one month." Sita, emaciated in her limbs and following dharma, addressed me in this way. With large eyes like those of a doe, she is confined to Ravana's inner quarters. O Raghava! I have told you everything, exactly as it occurred. Every means possible should be used to cross over the ocean.' Realizing that the two princes were reassured, he gave Raghava the token of recognition. Vayu's son told him everything about the queen's account, as it happened.

Chapter 5(64)

Hanumat spoke in this way to Rama, Dasharatha's son. With Lakshmana, he clutched that jewel to his heart and wept.

---

[299] For whatever reason, Hanumat does not mention Rama's ring, which he had carried with him, to win Sita's confidence.

[300] The jewel.

On seeing that excellent jewel, Raghava was afflicted with grief. With his eyes overflowing with tears, he spoke to Sugriva. 'A cow is affectionate towards her calf and her affection oozes out.[301] On seeing this jewel, that is what is happening with my heart. My father-in-law gave this excellent jewel to Vaidehi, when she became a bride. When it was fixed to her head, it became even more beautiful. This jewel was produced from the water and was worshipped by his ancestors. Extremely satisfied at a sacrifice, the intelligent Shakra had bestowed it as a gift. O amiable one! On seeing this excellent jewel, right now, I feel as if I am seeing my father and the lord of Videha.[302] This is the jewel that used to look beautiful on my beloved's head. On seeing it, I think that I have met her. O amiable one![303] Tell me again and again what Sita Vaidehi said. Your words are like water, like water sprinkled on a senseless person. O Soumitri! What can be more painful than this? Without Vaidehi having returned, I am seeing this jewel that has been produced from the water. If Vaidehi can sustain herself for a month, she will remain alive for a long time. O amiable one! Without that dark-eyed one, I cannot remain alive even for an instant. Take me to the spot where my beloved was seen. After getting to know where she is, I cannot remain here even for an instant. She is most timid among the timid. How can the one with excellent hips remain in the midst of terrible rakshasas who generate fear? Her face is like the autumn moon, when it has freed itself from the darkness, but is enveloped by clouds. Therefore, among those rakshasas, it is not radiant. O Hanumat! Tell me truthfully. What did Sita say? This is the way I will remain alive, like a diseased person is with medicine. She is sweet and her conversation is sweet. What did my beautiful one say? Without me, how is the beautiful one? O Hanumat! Tell me. Facing a greater and greater misery, how has Janakee remained alive?'

[301] In the form of milk.
[302] Janaka.
[303] This is addressed to Hanumat.

Chapter 5(65)

Hanumat was thus addressed by the great-souled Raghava. He told Raghava everything that Sita had said. 'O bull among men! This is what Queen Janakee said. As a sign, she spoke about something that had occurred earlier in Chitrakuta. Janakee was happily asleep with you, but awoke before you. A crow suddenly descended and pecked at her, between her breasts. O Bharata's elder brother! Taking your turn, you were asleep on the queen's lap. However, that bird again caused pain to the queen. It repeatedly tore at her, severely. When she was wet with blood, she awoke you. O scorcher of enemies! You were happily asleep. However, repeatedly suffering from the crow, the queen awoke you. O mighty-armed one! You saw that she had been injured between the breasts. Sighing like an angry serpent, you spoke to her. "O timid one! Who has lacerated you between the breasts with his talons? Who is sporting with an enraged five-hooded serpent?" Looking around, she suddenly pointed to the crow. "There it is, stationed in front of me, with blood on its sharp talons. Does this crow, supreme among birds, indeed belong to Shakra? It swiftly roams around on earth, with a speed like that of the wind. O mighty-armed one![304] At this, your eyes rolled around in rage. O supreme among intelligent ones! You decided to act cruelly towards that crow. You picked up a blade of darbha grass and invoked brahmastra on it. It blazed like the flaming fire of destruction and headed in the direction of the bird. You flung the blazing darbha towards the crow. The blazing darbha followed the crow. It was abandoned by its father[305] and by all the gods and the maharshis. It circled around the three worlds, but could not find a protector. O one who is a refuge! It fell down on the ground and sought refuge with you. O Kakutstha! Though it deserved to be killed, because of your compassion, you saved it. O Raghava! It was not possible to render the weapon futile. Therefore, it robbed the crow of its right eye. O Rama! Having

[304] These are Sita's words, being quoted by Hanumat.
[305] Indra.

bowed down to you and to King Dasharatha, the crow then took leave of you and returned to its own abode. In this way, you are supreme among those who know about weapons. You are spirited and good in conduct. O Raghava! Why are you not using your weapons against the rakshasas? The serpents, the gandharvas, the asuras and all the large numbers of Maruts are incapable of standing before Rama in a battle. If that valiant one has the slightest bit of respect for me, let him swiftly use his extremely sharp arrows to kill Ravana in a battle. Why is Lakshmana, scorcher of enemies, not following his brother's command? Why is that Raghava, supreme among men, not protecting me? Those two capable tigers among men are like Vayu and Agni in their energy. Even the gods find them to be invincible. Why are they ignoring me? There is no doubt that I have committed an extremely grave crime. Though they are capable, this is the reason those two scorchers of enemies are ignoring me." I heard Vaidehi's piteous words, spoken amidst tears. I again addressed the noble one in these words. "O queen! I swear truthfully that Rama has become indifferent because of his grief over you. Rama is overcome by sorrow and Lakshmana is tormented. Sustain yourself in some fashion and you will no longer confront a period of sorrow. O beautiful one! In a short while, you will see an end to your misery. Those two princes, tigers among men, are the destroyers of enemies. In their eagerness to see you, they will reduce Lanka to ashes. In a battle, Raghava will slay the terrible Ravana and his relatives. The mighty-armed one will certainly take you back to his own city. O unblemished one! Give me a sign so that Rama can recognize it. You should give something that will generate joy in him." She looked in all the directions and unbraided her excellent braid. O immensely wise one! She freed this jewel and gave it to me in this piece of cloth. O supreme among the Raghu lineage! For your sake, I accepted the divine jewel. Desiring to return here quickly, I bowed my head down before her. On seeing that I was preparing to leave and had expanded my body, Janaka's daughter, the one with the beautiful complexion, spoke to me. Her face overflowing with tears, in a distressed and choking voice, she said, "O Hanumat! Rama and Lakshmana are like lions. When you

reach them, ask about their welfare and that of Sugriva and all his
advisers. You must act so that the mighty-armed Raghava can make
me cross over this ocean of grief. This flood of sorrow is fierce. The
guards are censuring me. O supreme among apes! When you reach
Rama, tell him this. May your journey be auspicious." O king! O
lion among kings! Full of sorrow, these are the words spoken by the
noble Sita. Accept the words uttered by me and believe that Sita is
safe in every possible way.'

Chapter 5(66)

'O tiger among men! Out of affection, love and respect for you,
though she had respectfully replied to me, the queen spoke
again. "You must speak many such words to Rama, Dasharatha's
son, so that he quickly gets me back, after having killed Ravana
in a battle. O brave one! O destroyer of enemies! If you so think,
reside here for one day. Hide yourself in some spot. Having rested,
leave tomorrow. O ape! I am limited in fortune. However, because
of your presence, my sorrow and hardship will be dispelled for an
instant. O valiant one! Between your going and your return, there
is no doubt that there will be a threat to my life. The sorrow of not
being able to see you will also torment me. On top of the present
misery, I will be overcome by another misery. From this state of
hardship, I will suffer a greater unhappiness. O brave one! A doubt
presents itself before me. There is no doubt that you possess a large
number of apes and bears as aides. How will they cross the great
ocean, which is extremely difficult to cross? How will the soldiers of
the apes and the bears do this? How will those two supreme men?
O unblemished one! There are only three creatures who have the
capacity to cross the ocean—Vinata's son,[306] Vayu and you. O brave
one! This is extremely difficult to cross. Therefore, engage yourself
in this task. O supreme among those who can accomplish tasks!

[306] Garuda.

What solution do you perceive? If you wish, you alone are capable of accomplishing this task. O slayer of enemies! Your fame and ability to enhance your strength is sufficient. If Rama kills Ravana and all his soldiers in a battle and having become victorious, takes me back to his own city, this would bring him fame. I belong to the brave one and was secretly abducted from the forest. Out of fear of the rakshasas, Raghava should not do that.[307] Lanka is full of soldiers. If Kakutstha, the afflicter of enemy soldiers, takes me away in this way, this will be worthy of him. You must act so that the valiant and great-souled one behaves in this way and exhibits his valour in battle." I heard the words spoken by her and they were full of meaning and reason. Having heard what she said, I spoke my final words of reply. "O queen! The ape and the bear soldiers and Sugriva, the lord of the apes who is full of spirit, have made up their minds for your sake. They are full of valour. They are spirited and immensely strong. The apes have made up their minds and are waiting for the command. There is nothing that can obstruct their path, above, below and diagonally. They are great and infinitely energetic and do not suffer in any task. Those immensely fortunate apes are full of strength and resorting to the path followed by the wind, have circumambulated the earth several times. Those residents of the forest are equal to me and superior. There is no one in Sugriva's presence who is inferior to me. I came from there to here. Why can't those extremely strong ones? Usually, the better ones are not sent. It is the ordinary ones who are sent.[308] O queen! Therefore, enough of this lamentation and grieving. The leaders of the apes will arrive here in a single leap. Those two immensely fortunate ones, lions among men, will arrive before you riding on my back, like the rising moon and the sun. You will soon see Raghava, who is like a lion and is the slayer of enemies. With a bow in his hand, Lakshmana will present himself at the gate of Lanka. You will soon see the apes assemble, with complexions like Indras among elephants. Those brave ones are like lions and tigers

---

[307] Take me away in secret.
[308] That is, the others are superior to me.

in their valour and use their nails and teeth as weapons. They are like mountains and clouds. You will soon hear the sound of the best among apes roaring in Lanka, on the summit of Malaya. With the destroyer of enemies, you will return from exile in the forest. You will soon see Raghava consecrated in Ayodhya." At these words spoken by me, her voice was no longer distressed. I comforted her with these auspicious and beneficial words. The daughter of the king of Mithila obtained peace, though she was still suffering on account of you. I left.'

This ends Sundara Kanda.